METHODS FOR OBTAINING AND HANDLING
MARINE EGGS AND EMBRYOS

Methods for Obtaining and Handling

Marine Eggs and Embryos

D. P. Costello, M. E. Davidson

A. Eggers, M. H. Fox and C. Henley

MARINE BIOLOGICAL LABORATORY

WOODS HOLE, MASSACHUSETTS

1957

Copyright 1957 by Donald P. Costello

First edition

CONTENTS

vi   CONTENTS

INTRODUCTION

This manual represents a compilation of the methods for handling embryological materials available at Woods Hole, Massachusetts. The material outlined was assembled from personal communications, from the laboratory guides prepared by members of the Embryology Course staff of the Marine Biological Laboratory at Woods Hole, from the observations made by Marjorie Hopkins Fox, Annette Eggers and Margaret E. Davidson as Embryology Course research assistants, and from the work on marine forms done by the senior author and Catherine Henley.

In the past, much valuable time-saving information has been lost because it passed from investigator to investigator merely by word of mouth. E. E. Just's articles in the *Collecting Net* (1928) and his book, "Basic Methods for Experiments on Eggs of Marine Animals" (1939), were the first attempts to preserve this type of knowledge for the younger generations of investigators. This manual was started as an extension of Just's book, giving more details about the forms he described, and including data on additional species. Wherever possible, we have avoided descriptions of standard technical laboratory procedures which are available in other books.

Although our account is based upon those animals available at Woods Hole, it is apparent that the methods may be used to advantage elsewhere. Many of the forms described here are available along the entire Atlantic coast, and closely related forms (with similar breeding-habits and similar embryonic development) are to be found on the European, Pacific and southern Atlantic coasts. The breeding seasons listed in this account apply in most cases only to the Woods Hole region.

Many workers at Woods Hole have been limited in the scope of their work by lack of information concerning the local fauna. Given a concise source of information, an investigator should be able to select the egg best suited for any purpose: large or small; transparent and colorless, or opaque and pigmented; with a tough membrane, or with a delicate one; with external jelly, or free of it. It is possible to utilize eggs at each of the four recognized stages of attainment of the fertilizable condition; eggs with a pronounced cortical change at activation, or with little or no change; eggs with or without micropyles; eggs with slow or rapid sperm penetration, and with slow or rapid development; eggs with any of the various types of cleavage; etc.

The present volume is admittedly incomplete, and better methods for handling certain of the materials may be forthcoming, or even already in use. We hope that workers will report errors, and make suggestions concerning improvements; gaps in the data should be filled in, and information for additional forms added. Each genus of animal at Woods Hole probably provides embryological materials worthy of investigation, and it is hoped that eventually all the most useful forms will be included in a later revision of this work.

The listing of the names of the co-authors is on an alphabetical basis. Mrs. Fox served as research assistant in the Embryology Course at the M. B. L. during the summers of 1945, 1946, and 1947, obtaining information for this manual. She was succeeded by Miss Eggers for the summer of 1948, and by Miss Davidson for the summers of 1949 and 1950. After a lapse of several years, the work was resumed in 1956 under a National Science Foundation grant (NSF-G2477) with the aid of Miss Henley, who edited the sections previously prepared and added several new ones.

In general, the nomenclature which we have adopted for the forms considered is that used in the classic earlier papers in the field of embryology, since we feel that these are the names by which the animals are best known to workers at Woods Hole. Thus, we have retained the generic names "Nereis" and "Mactra," for example, even though recent taxonomic revisions have assigned other names to both these forms. All the common synonyms known to us for the names of animals considered are included in the index to this volume, and in the heading of each description.

The arrangement of sections is based on a phylogenetic sequence from "lowest" to "highest," and within each sub-division, the genera are described in alphabetical sequence.

A bibliography has been compiled for each section, listing (1) those papers and books on which our description is based, and (2) some of the reports in the literature which have utilized the form under consideration. We have made no effort to include all the papers describing work done on a given animal, but only those which were most useful to us in our compilation.

There were many early investigators at Woods Hole who worked out the details of obtaining and handling one or more types of embryological materials, as well as the fundamental aspects of the embryology of such forms. Sometimes they incorporated this information into their papers, but more often it was omitted. About 1940, when the older generation of embryologists at Woods Hole (including E. B. Wilson, E. G. Conklin, F. R. Lillie, A. D. Mead, A. L. Treadwell, C. M. Child, H. E. Crampton and others) was beginning to dwindle in numbers, Dr. Viktor Hamburger suggested that plans be made for a manual which would put on record some of the methods utilized by those studying the development of marine animals; he obtained funds from the Marine Biological Laboratory for a summer research assistant to help with the project, beginning in 1945.

Another factor contributing to the initiation of the work was the almost total disappearance of the sea urchin, Arbacia, from the usual collecting grounds near the Laboratory; this occurred about 1945. Earlier, when sea urchins were abundant at Woods Hole and thousands were often collected at a time, the Arbacia egg was the "standard living cell" upon which much of the physiological, biochemical and cytological work was done. With the marked decrease in numbers of Arbacia, however, it became impossible for many investigators to utilize this form, and there were frequent inquiries as to the availability of other egg-species.

A collector-curator, George M. Gray (head of the Supply Department for many years), had very extensive and readily available knowledge of the Cape Cod marine organisms. He was succeeded in 1933 by James McInnis, and the staff of the Supply Department was trained under the able direction of Mr. Gray, Mr. McInnis and the older, experienced men. It would have been impossible to produce this guide without the willing help given by members of the Department.

Although it is impossible for us to mention the names of all those who directly or indirectly contributed to the M. B. L. Embryology Course outlines (which served as a basis for some of the sections in this book), we should like to acknowledge their contributions, as well as the assistance given us by investigators at the Laboratory, course instructors, teaching assistants, students and others. Some of these persons are mentioned in the list which follows: M. Jean Allen, P. B. Armstrong, W. W. Ballard, C. G. Bookhout, F. A. Brown, Jr., Eugenie Clark, A. C. Clement, Preston Cloud, A. L. and L. H. Colwin, D. E. Copeland, J. D. Costlow, Jr., Sears Crowell, Katsuma Dan, H. B. Goodrich, M. B. Gray, Viktor Hamburger, H. L. Hamilton, E. B. Harvey, L. V. Heilbrunn, A. M. Hilton, Shinya Inoué, C. E. Jenner, V. L. Loosanoff, F. M. MacNaught, James McInnis, C. B. Metz, J. A. Miller, J. A. Moore, J. A. Moulton, J. M. Oppenheimer, Charles Packard, Helen Padykula, M. H. Pettibone, J. S. Rankin, M. D. Rogick, S. M. Rose, Arlene Seaman, Allan Scott, Sister Florence Marie Scott, H. P. Smith, Ralph Smith, Lois TeWinkel, J. P. Trinkaus, Ruth Turner, Albert Tyler, R. L. Watterson, D. J. Zinn and Edgar Zwilling.

Mrs. T. H. Montgomery and Mrs. Seaver Harlow, Laboratory Librarians, and members of the Library staff were always most helpful and courteous, and we should like to express our thanks to them.

Our special appreciation is due Miss Louise Dalton for her careful typing of the entire final manuscript and many of the earlier drafts.

GENERAL METHODS

Collection of animals

At the Marine Biological Laboratory, the collecting is done, for the most part, by the Supply Department, and the investigators usually do not obtain their own material. This system is a very convenient one when the collecting staff is experienced, so that they realize the advantages of freshly collected material over that aged in a floating stage; in addition, the collectors must know the best means of transporting the animals from the collecting grounds to the Supply Department, the handling and maintenance of material after it reaches the Department, and the importance of delivery to the investigator as soon after collection as possible. It goes without saying that they must also be equipped with the best possible boats, dredges and other collecting apparatus, and that they must have an accurate knowledge of the availability of a given form. The Supply Department has met all these requirements with a high degree of success.

In other laboratories, where experienced collectors are not a part of the staff, the investigator has an opportunity to learn at first hand the breeding-habits and general ecology of the animals with which he is working; he can ascertain the best methods of collecting, transporting and maintaining them in order to provide himself with the best possible experimental material. Some of the general factors to be kept in mind include the following:

(1) Avoid trauma to the animals, both during and after collection.

(2) Avoid marked temperature changes, maintaining the specimens at all times as nearly as possible at the temperature of their natural environment.

(3) Do not crowd the animals; adequate supplies of sea water and oxygen should be provided during collection, transportation, and maintenance in the laboratory.

(4) Conserve the supply of living material, taking no more of a given species than necessary and leaving an adequate breeding population. Whenever possible, unused animals, or spent animals which have been induced to shed, should be returned to their natural habitat.

Sexing adults

If the differences between the two sexes of a dioecious species are such that the investigator cannot distinguish them on the basis of external characteristics, there are several methods for ascertaining sex without wasting material. (1) A few drops of gonad material can be withdrawn, by means of a hypodermic syringe and fine needle. The needle is inserted at the hinge-line in the case of Mactra, through the peristome of Arbacia, or through an arm for Asterias. This material, when examined, should contain eggs or sperm if the individual is mature. (2) Certain of the methods used for inducing shedding (electrical stimulation, KCl-treatment, or reactions to gamete-water) enable one to ascertain sex merely by looking at the gametes.

Obtaining gametes

After the adult animals are collected and brought into the laboratory, they are usually kept in aquaria or other containers supplied with running sea water. Only a few species shed their gametes spontaneously, and it is therefore necessary to have methods for inducing them to shed at the time when the gametes are needed by the worker. The crude older technique of cutting open the animals and removing the gonads is wasteful of material, and often yields gametes so contaminated with body fluids that they are non-fertilizable. Recent methods that have been developed to induce shedding include (1) injection of isosmotic KCl (first described by L. P. Wilson for Arbacia and subsequently modified in various ways for use with a number of other forms) ; (2) temperature shock (an imitation of one of the tidal effects on littoral animals) ; (3) electrical stimulation (used very successfully by Iwata in Japan for several echinoderms and subsequently adopted, with modifications, by E. B. Harvey in this country) ; (4) mechanical stimulation, such as shaking the adults in a bucket of sea water; (5) altering the normal periods of light and darkness (see the section on Styela, for example) ; and (6) adding gametes (or gamete-sea water) of the opposite sex. For species which fertilize their eggs internally, of course, such methods do not apply, and there are certain other forms for which removal of the excised gonads to dishes of sea water is apparently the only practicable method for obtaining eggs and sperm. "Stripping" the gametes is the method of choice for most teleosts.

Insemination

Generalizations about the exact conditions which will result in normal fertilization are difficult, because the several species vary considerably in such particulars as optimal sperm concentration, degree of washing (if any) of the eggs prior to insemination, etc. However, it is, in general, important to avoid excessive concentrations of sperm. In addition to promoting polyspermy and abnormal development in some species, excess sperm also contribute (after a short time) excess carbon dioxide, decomposing proteins, and a rich culture medium for bacteria which hasten the fouling of the culture. Another general principle is to avoid contaminating the eggs with body fluids (or portions of the shell or test, in the case of echinoderms) ; as Lillie early demonstrated, such fluids have a deleterious effect on the fertilization-reaction. Mucous secretions of the female (as in the case of Chaetopterus) may also constitute a structural barrier to fertilization. A third generalization is that the eggs should never be crowded: one layer on the bottom of a dish gives much better results than multiple layers. For eggs that elevate fertilization membranes or extrude marked quantities of jelly as a part of the fertilization-reaction, the eggs should be even more widely spread.

Raising larvae to later stages of development

After embryos have used up the stored yolk, oil, and other nutritive materials originally present in the egg, they must be supplied with appropriate food if development is to continue. Diatoms are the chief food for marine invertebrate larvae such as trochophores, bipinnaria, etc. Diatom-culture methods are described in the papers by Just (1922, 1939), Galtsoff *et al.* (1937) and Grave (1902). There are several laboratories which maintain one or more strains of Nitzschia and other diatoms in pure and in mixed cultures, and it is often possible to obtain inocula from such cultures. Certain marine protozoa are useful for feeding some types of larvae, and older stages will often thrive on a diet of mixed plankton. Fundulus hatchlings can be fed Nereis trochophores.

Methods of observation

In addition to the usual light-field and dark-field microscope, excellent use can be made of several other types of optical equipment. These include:

(1) The phase contrast microscope. This is especially useful for sperm and for very slender structures, such as sperm filaments. However, it is much less useful for larger structures (such as eggs), especially those with jelly-layers and membranes which refract light.

(2) The polarization microscope gives superb visualization of living spindle fibers and of other structures with oriented molecules, such as the spicules of echinoderm larvae. Unfortunately, the birefringence of most organelles (except calcified structures) of eggs and embryos is rather low. A quarter-wave plate greatly enhances the beauty of polarization-images.

(3) The ultraviolet microscope may be used to demonstrate relative concentrations of ultraviolet-absorbing materials (proteins, amino acids, DNA, etc.) in various regions of *thin* structures. By means of a quartz monochromator and the use of special stops, it is possible to obtain a crude absorption spectrum of certain cell-components. Obviously, quartz slides and coverslips must be used with the ultraviolet microscope.

(4) The newly designed interference microscope may eventually be put to interesting uses.

(5) The electron microscope is of no value with living material. Under carefully controlled conditions of fixation and drying of thin material, or by still more carefully controlled embedding and sectioning methods, in the hands of experts, some useful information about the micro-structure of eggs, sperm and embryos may be obtained.

(6) Water-immersion lenses (with all metal parts coated, so that heavy metals cannot affect the eggs) are very useful.

For investigators who are not burdened with excessive and elaborate equipment, but who are capable of making their observations largely with the use of a good compound microscope, there are a few refinements of technique which will greatly aid the perception of microscopic detail:

(1) A good north light, and centered microscope diaphragm (to reduce the illumination and reveal delicate structures).

(2) Critical illumination, if artificial light is to be used.

(3) The use of a Chinese ink suspension to provide a background against which will be revealed the thickness of transparent jelly-layers, etc. This must always be prepared *fresh,* immediately before use: carefully rub the end of a dry stick of Chinese ink on a finely ground glass slide (wet with sea water) until a dark, fine and uniform suspension is obtained.

(4) A very dilute suspension of Janus green (two drops of a 1:1000 solution, made up in distilled water, added to about 20 cc. of sea water) will faintly stain the jelly of certain eggs (Arbacia, Asterias, etc.), without injuring them appreciably. The membranes, only, of certain other eggs will absorb the dye, and there are also cases where both the jelly and the membranes are stained. For true *intra vitam* staining with Janus green, however, a zinc-free preparation must be obtained.

(5) For quieting larvae, so that details of larval structures (including ciliation) are more easily seen, the following methods can be used:

(a) More concentrated Janus green (one cc. of 1% Janus green in distilled water, added to 10 cc. of sea water).

(b) Squid egg-string extract, especially for echinoderm larvae (see the section on Asterias, p. 172).

(c) Shredded lens paper (usually not very satisfactory).

(d) Chloral hydrate or magnesium sulfate (the concentration for each species must be ascertained by trial and error).

Glassware

It is essential that the glassware used for living material be completely free of all toxic substances. Washed new glassware (which should then be reserved specifically for living material) is much safer than glassware previously used for various unknown chemical procedures. Just (1939) discusses this problem in detail. He has given excellent advice, also, on utilization of sea water, and on the uses of thermometers and stop-watches in embryological research.

Moist-chambers, for keeping embryos or larvae so that there is relatively little evaporation of the sea water medium in which they are being raised, can be made from crystallization-dishes with covers. Large fingerbowls (with provision made for covering them, either with large glass plates or with other fingerbowls) may be used if crystallization-dishes are not available. The culture dishes (Columbia watch glasses, depression slides, small stender dishes, etc.) are supported on a platform composed of a round glass plate cut to slightly less than the diameter of the moist-chamber; this platform can conveniently be arranged to rest on four square embryological watch glasses ("salt cellars"). The bottom of the moist-chamber is filled to a depth of about one-fourth inch with slightly diluted (about 90%) sea water, to maintain the proper humidity. Some workers prefer a paraffin-coated low hardware-cloth rack to the round glass platform.

Instruments and miscellaneous equipment

The experimental embryologist who works with marine material makes use of many of the instruments originally devised for operative techniques in vertebrate experimental embryology. (See the book by Hamburger, 1942.) These include iridectomy scissors, watchmaker's forceps, hair loops, sharp steel beading needles (which can be fused into handles made of glass tubing), glass needles, etc. Another most useful implement for moving eggs without injury from one container to another is the mouth pipette. This consists of a pipette drawn out to the requisite bore, attached to a piece of clear gum-rubber tubing (about 3 mm. in outside diameter and about 36 inches long); a mouthpiece made of fire-polished glass tubing is provided. Wooden blocks about two inches in thickness, with a series of holes drilled in them, are useful as racks for glass needles, hair loops, etc. They should be provided with glass or rigid plastic bell-jar covers.

Since most of the marine invertebrate eggs are very much smaller than the traditional amphibian and chick material, the hair loops should be smaller in diameter and made of finer hair than those used by the worker with vertebrate eggs and embryos. The steel forceps and needles must be sharpened to very fine points (utilizing an Arkansas stone and a dissecting binocular microscope for the sharpening process), and the glass needles drawn out to points of the requisite diameter, length, sharpness and flexibility for particular purposes on a given material. It goes without saying that all precautions should be taken to protect expensive steel instruments from the corrosive effects of sea water.

Operating dishes for the small invertebrate eggs can be readily made by filtering a few drops of hot, freshly prepared 2% agar in sea water into Columbia watch glasses. (It is convenient to use a metal, water-jacketed funnel for filtering the agar, so that the material remains liquid until it touches the glass dish.) Hardening of the agar occurs as it cools, and it makes a resilient surface on which eggs can be cut with glass needles. Such dishes are used, also, for raising embryos denuded of their membranes, for isolated blastomeres, and for other delicate embryos or embryo-parts; the agar prevents cells from attaching and sticking to the glass bottoms of the dishes. Hörstadius (1937) uses washed photographic film for an operating surface.

At most marine laboratories, high atmospheric humidity presents a number of problems to workers, especially when histological or cytological preparations are being made. We have found it most helpful to use an ordinary commercial infra-red lamp (either red, with a "built-in filter," or plain white) in a goose-neck desk lamp from which the shade has been removed so that the large bulb will fit. The beam from such a set-up can be directed toward the area where one is working, to facilitate the final steps of dehydration and clearing. Sometimes, it will also prove helpful to pre-heat the slides and/or coverslips to be used; an ordinary slide-warmer is convenient for this purpose.

Other useful but more specialized items of miscellaneous equipment are described in connection with the forms for which they are most often utilized.

Formulae

Formulae for artificial sea water, calcium-free sea water, fixatives, stains, etc., have, for the most part, been omitted from this manual. The Chemical Room of the Marine Biological Laboratory at Woods Hole publishes, from time to time, a revision of its compilation, "Formulae and Methods," which includes such information.

REFERENCES:

GALTSOFF, P. S., F. E. LUTZ, P. S. WELCH AND J. G. NEEDHAM, 1937. Culture Methods for Invertebrate Animals. Comstock Publishing Co., Inc., Ithaca, New York.

GRAVE, C., 1902. A method of rearing marine larvae. *Science,* **15**: 579–580.

HAMBURGER, V., 1942. A Manual of Experimental Embryology. The University of Chicago Press, Chicago.

HÖRSTADIUS, S., 1937. Section on free-hand manipulations. *In:* Handbook of Microscopical Technique, edit. by C. E. McClung. P. B. Hoeber, Inc., New York, pp. 43–50. (Rev. ed.)

JUST, E. E., 1922. On rearing sexually mature *Platynereis megalops* from eggs. *Amer. Nat.,* **56**: 471–477.

JUST, E. E., 1939. Basic Methods for Experiments on Eggs of Marine Animals. P. Blakiston's Son & Co., Inc., Philadelphia.

PRATT, H. S., 1951. A Manual of the Common Invertebrate Animals. The Blakiston Co., Philadelphia. (Rev. ed.)

PORIFERA

Mycale (formerly *Esperella*) *fibrexilis*

LIVING MATERIAL:

Mycale is a small, yellowish-brown encrusting sponge, with a poorly developed skeleton. It is reported by Wilson (1937) to be common on wharf piles at Woods Hole, Mass.

BREEDING SEASON:

Asexual larvae (gemmules) are released in July and August. At this time, a few small eggs in the germinal vesicle stage can be found, but sexual reproduction and the release of sexual larvae probably occur in the early fall.

PROCURING AND HANDLING MATERIAL:

A. Care of Adults: This sponge is easily kept in aquaria. It requires no special care, beyond the provision of an adequate supply of running sea water.

B. Preparation of Cultures: Larvae may be obtained during the breeding season by placing the adult sponge in a two- or three-gallon jar containing sea water. Exposure to air should be avoided. Release of the ciliated larvae seems to be stimulated by confinement in a limited amount of water and may occur within a few minutes, although sometimes it is necessary to leave the animal overnight. The larvae can be collected with a pipette and transferred to a fingerbowl of filtered sea water. The water should be changed several times a day. The free-swimming stage lasts only one or two days. Shells, pieces of wood, or glass slides placed in the bowl will provide attachment surfaces for the metamorphosing larvae, which can then be easily transferred to live-boxes if further growth is desired.

NORMAL DEVELOPMENT:

A. The Unfertilized Ovum: The oöcyte is small; it has a large nucleus containing a prominent nucleolus.

B. Fertilization and Cleavage: Sexual reproduction in this species has not been thoroughly studied. If development is similar to that of *Tedanione foetida* or *Hircinia aeuta,* fertilization is internal and cleavage equal and regular. In these forms, a morula develops into a ciliated larva very similar to the asexually-produced gemmule larva of Mycale (Wilson, 1894).

C. Rate of Development: The developmental rate for this species has not been recorded. The free-swimming larval stage is short, lasting only a day or two.

D. Later Stages of Development and Metamorphosis: A ciliated larva is produced, which escapes through an osculum as a free-swimming form. The gemmule larva at this stage is a solid, oval body, measuring a millimeter or less. The flat posterior pole is non-ciliated and contains a bundle of long straight spicules. The rest of the animal is covered by ciliated ectoderm cells which contain orange pigment granules. The inner, parenchymatous mass contains several types of scattered spicules.

1

At metamorphosis the swimming larva settles and attaches obliquely at the posterior pole.   At this time there is a flattening of cells and loss of cilia.   In the course of two or three days, epidermis, canals, pores, and flagellated chambers appear.

E. Asexual Gemmules: The gemmules develop from mesenchyme cells within the body of the parent.   When mature, they burst into one of the excurrent canals and are carried by the water currents out through an osculum.

SPECIAL COMMENTS:

This culture method has been successfully used by H. V. Wilson for several species of sponges, although Mycale seems to have been the only Woods Hole form studied.

REFERENCES:

WILSON, H. V., 1891. Notes on the development of some sponges. *J. Morph.,* **5**: 511–519.
WILSON, H. V., 1894. Observations on the gemmule and egg development of marine sponges. *J. Morph.,* **9**: 277–406.
WILSON, H. V., 1898. On the feasibility of raising sponges from the egg. *Bull. U. S. Fish Comm.,* **17**: 241–245.
WILSON, H. V., 1935. Some critical points in the metamorphosis of the halichondrine sponge larva. *J. Morph.,* **58**: 285–353.
WILSON, H. V., 1937. Notes on the cultivation and growth of sponges from reduction bodies, dissociated cells, and larvae. *In:* Culture Methods for Invertebrate Animals, edit. by Galtsoff *et al.,* Comstock, Ithaca, pp. 137–139.

COELENTERATA *

(HYDROZOA)

Introduction

LIVING MATERIAL:

There is much fluctuation from year to year in the availability of material, certain species, only, being available some years. The species listed in this manual include forms showing the range from types such as Obelia, with perfect medusae, to types such as Hydractinia, in which the medusae are degraded to mere sporosacs. Unfortunately, species such as Gonionemus and Eutima, in which the hydroid generation is very inconspicuous and the medusa generation is the important phase of the life history, are not common at Woods Hole.

The "typical" hydrozoan exhibits an alternation of generations—the succession of two morphologically different adult types, each characterized by a different manner of reproduction. In the hydroid generation, the animal is usually attached and colonial; individual members of the colony may be alike, or the colony may exhibit polymorphism with some members being specialized for securing food and others for reproduction. Asexual reproduction, by budding, results in formation of the medusa; in general, a colony produces either male or female medusae. These individuals leave the colony and carry on a free-living existence; gonads develop on the radial canals or on the sides of the manubrium, and liberation of the gametes from these gonads results in sexual reproduction. The fertilized egg typically develops into a planula larva, which eventually becomes attached and develops a hydranth; lateral budding occurs, and in this manner a new colony is formed.

In general, the Hydrozoa are very sensitive to environmental conditions and do not survive well in the laboratory, even in aquaria containing running sea water. When they are removed to fingerbowls or other smaller vessels, the animals are likely to die very soon unless they are kept at a temperature below that of the room. In working with hydroids, it is advisable to use only a few stems in a large volume of sea water, and to change the sea water frequently. *Do not crowd* either the adults or the eggs and embryos.

BREEDING SEASON:

The height of the hydroid breeding season for some species is during the spring, and warm weather seems to be detrimental to these colonies. A good many forms are available through the summer months for embryological work, however, and the individual breeding season for each species (as far as it has been ascertained) is indicated in the following accounts. Colonies which are excellent for work on regeneration problems are available in the fall.

* Much of the information describing the development of coelenterates was furnished by Dr. W. W. Ballard, to whom we are most grateful.

COELENTERATA

(Hydrozoa)

Bougainvillia superciliaris and *B. carolinensis*
(Perfect but relatively inconspicuous medusae)

LIVING MATERIAL:

The trophosome of *B. superciliaris* is about two inches tall, irregularly branched and light green in color. The pale rose hydranths have 15–20 tentacles in a single whorl about an inconspicuous hypostome. *B. carolinensis* is usually three to six inches tall; it is by far the commoner species at Woods Hole, Mass. The colony is light brown in color, with a greenish tinge; the red hydranths bear about 12 stiff, filiform tentacles on a long, flexible eversible proboscis. Both species are found attached to Fucus and floating timbers, and *B. carolinensis* has also been collected from the dock of the U. S. Fish Commission. See the paper by Nutting (1901) for details and diagrams.

BREEDING SEASON:

June, July and August. The medusae are reported to be present in August; the hydroids are available all summer, although some years they are difficult to find in June.

PROCURING AND HANDLING MATERIAL:

A. Care of Adults: The hydroid colonies should be kept in large dishes, supplied with running sea water. They should not be crowded.

B. Methods of Observation: Medusa development can be studied by clipping off the gonophores and mounting them on slides under a coverslip. Withdrawing a little of the water from under the coverslip (by absorbing it with a piece of lens paper) will exert a slight pressure on the gonophores and will bring out the structural details of the buds. The mature medusa buds can be dissected from the gonophores for study.

NORMAL DEVELOPMENT:

A. Asexual Reproduction: The gonophores are borne singly or in clusters on the main stem and branches; they have the appearance of stalked sacs, and a single medusa is produced within each. The buds are scattered irregularly throughout the colony and there is no orderly arrangement as to age. The medusae develop within the gonophores until all the organs except the gonads are fully formed; then they break away and take up a free-swimming existence. Details concerning formation of the medusae are to be found in the papers by Goette (1907) and Hyman (1940).

The medusae of both species are similar, being sub-globular in shape and possessing four radial canals and a velum. The tentacles are in four groups, each group having a conspicuous eyespot at its base. The brick-red manubrium of *B. carolinensis* is shorter and more slender than that of *B. superciliaris,* but both

4

species have four branched mouth tentacles. The free-swimming life lasts one or two months, during which time the gonads develop along the manubrium.

B. Sexual Reproduction: In *B. superciliaris* the fertilized eggs are retained in folds on the manubrium until the planula stage. A series of cleavages leads to the formation of a single-layered coeloblastula, which is transformed to a solid mass by a multipolar migration of cells. For details of this process, see the paper by Gerd (1892).

REFERENCES:

BERRILL, N. J., 1949. Growth and form in gymnoblastic hydroids. I. Polymorphic development in Bougainvillia and Aselomaris. *J. Morph.,* **84**: 1–30.

GERD, W., 1892. Zur Frage über die Keimblätterbildung bei den Hydromedusen. *Zool. Anz.,* **15**: 312–316.

GOETTE, A., 1907. Vergleichende Entwicklungsgeschichte der Geschlechtsindividuen der Hydropolypen. *Zeitschr. f. wiss. Zool.,* **87**: 1–336.

HYMAN, L. H., 1940. The Invertebrates: Protozoa through Ctenophora. McGraw-Hill Book Co., New York.

NUTTING, C. C., 1901. The hydroids of the Woods Hole region. *Bull. U. S. Fish Comm.,* **19**: 325–386.

COELENTERATA

(HYDROZOA)

Campanularia flexuosa
(Degenerate medusae)

LIVING MATERIAL:

This form is so similar to Obelia that one cannot differentiate between the two, using the anatomy of the feeding individuals as the sole criterion. Even the gonosomes are similar in the two genera, each consisting of a transparent gonotheca with the blastostyle extending from base to tip, and the gonophores budding from it. The gonophores of Campanularia are very degenerate, however, and their medusa-like structure can be distinguished only in sections. Because the gonophores are so inconspicuous and the embryos so obvious, the colonies which produce female gonophores and which later contain embryos are loosely spoken of as "female" colonies, although actually they are asexual.

The colonies are very abundant on floating sea-weed and timbers in shallow water.

BREEDING SEASON: June and July.

PROCURING AND HANDLING MATERIAL:

A. Care of Adults: The colonies can be kept in large dishes or beakers supplied with sea water.

B. Methods of Observation: The eggs and planulae may be studied either by mounting a gonosome in sea water on a slide, or by dissecting the embryos from the gonophores with fine needles.

The mature planulae will metamorphose readily if two or three are placed in a covered Syracuse dish of sea water. Once the planulae attach, the water in the dish should be changed at least twice a day.

NORMAL DEVELOPMENT:

A. Asexual Reproduction: The gonosomes of a female colony are larger than those of the male, and contain a series of embryos which are budded off from the blastostyle in a regular order, so that the older buds are closer to the mouth of the gonotheca. A single egg or embryo develops in each gonophore.

The smaller, oval, male gonosomes resemble those of the female, and bear rounded gonophores filled with milky-grey sperm which become active when they are discharged into sea water.

Details of gonophore development may be found in the paper of Goette (1907).

B. Sexual Reproduction: The maturation and development of the eggs have been studied by Hargitt (1913). There are no nurse cells present; a conspicuous release of chromidia from the nucleus occurs during the maturation process. The large, irregularly-shaped eggs (approximately 160 microns in diameter) are fertilized *in situ,* cleave, form a morula, gastrulate by delamination, and reach a free-swimming planula stage within the gonophores. Mature planulae are two or three times longer than they are broad, and show maggot-like movements while they are still within the gonotheca.

C. Later Stages of Development and Metamorphosis: Four to ten hours after leaving the gonotheca, the mature planulae will attach. Each then opens a mouth, puts forth tentacles, secretes a hydrotheca and perisarc, and becomes a fully-formed individual polyp in two or three days.

REFERENCES:

BERRILL, N. J., 1950. Growth and form in calyptoblastic hydroids. II. Polymorphism within the Campanularidae. *J. Morph.,* **87**: 1–26.

GOETTE, A., 1907. Vergleichende Entwicklungsgeschichte der Geschlechtsindividuen der Hydropolypen. *Zeitschr. f. wiss. Zool.,* **87**: 1–336.

HARGITT, G. T., 1913. Germ cells of coelenterates. I. *Campanularia flexuosa. J. Morph.,* **24**: 383–413.

HARGITT, G. T., 1919. Germ cells of coelenterates. VI. General considerations, discussion, conclusions. *J. Morph.,* **33**: 1–58.

COELENTERATA

(Hydrozoa)

Clava leptostyla

(Degenerate medusae)

LIVING MATERIAL:

The colony consists of solitary brick-red hydroids branching from a filiform hydrorhiza. The polyps are about two cm. high, and have approximately 20 filiform tentacles arranged irregularly about a long hypostome. See the diagram by Hyman (1940).

The colonies are found in shallow water, attached to fronds of rock-weed (*Fucus nodosus*).

BREEDING SEASON: June and July.

PROCURING AND HANDLING MATERIAL:

A. Care of Adults: The colonies should be kept in large dishes, supplied with sea water.

B. Methods of Observation: All stages of development up to the mature planulae can be teased from the female gonophores with fine needles. Larvae, released from ripe colonies, should be pipetted to fingerbowls of fresh sea water. They will then attach and metamorphose.

NORMAL DEVELOPMENT:

A. Asexual Reproduction: The gonophores develop in dense, bud-like clusters just below the tentacles. Those of the male colonies are pink, those of the female colonies purple. In both sexes they are very degenerate, retaining few traces of the medusa structure. Although there are only a few eggs present in each of the female gonophores, there is no evidence of a phagocytosis of nurse cells. Details of gonophore development are available in the papers by Harm (1902) and Kühn (1910).

B. Sexual Reproduction: The large eggs (131 microns in diameter, according to Hargitt, 1919) possess a delicate blue pigment, which appears during maturation and increases and spreads during the cleavage process. Fertilization is internal, and regular or irregular cleavage leads to the formation of a solid morula. The endoderm is formed by a secondary delamination within this mass (Harm, 1902). The oval embryo then elongates, becomes ciliated, and acquires the beginning of the coelenteron. At this stage, the planulae burst from the gonophores.

C. Later Stages of Development and Metamorphosis: The free-swimming planula creeps about for some time, exhibiting marked muscular contractions. Gland cells and nematocysts develop in the ectoderm, and the coelenteron increases in size. Eventually the larva becomes fixed at its broad anterior end, loses its cilia, and flattens out somewhat. It then elongates in the direction of the main body axis, and the first tentacles appear at the free end; this produces a functional hydroid. See the paper by Harm (1902), for further details.

REFERENCES:

HARM, K., 1902. Die Entwicklungsgeschichte von *Clava squamata*. *Zeitschr. f. wiss. Zool.*, 73: 115–166.

HARGITT, C. W., 1906. The organization and early development of *Clava leptostyla* Ag. *Biol. Bull.*, 10: 207–232.

HARGITT, C. W., 1911. Some problems of coelenterate ontogeny. *J. Morph.*, 22: 493–549.

HARGITT, G. T., 1916. Germ cells of coelenterates. II. *Clava leptostyla*. *J. Morph.*, 27: 85–97.

HARGITT, G. T., 1919. Germ cells of coelenterates. VI. General considerations, discussion, conclusions. *J. Morph.*, 33: 1–60.

HYMAN, L. H., 1940. The Invertebrates: Protozoa through Ctenophora. McGraw-Hill Book Co., New York.

KEMP, N. E., 1952. Regeneration in isolated and fused pieces of *Clava leptostyla*. *Biol. Bull.*, 102: 141–148.

KÜHN, A., 1910. Die Entwicklung der Geschlechtsindividuen der Hydromedusen. *Zool. Jahr. abt. Anat. u. Ontog. der Tiere,* 30: 43–174.

COELENTERATA

(Hydrozoa)

Eudendrium ramosum

(Degenerate medusae)

Living Material:

The colonies are profusely branched, and between 10 and 15 cm. in height. The hydranths have a trumpet-shaped hypostome surrounded by a single row of about 20 filiform tentacles. They are very common on piles or docks in shallow water.

Breeding Season: July and August.

Procuring and Handling Material:

A. Care of Adults: Colonies should be provided with adequate supplies of fresh sea water.

B. Methods of Observation: The release of planulae from ripe colonies occurs about mid-day, if the colonies are collected in the morning. Few larvae can be obtained from colonies collected late in the afternoon.

Eggs dissected from the gonophores will not cleave normally; if a study of normal development is desired, it is necessary to clip off not only the intact gonophore but also a considerable portion of the hydroid colony.

Normal Development:

A. Asexual Reproduction: The gonosomes are rudimentary, sessile medusa-forms or gonophores, borne at the bases of special hydranths which lose their tentacles and degenerate during the period in which the gonophores are ripening. The gonophores are strikingly different in the two sexes. The "female" colonies bear loose irregular tufts of sporosacs attached to the stems, each ripe sporosac being bright orange in color. "Male" colonies bear strings of light pink sporosacs (two to four or more per string), radiating like the spokes of a wheel from a common point on the base of the degenerate hydranth. Hyman (1940) shows illustrations of the gonophores; the paper of Goette (1907) may be consulted for the details of gonophore development.

B. Sexual Reproduction: The eggs are fertilized within the gonophores; they are large (230 microns in diameter) and very opaque, due to the presence of a large supply of orange-colored yolk. The details of cleavage can be ascertained only by histological study, but it has been shown that cleavage is very similar to that of insects and crustaceans, involving the formation of yolk-pyramids and an early period during which nuclear, but not cytoplasmic, divisions occur. Following a migration of nuclei to the surface of the syncytial mass, an outer layer of ectoderm is cut off. The inner mass remains syncytial for a considerable period of time and the endoderm is not fully differentiated until the time of metamorphosis.

10

C. Later Stages of Development and Metamorphosis: When first liberated, the ciliated planulae are elongated and pyriform; however, they become slender after a few hours of free-swimming existence. They show a marked positive phototropism when they are first released, but this later declines. Fixation normally occurs after two or three days; the broader aboral pole is attached to the surface and fixed there by a slimy secretion. Metamorphosis is completed in 12 to 24 hours.

For details of cleavage and planula formation, see the paper by Hargitt (1904); metamorphosis is described by Hargitt (1904), and by Allman (1871).

REFERENCES:

ALLMAN, J. G., 1871. A monograph of the gymnoblastic or tubularian hydroids. London, The Ray Society.

BERRILL, N. J., 1952. Growth and form in gymnoblastic hydroids. II. Sexual and asexual reproduction in Rathkea. III. Hydranth and gonophore development in Pennaria and Acaulis. IV. Relative growth in Eudendrium. *J. Morph.,* **90**: 1–32.

GOETTE, A., 1907. Vergleichende Entwicklungsgeschichte der Geschlechtsindividuen der Hydropolypen. *Zeitschr. f. wiss. Zool.,* **87**: 1–336.

HARGITT, C. W., 1889. Origin of sex-cells in Eudendrium. *Proc. Amer. Assoc. Adv. Sci.,* *1889.*

HARGITT, C. W., 1904. The early development of Eudendrium. *Zool. Jahrb. abt. Anat. u. Ontog.,* **20**: 257–276.

HYMAN, L. H., 1940. The Invertebrates: Protozoa through Ctenophora. McGraw-Hill Book Co., New York.

COELENTERATA

(HYDROZOA)

Eutima mira
(Conspicuous medusa generation)

LIVING MATERIAL:

The medusae were formerly abundant at Woods Hole, Mass., in August, but at the present time they are relatively rare. Adult medusae are low and bell-shaped, with four long, tapering marginal tentacles. Three rudimentary tentacles are also present in each quadrant. The four-lobed mouth is located at the apex of a long manubrium which is borne on a gelatinous peduncle. The manubrium is two or three times the height of the bell. The gonads are located along the mid-section of the four radial canals. (See the paper of Hargitt, 1904, for a diagram.)

BREEDING SEASON:

This species breeds during the summer months at Beaufort, N. C., but the breeding season at Woods Hole has not been determined.

PROCURING AND HANDLING MATERIAL:

A. Care of Adults: An adequate supply of fresh sea water is important.

B. Methods of Observation: Fertilized eggs can be obtained by placing several ripe animals in a small aquarium or battery jar of sea water. Shedding usually occurs between 7:30 and 8:30 P.M. on the night when the animals are collected.

NORMAL DEVELOPMENT:

A. The Unfertilized Ovum: The eggs are said to be very clear and transparent, so that it is possible to observe details of development quite completely.

B. Cleavage and Gastrulation: Fertilization is apparently external. Segmentation is total but not entirely regular, leading to the formation of a hollow, ciliated, one-layered blastula. The endoderm layer first appears at the posterior pole, but it is not clear as to whether this is a process of delamination or of cellular migration.

C. Time Table of Development: Details of the developmental time sequence are not available, although development is rapid. Eggs shed at 8 P.M. develop into rapidly swimming planulae by the next morning.

D. Later Stages of Development and Metamorphosis: About 12 hours after fertilization, a ciliated, elongate planula is formed. The cleavage cavity is reduced in the larva, but is still visible between the endoderm cells. The anterior end of the planula is the broader, and on the opposite end an invagination soon appears. This invagination is gradually pushed toward one side of the larva (termed the "ventral" side) by the enlargement of one of the lips of the invagination. At the time of attachment, the invaginated "ventral" sac is everted and the glandular cells which cover it secrete an adhesive cement. The free end of the attached

12

"root" then increases in length and the first hydranth develops at its apex. Subsequent hydranths are produced in a regular order behind this first individual.

The hydroid colonies are inconspicuous. The hydroids have a prominent round manubrium surrounded by a single circle of ten tentacles. The elongate, cylindrical hydranth body is not covered by the perisarc, and the stem lacks annulations.

REFERENCES:

BROOKS, W. K., 1886. The life-history of the Hydromedusae. *Mem. Boston Soc. Nat. Hist.,* 3: 359–430.

HARGITT, C. W., 1904. The medusae of the Woods Hole region. *Bull. Bur. Fish.,* 24: 21–79.

COELENTERATA

(Hydrozoa)

Gonionemus murbachii
(Conspicuous medusa generation)

LIVING MATERIAL:

Gonionemus was formerly very abundant in the Eel Pond at Woods Hole, Mass., but has now practically disappeared from the vicinity; this seems to be associated with the disappearance of eel grass.

The adults measure about 20 mm. in diameter and are about 10 mm. high; they possess four radial canals on which are located the yellow, ribbon-like gonads. The marginal tentacles vary in number from 16 to 80 and have characteristic adhesive pads near their tips. The sex can be ascertained by examining the animals with a dissecting microscope; the ovaries have a granular appearance, while the testes are homogeneous and translucent.

BREEDING SEASON:

July to the last week of September; the height of the season is from mid-July to mid-August.

PROCURING AND HANDLING MATERIAL:

A. Care of Adults: The adults are hardy and will survive in aquaria for several months. Neither larvae nor adults need running sea water, but they seem to survive best in balanced aquaria where they have a constant supply of diatoms for food.

B. Methods of Observation: Adults gathered in the morning will normally shed their eggs between 6 and 8 P.M. on the day of collection. They can be induced to shed in the morning by keeping them in artificial light during the night to prevent shedding, and then placing them in the dark for an hour. If eggs are desired in the afternoon, the adults should be gathered in the morning and then placed in the dark for an hour, beginning at about 3 P.M. A single animal kept in the laboratory will produce eggs nightly for as long as a week, although the number of eggs obtained decreases after the third day.

Since the fertilized eggs adhere to the surfaces with which they come into contact, it is suggested that the dishes in which shedding animals are placed contain microscope slides. These slides, with the attached eggs and larvae, are then easily manipulated for study.

NORMAL DEVELOPMENT:

A. The Unfertilized Ovum: The eggs are yellowish in color and measure about 70 microns in diameter. When shed, they are covered with a sticky jelly membrane; after fertilization they rapidly sink to the bottom and adhere to the container. Maturation apparently takes place before shedding, since polar bodies are not found on shed eggs.

14

B. *Cleavage and Gastrulation:* Cleavage is total and equal.   At the 8-cell stage, there is a rotation of some of the blastomeres to form a flat plate of cells.   Continued cleavage gives rise to a hollow blastula consisting of a single layer of cells. These cells develop cilia and, while the blastula is still rotating within its membrane, the endoderm is formed by multipolar delamination.   With the formation of this inner layer the blastocoele is eliminated.

C. *Time Table of Development:* Perkins (1902) gives the following schedule. The times are given in minutes after fertilization; no temperature is specified.

Stage	Time
First cleavage	60 minutes
Second cleavage	110 minutes
Third cleavage	160 minutes
Planula	12 hours
Attachment	2 weeks
First tentacles on hydroid	3 weeks

D. *Later Stages of Development and Metamorphosis:* After leaving the membranes, the larvae elongate and the anterior end (aboral pole) broadens.   At this time the planulae are bottom-swimmers.   The coelenteron begins to form in the posterior portion of the larva by a rearrangement of the endoderm cells, shortly before metamorphosis.   At the same time the cell boundaries of the posterior (oral) pole disappear and this region becomes syncytial.   At metamorphosis the larva stops swimming, loses its cilia, and attaches by the broad anterior end.   A mouth forms at the free end, and is surrounded at first by two tentacles and later by four. The polyps remain solitary but may give off non-ciliated planula-like buds (frustules) which creep along the bottom and develop into hydroids.

REFERENCES:

JOSEPH, H., 1925. Zur Morphologie und Entwicklungsgeschichte von Haleremita und Gonionemus. *Zeitschr. f. wiss. Zool.,* **125**: 374–434.

MURBACH, L., 1895. Preliminary note on the life-history of Gonionemus. *J. Morph.,* **11**: 493–496.

PERKINS, H. F., 1902. The development of *Gonionema murbachii. Proc. Acad. Nat. Sci., Philadelphia,* **54**: 750–790.

RUGH, R., 1929. Egg laying habits of *Gonionemus murbachii* in relation to light. *Biol. Bull.,* **57**: 261–266.

COELENTERATA

(Hydrozoa)

Gonothyrea loveni

(Imperfect medusae)

Living Material:

The colony consists of an erect, irregularly branching stem about one-half to three-fourths of an inch high. The hydrothecae are bell-shaped and have a toothed margin. The hydroids possess a single whorl of filiform tentacles. Gonothyrea is not common at Woods Hole, Mass.

Breeding Season: July and August.

Procuring and Handling Material:

A. Care of Adults: The colonies should be provided with an adequate supply of fresh sea water.

B. Methods of Observation: The eggs and larvae are difficult to dissect from the gonophores, and can best be studied by mounting whole gonophores on slides. Free-swimming planulae will readily attach and metamorphose in the laboratory if they are placed in covered Syracuse dishes of sea water.

Normal Development:

A. Asexual Reproduction: The gonangia, which are borne in the axils of the branches, consist of a central blastostyle surrounded by a long, oval gonotheca. The gonophores, which are actually degenerate medusae, do not break away from the blastostyle but remain attached to it by means of short stalks, projecting outside the gonotheca in groups of three or four. In the development of the gonophores of both sexes, there are traces of radial and ring canals, and stubby tentacles are present on the distal ends of the sporosacs.

B. Sexual Reproduction: The eggs, of which there may be one or more present in each gonophore, are comparatively small (102 microns, according to Hargitt, 1919). They are fertilized *in situ* before maturation by sperm which are released by the male gonophores. Cleavage may be either regular or irregular. If it is regular, a coeloblastula is formed and the endoderm is formed by multipolar migration; if it is irregular, a solid morula is formed and both ectoderm and endoderm differentiate directly from this. In either type of development the resulting planula is a solid, oval mass of cells. This soon elongates, becomes ciliated, and develops traces of a coelenteron. At this time it escapes from the gonophore.

C. Later Stages of Development and Metamorphosis: The planula, which shows a well-developed coelenteron, swims about for 6–12 hours and then attaches by its broader, anterior pole. At the time of attachment, it loses its cilia and flattens out. The widened base soon begins to secrete a perisarc. Following these events, there is an elongation perpendicular to the attachment, and the development of a mouth and tentacles at the free end. Details of gonophore formation are available

16

in the paper by Goette (1907) and the entire development, through metamorphosis, is described by Wulfert (1902).

REFERENCES:

BERRILL, N. J., 1950. Growth and form in calyptoblastic hydroids. II. Polymorphism within the Campanularidae. *J. Morph.,* **87**: 1–26.

GOETTE, A., 1907. Vergleichende Entwicklungsgeschichte der Geschlechtsindividuen der Hydropolypen. *Zeitschr. f. wiss. Zool.,* **87**: 1–336.

HARGITT, G. T., 1919. Germ cells of coelenterates. VI. General considerations, discussion, conclusions. *J. Morph.,* **33**: 1–58.

WULFERT, J., 1902. Die Embryonalentwicklung von *Gonothyraea loveni* Allm. *Zeitschr. f. wiss. Zool.,* **71**: 296–327.

COELENTERATA

(Hydrozoa)

Hydractinia echinata
(Degenerate medusae)

LIVING MATERIAL:

Colonies of this form are fairly common on the Littorina shells inhabited by the small hermit crab, Pagurus. There are three types of individuals in the fully-developed colony: (1) ordinary polyps (feeders), with a single whorl of tentacles; (2) thread-like coiling forms with no mouth and an apical knob of nematocysts (stingers, commonest around the lip of the shell); and (3) gonosomes. All three types arise singly from a hydrorhiza network covered by a rust-red spine-studded crust (Nutting, 1901).

The snails on which the colonies grow are common in the littoral near Woods Hole, Mass., and can be gathered in considerable numbers at Sheep Pen Harbor and Tarpaulin Cove.

BREEDING SEASON: June, July and August.

PROCURING AND HANDLING MATERIAL:

A. Care of Adults: Colonies may be kept in large beakers or other deep vessels, supplied with running sea water.

B. Methods of Observation: If a number of snail-shells bearing "male" and "female" colonies are placed in a large uncovered dish of sea water and left overnight, eggs will usually be shed and fertilized between 7 and 9 A.M. on the following morning. Colonies kept in running sea water have been known to shed daily for a week before becoming exhausted. The shedding can be controlled by light, however, if eggs are desired at some other time of day. Colonies should be kept in running sea water, under a glowing 100-watt bulb, from the time of collection until gametes are needed. They should then be placed in the dark for one or more hours and subsequently re-exposed to light. By the use of a hand lens or dissecting microscope, the sexes can be segregated to separate fingerbowls of fresh sea water. The males will shed 50 minutes after re-illumination, the females five minutes later. The eggs should be transferred to fingerbowls of fresh sea water and inseminated with one or two drops of water taken from a dish of shedding males. Ballard (1942) gives further details of this method for controlling shedding.

NORMAL DEVELOPMENT:

A. Asexual Reproduction: The gonosomes, or reproductive individuals, are usually without tentacles and have a large knob of nematocysts on the proboscis; each bears a number of gonophores, which are medusa-buds reduced to the status of sporosacs. Ripe "male" and "female" colonies can be distinguished from one another with the unaided eye, since the eggs within the sporosacs are dull green against the red hydrorhiza, and the sperm, when mature, are a white mass.   For details of gonophore development, see the papers by Goette (1907, 1916).

B. Sexual Reproduction: The maturation of the eggs within the gonophores occurs as a direct response to light and can be seen in eggs dissected from colonies placed in the light after several hours of darkness.   In such eggs, the large germinal vesicle begins to break down soon after the exposure to light.   The first polar body is given off 45 minutes after exposure to light, the second polar body ten minutes later.   Occasionally the first polar body may divide.   The eggs are shed immediately after the second maturation division (Ballard, 1942).

The eggs are yolky and usually green; occasionally grey, orange or pink ova are shed.   Teissier and Teissier (1927) give the average egg-diameter as between 160 and 170 microns.   When shed, the eggs are covered by a highly transparent, radially striated jelly, which swells on exposure to sea water.   The swelling of this layer causes the polar bodies to be lifted from the egg surface and they are soon lost.   Cleavage may be irregular, but usually the somewhat amoeboid egg undergoes three equal, total cleavages, each of which is at right angles to the preceding one.   The separating pairs of blastomeres tend to retain broad protoplasmic connections with one another on the side opposite the cleavage furrow, until just before the succeeding cleavages begin.   There is much variation in the time and degree of shifting of positions of the blastomeres, but the bizarre cleavage patterns often seen in the laboratory are commonly the result of evaporation of the sea water, or other unfavorable factors.

Mitotic synchronism quickly disappears.   Gastrulation is said to start as early as the 16-cell stage, by mixed delamination and multipolar proliferation.   The gastrula loses its spherical form and remains for a few hours an irregular mass; then it returns to the spherical form and gradually lengthens into the planula form. For illustrations of the cleavage pattern, see the papers by Beckwith (1914) and Bunting (1894).

C. Later Stages of Development and Metamorphosis: At the end of 24 hours the embryo is a "preplanula" (Teissier and Teissier, 1927) with an elongated oval form, recognizable polarity and ciliation.   During the course of a few days, it lengthens, one end becoming progressively slimmer, while it rolls and crawls along the bottom like a planarian.   The large end (which goes first in this movement) is the end which later produces the adhesive disc by which the larva attaches for metamorphosis; it becomes the aboral end of the polyp.

Following attachment of the attenuated planula, there is a delay of a few hours to several days, and then the tapering free end shrinks down almost to the substrate, where it produces a mouth and a succession of tentacles.   The new polyp elongates, its attached end meanwhile actively sending out a number of anastomosing and encrusting hydrorhiza processes from which branch new polyps.   For further details of planula development and metamorphosis, see the paper by Teissier and Teissier (1927).

REFERENCES:

BALLARD, W. W., 1942.   The mechanism for synchronous spawning in Hydractinia and Pennaria.   *Biol. Bull.,* **82**: 329–339.
BECKWITH, C. J., 1914.   The genesis of the plasma-structure in the egg of *Hydractinia echinata.* *J. Morph.,* **25**: 189–251.

BERRILL, N. J., 1953. Growth and form in gymnoblastic hydroids. VI. Polymorphism within the Hydractiniidae. *J. Morph.,* **92**: 241–272.

BUNTING, M., 1894. The origin of sex cells in Hydractinia and Podocoryne, and the development of Hydractinia. *J. Morph.,* **9**: 203–236.

GOETTE, A., 1907. Vergleichende Entwicklungsgeschichte der Geschlechtsindividuen der Hydropolypen. *Zeitschr. f. wiss. Zool.,* **87**: 1–336.

GOETTE, A., 1916. Die Gattungen Podocoryne, Stylactis und Hydractinia. *Zool. Jahrb. abt. Syst., Geog., Okol. der Tiere,* **39**: 443–510.

NUTTING, C. C., 1901. The hydroids of the Woods Hole region. *Bull. U. S. Fish Comm.,* **19**: 325–386.

TEISSIER, L., AND G. TEISSIER, 1927. Les principales étapes du développement d'*Hydractinia echinata* (Flem.). *Bull. Soc. Zool. France,* **52**: 537–547.

COELENTERATA

(Hydrozoa)

Obelia commissuralis and *O. geniculata*
(Perfect but relatively inconspicuous medusa generation)

LIVING MATERIAL:

The colonies of *Obelia commissuralis* are tree-like in form, and reach a height of 6 to 8 inches. The annulated, rather sparse side branches are given off at right angles from a long central trunk. Colonies of *O. geniculata* are not more than 30 mm. high and usually consist of a single stem bearing alternate hydranths on broad processes. Hydroids of both species have cup-like hydrothecae and a single row of filiform tentacles surrounding the hypostome.

The hydroid colonies are commonly found attached to docks, sea-weed or floating timbers at Woods Hole, Mass. The medusae are often caught in tow nets during the summer.

BREEDING SEASON: June, July and August.

PROCURING AND HANDLING MATERIAL:

A. Care of Adults: Colonies are easily maintained in the laboratory, if they are provided with an adequate supply of fresh sea water.

B. Methods of Observation: To obtain medusae, ripe hydroid colonies should be placed, without crowding, in large fingerbowls of sea water. Within an hour or two, swimming medusae are usually released; these can be removed to depression slides for study. Young stages of medusa formation must be teased from the gonosomes with needles; older gonophores will usually be released if a well-matured gonosome is mounted on a slide under a coverslip and pressure applied to the coverslip with needles.

To obtain fertilized eggs, several mature medusae should be placed together in a jar of sea water. Although it has not been demonstrated for the Woods Hole form, Merejkowsky (1883) states that the Mediterranean species of Obelia always sheds in the early morning hours.

NORMAL DEVELOPMENT:

A. Asexual Reproduction: The gonosomes of both species are borne in the axils of the branches, and are several times as large as the hydranths. Each consists of a vase-like gonotheca surrounding a central blastostyle whose expanded tip forms a loose plug for the mature gonotheca. The gonophores which mature as medusae develop as buds along the blastostyle, the most mature buds being found toward the neck of the gonotheca. When fully mature, they break loose and escape past the blastostyle plug to the outside. Details and diagrams of the development of the medusae can be found in the paper of Goette (1907).

B. Sexual Reproduction: When first shed, the medusae of *O. geniculata* have 24 tentacles, while those of *O. commissuralis* have only 16. Both species have

21

four radial canals and a rather short manubrium. The velum is reduced to a narrow and somewhat lobed membrane near the bases of the tentacles. This reduction of the velum makes possible an eversion of the bell when the medusa comes to rest, so that the manubrium protrudes from the center of the convex surface. The gonads are not visible when the medusae are shed, but slowly mature during the two months of free-swimming existence. When mature, they appear as oval structures hanging from the mid-part of the radial canals. Diagrams of the medusae of the two species are presented by Nutting (1901).

Merejkowsky (1883) gives the details of sexual reproduction in an undesignated species of the genus Obelia. The eggs (about 130 microns in diameter, according to Hargitt, 1919) are fertilized externally after the gametes have been shed. No fertilization membrane is produced. A single polar body is given off after the eggs are shed. Regular and total cleavage leads to the formation of a one-layered coeloblastula, which soon becomes ciliated and motile. A few hours after the blastula is formed, the endoderm develops by an inward migration of cells from the posterior pole of the larva, which is now elongated. Continued multiplication of the endoderm cells leads to the formation of a typical solid, ciliated planula, with a broad anterior end and a narrow, pointed posterior end. This planula remains as a surface-swimmer for about a day, gradually developing nematocysts and epithelio-muscular cells. It then drops to the bottom, loses its cilia, and becomes affixed by the broader anterior end. Tentacles and mouth develop at the free end of the attached larva, and eventually asexual budding leads to the formation of a new hydroid colony.

REFERENCES:

FAULKNER, G. H., 1929. The early prophases of the first oocyte division as seen in life, in *Obelia geniculata. Quart. J. Micr. Sci.,* **73**: 225–242.

GOETTE, A., 1907. Vergleichende Entwicklungsgeschichte der Geschlechtsindividuen der Hydropolypen. *Zeitschr. f. wiss. Zool.,* **87**: 1–336.

HARGITT, G. T., 1919. Germ cells of coelenterates. VI. General considerations, discussion, conclusions. *J. Morph.,* **33**: 1–58.

MEREJKOWSKY, C., 1883. Histoire du développement de la méduse Obelia. *Bull. Soc. Zool. France,* **8**: 98–129.

NUTTING, C. C., 1901. The hydroids of the Woods Hole region. *Bull. U. S. Fish Comm.,* **19**: 325–386.

COELENTERATA

(Hydrozoa)

Pennaria tiarella

(Imperfect medusae)

LIVING MATERIAL:

The colonies vary from two to six inches in height, and grow in a branched, fan-like pattern. The terminal hydranths are large, with vermilion bodies and white tentacles. The hypostome is long and is covered with stubby, knobbed tentacles. In addition, there is a basal ring of about 12 long, slender tentacles. Diagrams are given by Hyman (1940) and Nutting (1901). The adult colonies are very common at Woods Hole, Mass., and can be collected from Fucus or other sea-weeds, or from pilings three feet below sea level. They are abundant on the vegetation of the Spindle.

BREEDING SEASON: Mid-July to September.

PROCURING AND HANDLING MATERIAL:

A. Care of Adults: The animals are extremely sensitive and should never be crowded. Place a few colonies bearing the best embryological material (large eggs and full spermaries) in large fingerbowls on a water table, allowing a gentle stream of sea water to flow through the dishes.

B. Methods of Observation: About 3 P.M. on the second afternoon after collection, cut a few small stems from ripe "male" and "female" colonies, carefully rinse them in sea water, and place them together in a fingerbowl containing filtered sea water. Cover the dish and return it to the water table. Examine the dish during the evening for evidence of shedding, and pipette the fertilized eggs to a fingerbowl of fresh sea water as soon as possible after they are shed. If unfertilized eggs are desired, the male and female colonies can be isolated in separate fingerbowls. Eggs procured in this manner can be artificially inseminated with a few drops of sperm solution taken from a dish containing a shedding male colony.

It is possible to modify the time of shedding and to procure gametes at any time of day which is convenient (Baker, 1936; Ballard, 1942). If colonies are placed in the dark for 24 hours, as soon as they are brought into the laboratory, and then exposed to continuous light (either artificial or natural), shedding can be expected 10–14 hours after the return to light. Since the animals do not live long in the laboratory, this procedure can be used only once.

The free-swimming larvae should be transferred to Syracuse dishes of sea water and kept in a moist-chamber on a sea water table until attachment. After attachment has occurred, the dishes can be stacked in an inverted position, in wooden racks placed in aquaria of running sea water.

NORMAL DEVELOPMENT:

A. Asexual Reproduction: The gonophores bud off singly from the hydranth body just above the proximal tentacles; there may be one to three per gonosome.

23

A single colony bears gonophores of one sex only, but in living individuals sex is difficult to ascertain until the gonophores are mature; the eggs will be pink and the sperm white (Smallwood, 1899). "Male" and "female" colonies are actually asexual, bearing male and female gonophores, respectively. For illustrations and details of gonophore development, see the paper of Goette (1907).

The mature medusae are similar in the two sexes; they have an elongate bell, a velum, four radial canals and four rudimentary tentacles. The vermilion manubrium (spadix), to which the gametes are attached, is short and there is no mouth. In southern waters, Pennaria medusae generally break away from the colony and swim about during the discharge of the sex products; in Woods Hole, however, they usually remain attached, and the eggs may not be ejected until long after fertilization.

At the onset of spawning, the ripe medusae gradually begin a rhythmic twitching. The males emit puffs of white sperm, the females eject three to six eggs. The spent medusae finally drop off, swim feebly if at all, and shrivel and die in a few hours.

B. Sexual Reproduction: The newly shed eggs are opaque and usually pale pink in color, although this can vary from a cream-white to orange. The irregular shape makes accurate measurements difficult; C. W. Hargitt (1900) gives 400–500 microns as the diameter, while G. T. Hargitt (1919) states that the average diameter is only 237 microns. The large size of at least some of the ova is probably associated with the fact that certain of the maturing oöcytes absorb other oöcytes during development. The polar bodies are given off and lost before the eggs are shed. Fertilization is external and is accompanied by amoeboid movements of the egg; no fertilization membrane is formed.

The cleavages, which begin about 30 minutes after insemination, are rapid. Although at times they may be quite regular until the 8-cell stage, they become chaotic and without pattern after this stage. Nuclear division with delayed cytoplasmic division is quite common. The embryo has a flat, disc-like appearance during the later cleavages, but rounds up to form a solid spherical morula. This differentiates an ectodermal layer, which becomes ciliated. In 12–24 hours, the pyriform embryo becomes a young free-swimming planula. See the papers of C. W. Hargitt (1900) and G. T. Hargitt (1909) for details of early development.

C. Later Stages of Development and Metamorphosis: The early, free-living planula is a solid, ciliated organism, but eventually the endoderm differentiates from the central mass and the beginnings of a coelenteron become visible. In about five days the larva attaches and begins to secrete a delicate perisarc. Two days later, the rudiments of the proximal tentacles of the first hydranth are visible about the mouth, which develops at the free end of the metamorphosing larvae. Hargitt (1900) presents diagrams and describes metamorphosis in detail.

REFERENCES:

BAKER, E. G. S., 1936. Photoperiodicity in the spawning reaction of *Pennaria tiarella* McCr. *Proc. Indiana Acad. Sci.,* **45**: 251–252.

BALLARD, W. W., 1942. The mechanism for synchronous spawning in Hydractinia and Pennaria. *Biol. Bull.,* **82**: 329–339.

BERRILL, N. J., 1952. Growth and form in gymnoblastic hydroids. II. Sexual and asexual reproduction in Rathkea. III. Hydranth and gonophore development in Pennaria and Acaulis. IV. Relative growth in Eudendrium. *J. Morph.,* **90**: 1–32.

GOETTE, A., 1907. Vergleichende Entwicklungsgeschichte der Geschlechtsindividuen der Hydropolypen. *Zeitschr. f. wiss. Zool.,* **87**: 1–336.

HARGITT, C. W., 1900. A contribution to the natural history and development of *Pennaria tiarella* McCr. *Amer. Nat.,* **34**: 387–415.

HARGITT, G. T., 1909. Maturation, fertilization, and segmentation of *Pennaria tiarella* (Ayres) and of *Tubularia crocea* (Ag.). *Bull. Mus. Comp. Zool., Harvard,* **53**: 159–212.

HARGITT, G. T., 1919. Germ cells of coelenterates. VI. General considerations, discussion, conclusions. *J. Morph.,* **33**: 1–58.

HYMAN, L. H., 1940. The Invertebrates: Protozoa through Ctenophora. McGraw-Hill Book Co., New York.

NUTTING, C. C., 1901. The hydroids of the Woods Hole region. *Bull. U. S. Fish Comm.,* **19**: 325–386.

SMALLWOOD, M., 1899. A contribution to the morphology of *Pennaria tiarella* McCrady. *Amer. Nat.,* **33**: 861–870.

SMALLWOOD, W. M., 1909. A reëxamination of the cytology of Hydractinia and Pennaria. *Biol. Bull.,* **17**: 209–240.

COELENTERATA

(Hydrozoa)

Podocoryne carnea

(Perfect but relatively inconspicuous medusa generation)

LIVING MATERIAL:

This genus is very similar to Hydractinia. The colony is composed of an encrusting mat of stolons covered with a perisarc which is beset with jagged spines. From these hydrorhizae arise the feeding polyps, each having a single whorl of tentacles around a conical proboscis; the slender protective hydranths lack tentacles but are armed with batteries of nematocysts. The reproductive hydranths bear clusters of gonophores just below the tentacles. For a further description, see the paper of Hargitt (1901).

The species is rare at Woods Hole, Mass.; it is occasionally collected with colonies of Hydractinia from Sheep Pen Harbor. Like the latter species, it is found as an encrusting mat on snail shells, but the ratio of Hydractinia to Podocoryne colonies is about 100 to 1.

BREEDING SEASON: June and July.

PROCURING AND HANDLING MATERIAL:

A. Care of Adults: The colonies should be maintained in adequate supplies of sea water.

B. Methods of Observation: If ripe colonies are isolated in fingerbowls of sea water, the medusae are often discharged. Stages of medusa development can be obtained by dissection from the gonophores.

NORMAL DEVELOPMENT:

A. Asexual Reproduction: A single medusa develops within each gonophore, and only male or female medusae are produced by any one colony. The details of medusa development are described by Goette (1907). When they are fully formed, the nearly perfect medusae escape into the water. At the time of release, they have a marked bell-shape, a definite velum, and a short, reduced manubrium. At the end of the four radial canals can be seen four marginal tentacles, and between these there are four interradial tentacles. Although some strains of this species have mature gonads at the time when they are set free, the strain available at Woods Hole has only very immature gonads visible along the radial canals. Goette (1916) states that the medusae may give rise to several additional generations of medusae by budding before they produce gametes. Diagrams of the medusae are available in the paper by Hargitt (1901).

B. Sexual Reproduction: This phase of the life history has been studied by de Varenne (1882), in one of the strains having a free-swimming life of only a few hours. Fertilization is external and occurs before the breakdown of the germinal vesicle. The egg is said to exhibit marked amoeboid movements. Total cleavages lead to the formation of a solid, oval morula; an internal cavity soon appears and the elongating, ciliated larva quickly develops into a free-swimming planula.   After a few hours the planula loses its cilia, fixes by its anterior end, and secretes a perisarc.   The free end develops the mouth and tentacles of a typical hydroid.

REFERENCES:

BERRILL, N. J., 1953. Growth and form in gymnoblastic hydroids. VI. Polymorphism within the Hydractiniidae. *J. Morph.*, **92**: 241–272.
BUNTING, M., 1894. The origin of the sex cells in Hydractinia and Podocoryne; and the development of Hydractinia. *J. Morph.*, **9**: 203–236.
GOETTE, A., 1907. Vergleichende Entwicklungsgeschichte der Geschlechtsindividuen der Hydropolypen. *Zeitschr. f. wiss. Zool.*, **87**: 1–336.
GOETTE, A., 1916. Die Gattungen Podocoryne, Stylactis und Hydractinia. *Zool. Jahr. abt. Syst., Geog., Okol. Tiere,* **39**: 443–510.
HARGITT, C. W., 1901. Synopses of North-American Invertebrates. XIV. The Hydromedusae. *Amer. Nat.,* **35**: 301–315, 379–395, 575–595.
MAYER, A. G., 1910. Medusae of the world. I and II. The Hydromedusae. Carnegie Inst., Wash. Pub. 109.
DE VARENNE, M. A., 1882. Développement de l'oeuf de la *Podocoryne carnea*. *C. R. Acad. Sci.,* **94**: 892–894.

COELENTERATA

(Hydrozoa)

Tubularia crocea

(Imperfect medusae)

LIVING MATERIAL:

The colonies form dense tufts of long, tangled, sparsely branched stems, three to four inches high. The hydranths have two rows of short tentacles: a row about the mouth and a proximal row of 16–25 shorter tentacles. See the diagram by Hyman (1940). The colonies grow profusely on piles and docks in the Woods Hole, Mass., area.

BREEDING SEASON: June and July.

PROCURING AND HANDLING MATERIAL:

A. Care of Adults: Select a good-sized colony, examine it with a hand lens or dissecting microscope, and clip off those branches containing the best embryological material. The hydroids should not be crowded, and the sea water should be changed frequently. They are very sensitive to increases in temperature.

B. Methods of Observation: Motile sperm can be obtained by crushing the gonophores on a slide; eggs and larvae can be teased from the female gonophores with fine needles. Older larvae, close to the time of hatching, are visible *in situ*. Actinulae escaping from the parent colony will not develop without special feeding. If mature colonies are allowed to stand for several hours in a large dish, the actinulae will be shed first, followed by earlier and earlier developmental stages, until finally cleavage stages are obtained.

NORMAL DEVELOPMENT:

A. Asexual Reproduction: The gonosomes of a mature specimen are long, branched stalks which grow in a dense cluster between the two circles of tentacles. The gonophores are budded off along the length of the gonosomes; they are quite markedly reduced medusae which never become free-swimming, and usually show no signs of radial or circular canals. The male and female gonophores are produced by separate colonies. The male gonophores are balloon-like structures lacking tentacles; within them, a cloudy mass of sperm can be seen surrounding the dark red spadix, which is actually the manubrium of the medusoid. The female gonophores, containing the eggs and developing larvae, usually have four blunt, knob-like tentacles at the distal end, although occasionally one or more of these is slightly elongated. Details of gonophore development can be found in the paper by Goette (1907).

B. Sexual Reproduction: Although many oöcytes are present in the young gonophores, only a few reach maturity. These favored oöcytes engulf and absorb the "nurse" eggs, which are arrested in the primary oöcyte stage. The sperm probably enters the egg before the polar bodies are given off, although there is

28

some controversy on this point. When ripe, the egg is very large (approximately 400 microns) and somewhat irregular in shape (Allen, 1900; Hargitt, 1909, 1919). Fertilization and early development take place within the modified medusa. Cleavage is often irregular and apparently either a coeloblastula or a solid morula can be formed (Lowe, 1926; Hargitt, 1909). Gastrulation of the coeloblastula is described as a mixture of delamination and multipolar proliferation (Benoit, 1925; Hargitt, 1909). The embryo is thus converted into an oval, solid mass of cells which eventually flattens to a disc. Irregular coalescing spaces appear in the endoderm, marking the beginning of the adult coelenteron. Blunt protuberances at the edge of the disc are rudiments of the aboral tentacles of the adult; these rapidly elongate and bend toward the future aboral end of the body.

C. Later Stages of Development and Metamorphosis: The entire embryo elongates in the direction of the oral-aboral axis and becomes cylindrical. The oral end is perforated by the mouth and a series of small protuberances, the oral tentacles, develop about this opening. When this stage is reached, the "actinula," which may be considered a precociously metamorphosing form, part planula and part polyp, leaves the gonophore. It then creeps about on the substrate by means of the aboral tentacles; although the mouth is carried downward at this time, the attachment is made by the aboral pole. The attached polyp increases rapidly in height, and buds off daughter hydroids along its sides. The creeping stolons, which bud off secondary upright shoots, are developed from the base of the primary polyp. Details of actinula formation are described by MacBride (1914).

REFERENCES:

ALLEN, C. M., 1900. A contribution to the development of *Parypha crocea*. *Biol. Bull.,* 1: 291–315.

BENOIT, P., 1925. L'ovogénèse et les premiers stades du développement chez la Myriothèle et chez la Tubulaire. *Arch. de Zool. Exp.,* 64: 85–326.

BERRILL, N. J., 1952. Growth and form in gymnoblastic hydroids. V. Growth cycle in Tubularia. *J. Morph.,* 90: 583–601.

GOETTE, A., 1907. Vergleichende Entwicklungsgeschichte der Geschlechtsindividuen der Hydropolypen. *Zeitschr. f. wiss. Zool.,* 87: 1–336.

HARGITT, G. T., 1909. Maturation, fertilization, and segmentation of *Pennaria tiarella* (Ayres) and of *Tubularia crocea* (Ag.). *Bull. Mus. Comp. Zool., Harvard,* 53: 162–212.

HARGITT, G. T., 1919. Germ cells of coelenterates. VI. General considerations, discussion, conclusions. *J. Morph.,* 33: 1–58.

HYMAN, L. H., 1940. The Invertebrates: Protozoa through Ctenophora. McGraw-Hill Book Co., New York.

LOWE, E., 1926. The embryology of *Tubularia larynx* (Allm.). *Quart. J. Micr. Sci.,* 70: 599–627.

MACBRIDE, E. W., 1914. Text-Book of Embryology. Vol. I. Invertebrata. Macmillan and Co., Ltd., London.

COELENTERATA

(HYDROZOA)

Turritopsis nutricula
(Conspicuous medusa generation)

LIVING MATERIAL:

This is not a common Woods Hole form. The adult medusae are square in shape and have a large manubrium which nearly fills the upper part of the sub-umbrella cavity. Although the young medusae have only 8 tentacles, the adults have over 100. The large, oval, red-orange reproductive organs surround the upper portion of the manubrium and are found along the four radial canals. The branching hydroid colonies are 8 to 12 mm. high and bear yellowish-red hydranths. The medusa buds are found on the stem at the bases of the hydranths.

BREEDING SEASON:

This has not been ascertained for the Woods Hole region. At Beaufort, North Carolina, the animals breed during the summer months.

PROCURING AND HANDLING MATERIAL:

A. Care of Adults: The adults are relatively hardy and live well in aquaria, although they are very voracious.

B. Obtaining Gametes: The eggs are shed by dehiscence from the gonads about 5 or 6 A.M.

NORMAL DEVELOPMENT:

A. The Unfertilized Ovum: Approximately 20–35 eggs are shed at one time; they are spherical and measure 116 microns in diameter. The inner, dense, yellowish yolk-mass is surrounded by an outer clear ectoplasmic layer, but there is no visible fertilization membrane. Two polar bodies are produced shortly after shedding, but these soon disintegrate and are lost.

B. Cleavage and Gastrulation: Cleavage is total and approximately equal until the 8-cell stage, after which time it becomes very irregular. As in the case of Gonionemus, there is a rotation of cells at the 8-cell stage, so that a flat plate is formed. A solid, syncytial morula, with no trace of a cleavage cavity, develops in six to eight hours. Both the outer ectoderm and the inner endoderm develop from this syncytium.

C. Time Table of Development: The following time table is taken from the paper of Brooks and Rittenhouse (1907). No indication as to the temperature is given.

Stage	Time
Polar bodies	A few minutes after shedding
First cleavage	25–30 minutes after polar bodies
Second cleavage	50–60 minutes after the first cleavage

Stage	Time
Third cleavage	75–85 minutes after the second cleavage
Oval, morula-like embryo	6–8 hours
Free-swimming planula	11 hours
Top-swimming, contractile planula	24 hours
Attachment	48–60 hours
First hydroid well formed	72 hours

D. *Later Stages of Development and Metamorphosis:* The young, oval, ciliated embryo changes by the eleventh hour into a solid, bottom-swimming planula, which is elongated and has a broad anterior end. The planula continues to elongate, and after a day has the ability to contract. At this time, it becomes a top-swimmer. Forty to sixty hours after shedding, a cavity becomes visible in the endoderm of the planula, starting at the anterior end and extending posteriorly. Soon after this time, the larva again sinks to the bottom, and after a short interval, during which it glides along the bottom, the cilia are lost and the larva attaches by its side to the substrate. The root-like planula increases in size and a bud develops from the mid-region of its upper surface. Twenty-four hours after attachment, this bud becomes a young hydroid with three whorls of tentacles. The primary bud gives rise to a branching colony (much like that of Tubularia in general appearance) by asexual budding.

REFERENCES:

BROOKS, W. K., 1886. The life-history of the Hydromedusae. *Mem. Boston Soc. Nat. Hist.,* **3:** 359–430.

BROOKS, W. K., AND S. RITTENHOUSE, 1907. On *Turritopsis nutricula* (McCrady). *Proc. Boston Soc. Nat. Hist.,* **33:** 429–460.

COELENTERATA

(Scyphozoa)

Aurelia aurita (A. flavidula)

LIVING MATERIAL:

The number of animals available at Woods Hole, Mass., varies from year to year; at times they are abundant, at other times they are very scarce. Mature females are recognizable by the presence of pale-pink or purplish gonads; the gonads of the males are milky-white. The animals are usually abundant in the spring, but disappear in July.

BREEDING SEASON:

This is reported to extend from mid- to late summer.

PROCURING AND HANDLING MATERIAL:

A. Care of Adults: Aurelia is very difficult to maintain alive in the laboratory for any period of time; large aquaria, supplied with adequate amounts of running sea water, are probably desirable.

B. Methods of Observation: Eggs and developing planulae can be dissected from the brood-pouches located on the inner surfaces of the oral arms; they should be mounted in a drop of sea water for microscopic observation.

Active planulae, obtained in the above manner, will readily attach and metamorphose as far as the scyphula stage, if they are placed in clean watch glasses of sea water. Gilchrist (1937) gives directions for culturing the scyphistoma stage.

NORMAL DEVELOPMENT:

A. Early Stages of Development: The pinkish, transparent eggs measure about 120 microns in diameter. Fertilization occurs in the gastric pouches, and the eggs are transferred to small brood-pouches on the inner surfaces of the oral arms. Cleavage is total and quite regular, forming a hollow, single-layered blastula. Gastrulation is by invagination, occasionally accompanied by an in-wandering of cells. At the time of completion of the gastrulation process, the blastopore, which becomes the mouth of the scyphistoma, is almost completely closed. The spherical embryo develops cilia and elongates, taking on an egg-shape; the blastopore is located at the more pointed end. At this stage, the larva leaves the brood-pouch and takes up a free-swimming existence. For details of the early stages of development, see the papers by Hargitt and Hargitt (1910) and Smith (1891).

B. Later Stages of Development: In about two days the planula attaches by the aboral end and gradually flattens to a cup-shape, losing its ciliation; it is now a young scyphistoma. The mouth and a short hypostome soon become visible. Four primary tentacles arise in a circle about the gaping mouth, and, alternating with these, four endodermal ridges (the taeniolae) project into the coelenteron. The tentacle number is increased to 24 in about a month. Lateral buds can be produced, which either become free or form stolons from which new scyphistomae

32

arise. In the older scyphistomae, the gastric pouches can be seen to communicate by means of holes in the taeniolae, forming the ring sinus just below the oral disc. Sense organs are visible at the bases of each of the eight primary tentacles, appearing first as wart-like buds. Eight lobes from the ring sinus grow out as lappets towards the sense organs, each lappet eventually enclosing a sense organ in its forked tip. When this stage is reached, strobilization occurs. For details of scyphistoma formation, see the paper by Hein (1900).

C. Strobilization and the Ephyrula: The scyphistoma stage of Aurelia is long and strobilization does not usually occur until about April. At this time, the primary tentacles are lost and the tubular body is divided into a series of plate-like discs. Each of these discs becomes free as a small ephyrula, or young jelly fish. The ephyrula bears eight forked lappets, each of which is tipped with a sensory tentacle. The four gastric pouches, lined with gastric filaments which develop from the free edges of the original taeniolae, are clearly visible. Further growth over a period of four months leads to the formation of an adult jelly fish. Details of ephyrula formation and strobilization can be found in the papers by Friedemann (1902) and Percival (1923); the entire development of Aurelia is reviewed by MacBride (1914).

REFERENCES:

FRIEDEMANN, O., 1902. Untersuchungen über die postembryonale Entwicklung von *Aurelia aurita. Zeitschr. f. wiss. Zool.,* **71**: 227–267.

GILCHRIST, F. G., 1937. Rearing the scyphistoma of Aurelia in the laboratory. *In:* Culture Methods for Invertebrate Animals, edit. by Galtsoff *et al.,* Comstock, Ithaca, p. 143.

HARGITT, C. W., AND G. T. HARGITT, 1910. Studies in the development of Scyphomedusae. *J. Morph.,* **21**: 217–262.

HEIN, W., 1900. Untersuchungen über die Entwicklung von *Aurelia aurita. Zeitschr. f. wiss. Zool.,* **67**: 401–438.

MACBRIDE, E. W., 1914. Text-Book of Embryology. Vol. I. Invertebrata. Macmillan and Co., Ltd., London.

PERCIVAL, E., 1923. On the strobilization of Aurelia. *Quart. J. Micr. Sci.,* **67**: 85–100.

SMITH, F., 1891. The gastrulation of *Aurelia flavidula,* Pér. & Les. *Bull. Mus. Comp. Zool., Harvard,* **22**: 115–124.

COELENTERATA

(Scyphozoa)

Cyanea capillata (C. arctica)

LIVING MATERIAL:

The abundance of these animals varies from year to year; adults have been captured at all times of the year, but are not found near the surface during stormy weather.

BREEDING SEASON:

Usually in March and early May, but some animals in the breeding condition can be taken as late as July.

PROCURING AND HANDLING MATERIAL:

A. Care of Adults: No information is available.

B. Obtaining Embryos: Mature animals can be recognized by the white or cream-colored gonads lining the gastric pockets. Eggs and developing larvae are found in the brood-pouches along the oral lobes; they appear as greyish specks to the unaided eye, and can be dissected out into a drop of sea water on a slide, for examination. The early cleavage stages and blastulae are found in the region of the mouth.

C. Methods of Observation: If active planulae are placed in clean Syracuse dishes of sea water, they will attach and metamorphose. If the watch glasses with the attached scyphistomae are removed to aquaria and the larvae fed echinoderm larvae, copepods, etc., they will live for several months.

NORMAL DEVELOPMENT:

A. Early Stages of Development: Maturation probably occurs in the gonad. The mature eggs, each with the second polar body clinging to the delicate egg membrane, then dehisce into the gastric pouches where fertilization occurs; the eggs lodge in folds of the oral lips, where they continue to develop until the planula stage. Cleavage is total, and may or may not be equal; often it is slightly irregular. A cleavage cavity appears early and a hollow, single-layered blastula is formed. Gastrulation is by invagination, although at times this may be accompanied by delamination. The spherical gastrula soon becomes oval and elongates into an active planula which leaves the oral lobe. See the paper by Hargitt and Hargitt (1910) for details of early development; Okada (1927) describes the details of gastrulation.

B. Later Development: The free-swimming planulae are orange-red in color, well ciliated and opaque. The anterior end is distinctly broader than the posterior end, and the old blastopore, which develops into the mouth, may be visible. After a free-swimming life of from 20 to 40 days, the larva settles down and attaches by the narrow end to the substrate. There is an elongation of the body, followed by the acquisition of tentacles about the gaping mouth. The larva is now in the scyphula or scyphistoma stage. The number of tentacles increases from two to twenty-four. Agassiz (1862) gives diagrams of the planulae and young scyphulae.

Apparently, stolonization and colony formation occasionally occur; strobilization is inconspicuous, and often only one strobilus is given off at a time, although occasionally three to five are released. Ephyrae can be produced 20 days after attachment, but normally this process takes 30 to 40 days.

REFERENCES:

AGASSIZ, L., 1862. Contributions to the Natural History of the United States of America. Vols. 3 and 4. Little, Brown and Co., Boston.

HARGITT, C. W., AND G. T. HARGITT, 1910. Studies in the development of Scyphomedusae. *J. Morph.*, 21: 217–262.

McMURRICH, J. P., 1891. The development of *Cyanea arctica*. *Amer. Nat.*, 25: 287–289.

OKADA, Y. K., 1927. Sur l'origine de l'endoderme des discoméduses. *Bull. Biol. France et Belg.*, 61: 250–262.

COELENTERATA

(ANTHOZOA)

Metridium dianthus (M. marginatum)

LIVING MATERIAL:

Metridium is a large yellow-brown anemone, which is common along the Atlantic coast. It has a broad pedal disc and a lobed oral disc bearing many short tentacles.

BREEDING SEASON: Probably June and July.

PROCURING AND HANDLING MATERIAL:

A. Care of Adults: These anemones are easily kept in the laboratory for considerable periods of time, if they are maintained in aquaria with adequate supplies of running sea water.

B. Methods of Observation: The sex of the mature animals cannot be ascertained macroscopically. If a number of ripe individuals are placed together in large dishes containing sea water, natural spawning and fertilization will occur. The same individuals have been shown to spawn several times, at intervals of two to ten days, for a month. Since the eggs are heavy, they will sink to the bottoms of the containers; they can be picked up and transferred to fingerbowls with a pipette. The jelly, which may surround the eggs when they leave the stomodeum, soon dissolves. The larvae can be maintained in the laboratory if they are changed to dishes of fresh, aerated sea water at intervals of a few days.

NORMAL DEVELOPMENT:

A. The Unfertilized Ovum: The eggs are mature and surrounded by a delicate membrane at the time of shedding; they are spherical, opaque, and usually pink in color. McMurrich (1891) reports that they measure between 100 and 160 microns in diameter.

B. Fertilization and Cleavage: Fertilization occurs soon after the eggs are shed, as the eggs are sinking to the bottom. Cleavage is total and slightly irregular, being either equal or sub-equal. The hollow, single-layered blastula is converted into a gastrula by invagination.

C. Time Table of Development: No details of the exact developmental rate are available, although the first cleavage is said to occur 45 minutes after insemination. Fixation occurs in about a month.

D. Later Stages of Development: The young gastrula is top-shaped, the oral surface being somewhat flattened. In the older larva the body is lengthened, and a tuft of long, stiff cilia appears on the anterior (aboral) pole. The stomodeum is well formed, and the two lateral mesenteries appear as conspicuous folds in the gastric cavity. Nematocysts are present at both the oral and the aboral poles of the developing larva. Although temporary attachments (probably for feeding

36

purposes) are made by the oral surface, the permanent attachment occurs at the aboral pole.

REFERENCES:

GEMMILL, J. F., 1920. The development of the sea-anemones *Metridium dianthus* (Ellis) and *Adamsia palliata* (Bohad). *Phil. Trans. Roy. Soc., London, ser. B,* **209**: 351–375.
McMURRICH, J. P., 1891. Contributions on the morphology of the Actinozoa. II. On the development of the Hexactiniae. *J. Morph.,* **4**: 303–330.

CTENOPHORA

Mnemiopsis leidyi

LIVING MATERIAL:

Since Mnemiopsis is not common at Woods Hole, Mass., until August, it is often difficult to obtain animals in the breeding condition. The adults can best be collected at night with a hand net, although they have been found at the surface of the water on calm days, between the hours of 9 and 11 A.M., and 4 and 6 P.M.

BREEDING SEASON:

Eggs have been obtained from May through July (from animals collected in Buzzards Bay); it is possible that Mnemiopsis continues to breed even later in the season.

PROCURING AND HANDLING MATERIAL:

A. Care of Adults: The animals survive well in laboratory aquaria, if they are provided with adequate amounts of fresh sea water.

B. Methods of Observation: Fertilized eggs are usually released 12 to 24 hours after the animals are brought into the laboratory.

NORMAL DEVELOPMENT:

A. Egg Characteristics: The spherical eggs are very transparent, and consist of an inner yolky sphere surrounded by a clear outer zone. Each egg is enveloped in a thin, structureless membrane.

B. Fertilization and Cleavage: Since the animals are hermaphroditic, the eggs are fertilized before shedding occurs. Cleavage is total but unequal; the first two cleavages are longitudinal, cutting from the animal to the vegetal pole. The next cleavage is oblique, producing four large central cells and four small lateral cells which migrate towards the animal pole to form a flat plate of eight cells. These eight large "macromeres" produce an octet of smaller micromeres by a fourth cleavage. A continued production and division of the micromeres leads to an epibolic type of gastrulation.

C. Time Table of Development: Details of developmental rate are not available, but it is apparently quite rapid, since gastrulation occurs within six hours and the embryos are ready to hatch in 30 hours.

D. Later Stages of Development: At the time of hatching, the embryo is well formed. Four double rows of ciliated plates and two long lateral tentacles are present. The apical sense organ is prominent on the aboral pole. The endodermal gut is connected to a large stomodeum, and has six lateral diverticula: two to the tentacles, and one to each of the four rows of comb-plates. See the paper of Mayer (1912) for diagrams of the larvae.

REFERENCES:

AGASSIZ, A., 1874. Embryology of the Ctenophorae. *Mem. Amer. Acad. Arts and Sci.,* **10**: 356–398.

MAYER, A. G., 1912. Ctenophores of the Atlantic coast of North America. *Carn. Inst., Wash. Publ. 162.*

Note: Further descriptions of Ctenophore embryology and a complete bibliography can be found in the textbooks of MacBride, Hyman, and Korschelt.

PLATYHELMINTHES

Hoploplana (formerly *Planocera*) *inquilina*

LIVING MATERIAL:

The adult polyclads are found inhabiting the mantle cavity of *Busycon canaliculatum* and may easily be dissected from the gill chambers. They are numerous in freshly caught specimens of Busycon, but the worms rapidly decrease in number if the snails are allowed to remain in the aquaria for a few days.

BREEDING SEASON: June to September.

PROCURING AND HANDLING MATERIAL:

If adult worms are placed in jars of fresh sea water through which an air current is allowed to bubble, they will soon deposit their eggs on the bottom or sides of the dish.

Surface (1907) warns that the eggs do not develop normally after experimental handling, although untreated eggs and larvae are easily reared in the laboratory.

NORMAL DEVELOPMENT:

A. Egg Characteristics: The eggs are deposited without any special orientation in tough, gelatinous, spiral capsules. Each capsule contains from 100 to 200 eggs, each of which is surrounded by a membrane. The eggs measure 100 microns in diameter and are densely granular with yolk. Fertilization is internal, although the eggs are still in the germinal vesicle stage when they are laid.

B. Cleavage and Gastrulation: Cleavage is unequal and spiral. It is peculiar in that, after giving off the fourth quartet of micromeres, the macromeres are very small and eventually degenerate. The fourth quartet of micromeres thus takes over the function of forming both endoderm and mesoderm. Gastrulation is by epiboly.

C. Time Table of Development: The first polar body is formed an hour after the eggs are laid; the second polar body and early cleavages follow at one-hour intervals. Gastrulation is completed by the end of the second day; rotation within the capsules occurs on the third day; eyes appear on the fourth day; contractility and the development of ciliated lobes can be observed during the fifth day; and on the sixth day, the larvae leave the capsules.

D. Later Stages of Development: The larva is of the type known as Müller's larva. It is oval in shape, bearing at its lower pole an ectodermal stomodeum which leads to an irregular, ciliated, endodermal sac. Eight ciliated lobes can be seen just below the equator, and at the aboral pole a plate of very small cells covers a mass of ganglion cells. The further metamorphosis of the larva has not been followed in this species, although Lang (1884) has described the later development of a Müller's larva of another genus.

40

REFERENCES:

Lang, A., 1884. Die Polycladen (Seeplanarien) des Golfes von Neapel und der angrenzenden Meeresabschnitte. *Fauna u. Flora d. Golfes von Neapel,* **11**: 1–688.

MacBride, E. W., 1914. Text-Book of Embryology. Vol. I. Invertebrata. Macmillan and Co., Ltd., London, pp. 102–117.

Surface, F. M., 1907. The early development of a polyclad, *Planocera inquilina* Wh. *Proc. Acad. Nat. Sci., Phila.,* **59**: 514–559.

PLATYHELMINTHES

Polychoerus caudatus

LIVING MATERIAL:

This small orange-red flatworm is characterized by one or more filamentous tails between its two caudal lobes. It was formerly common on Ulva in Little Harbor at Woods Hole, and on the mud flats of Hadley Harbor (Mark, 1892). It disappeared from the Woods Hole region with the eel grass, but has since been found near the breakwater at Provincetown. A close relative, *Polychoerus carmelensis,* has been found in enormous numbers at Carmel Bay, on the coast of California (D. P. Costello and H. M. Costello, 1938).

BREEDING SEASON: June through August.

PROCURING AND HANDLING MATERIAL:

A. Care of Adults: After collection, the adults are placed in an aquarium through which sea water is gently flowing. The animals crawl about on the glass sides, or on Ulva placed in the water. Under these conditions, the adults may live for some weeks, but usually produce gametes only during the early part of this period.

B. Procuring Embryos: The following account is based on data for *Polychoerus carmelensis,* but probably applies equally well to *P. caudatus.*

The adults are hermaphroditic, and usually mate during the early morning hours (H. M. Costello and D. P. Costello, 1938). The sperm presumably pass from the anterior pocket of the vagina through the bursa, and fertilize the eggs while the latter are in the parenchyma. Egg-laying occurs by extrusion involving a disruption of the ventral body wall.

Deposition of the egg-masses usually occurs at sundown. These egg-masses are small gelatinous bodies containing from five to twenty eggs. They are fastened to the glass sides of the aquarium, or attached to Ulva. To collect egg-masses, it is convenient to remove 20 or 30 adults to fingerbowls of standing sea water on the sea water table. This sea water may be changed once or twice a day. Egg capsules are usually deposited on the side of the dish away from the light.

It is possible to dissect the fertilized eggs from the body, since they can be seen readily through the body wall, but their viability is not known. Past investigators have depended upon being present at the time of egg-laying to obtain the earliest developmental stages. The embryos are easily dissected from the gelatinous masses, but do not develop well after removal.

NORMAL DEVELOPMENT:

A. Egg Characteristics: The eggs originate in the *eilager,* which is situated just behind the statocyst. Two divergent streams of developing ova extend posteriorly toward the bursa. The full-grown oöcytes are found at the level of the bursa.

The egg is in the germinal vesicle stage when it is penetrated by a spermatozoon. This stimulus causes the egg to undergo its maturation division and to proceed to the metaphase of the first cleavage division, preceding egg-laying. The large "polar suns" of the first cleavage spindle may sometimes be seen through the body wall of a flattened animal.

After the eggs are laid, the polar bodies are not visible at the egg surface, and there is no marker for the animal pole. These unextruded polar bodies remain submerged in the egg cytoplasm, where they eventually degenerate.

The fixed eggs of *Polychoerus carmelensis* measure about 220 microns in diameter. Those of *Polychoerus caudatus* are probably about the same size, although Gardiner (1895) states that they measure 40 by 60 microns. The eggs lack a fertilization membrane, and contain flecks of red-yellow pigment. In the freshly-laid egg, these pigment granules extend throughout the cytoplasm except in the region of the amphiaster, which is thus outlined as an enormous dumb-bell. The pigment granules move along the cleavage furrows during division.

B. Cleavage and Gastrulation: Cleavage is total and, after the two-cell stage, unequal. According to Costello (1937, 1948) the cleavage is best described as spiral cleavage by duets, instead of by quartets. It was described earlier as bilateral. Gastrulation occurs by a curious pivoting type of epiboly. See the papers by Bresslau (1933) and Gardiner (1898) for figures of cleavage stages.

C. Later Stages of Development: Polychoerus has a direct development, and the embryo, when hatched from the egg mass, is a small worm with eyespots, and with typical caudal lobes.

REFERENCES:

BRESSLAU, E., 1933. Turbellaria. Kükenthal-Krumbach Handbuch der Zoologie, Bd. 2.

COSTELLO, D. P., 1937. The early cleavage of *Polychoerus carmelensis*. *Anat. Rec.,* **70**: Suppl. 1, 108–109.

COSTELLO, D. P., 1946. The giant cleavage spindle of the egg of *Polychoerus carmelensis*. *Anat. Rec.,* **96**: 561.

COSTELLO, D. P., 1948. Spiral cleavage. *Biol. Bull.,* **95**: 265. (See, also, *Erratum, Biol. Bull.,* **95**: 361.)

COSTELLO, D. P., AND H. M. COSTELLO, 1938. A new species of *Polychoerus* from the Pacific Coast. *Ann. and Mag. Nat. Hist.,* ser. 11, **1**: 148–155.

COSTELLO, H. M., AND D. P. COSTELLO, 1938. Copulation in the acoelous turbellarian *Polychoerus carmelensis*. *Biol. Bull.,* **75**: 85–98.

COSTELLO, H. M., AND D. P. COSTELLO, 1939. Egg laying in the acoelous turbellarian *Polychoerus carmelensis*. *Biol. Bull.,* **76**: 80–89.

GARDINER, E. G., 1895. Early development of *Polychoerus caudatus,* Mark. *J. Morph.,* **11**: 155–176.

GARDINER, E. G., 1898. The growth of the ovum, formation of the polar bodies, and the fertilization in *Polychoerus caudatus*. *J. Morph.,* **15**: 73–110.

LÖHNER, L., 1910. Untersuchungen über *Polychoerus caudatus* Mark. *Zeitschr. f. wiss. Zool.,* **95**: 451–506.

MARK, E. L., 1892. *Polychoerus caudatus,* nov. gen. et nov. spec. Festschr. z. 70. Geburtstage R. Leuckarts. Leipzig. S. 298–309.

NEMERTEA

Cerebratulus lacteus

LIVING MATERIAL:

Adults are found near or below the low-water mark, burrowing in mud, sandy mud, or sand in sheltered bays, harbors and estuaries. If not available at Woods Hole they can be shipped in from Maine or from north of Cape Ann, Mass. The sexes are separate. Sexually ripe males are bright red, ripe females dull, brownish red; in spent animals these colors fade (Coe, 1895).

BREEDING SEASON:

May and June in Long Island Sound, July in the Woods Hole region, and July and August in Massachusetts Bay and on the Maine coast (Coe, 1937).

PROCURING AND HANDLING MATERIAL:

A. Care of Adults: The sexes are best segregated. The female Cerebratulus may be kept for three weeks or more in the laboratory, but the eggs are less suitable for experimental purposes after the first week. The worms should be kept in tall battery jars, over the tops of which gauze covers are securely tied; the worms are active and will escape down the drain unless this precaution is taken. A sea water hose should extend through the gauze to the bottom of the jar, to insure a continuous supply of fresh sea water. A low temperature (around 10° C.) is optimal, but it is difficult to maintain with running sea water at Woods Hole.

B. Procuring Gametes: A continuous supply of gametes may be obtained by removing successive portions from the posterior end of a ripe individual. A large female, for example, may produce upwards of fifty million eggs.

Female gametes: Females kept in the manner described above will shed some eggs spontaneously, but to obtain large numbers a posterior piece, an inch long, should be cut off and placed on a five-inch square of cheesecloth in a fingerbowl of cool sea water. With scissors or scalpel make a slit on either side of the mid-dorsal line. The muscular contractions of the fragment will soon force the ripe ova into the water. The cheesecloth retains the slime and body section and allows the eggs to filter through. When they have settled, decant the water and add fresh, filtered sea water.

Male gametes: To obtain sperm, a half-inch posterior fragment of a male is placed in a dish of clean sea water and a puncture made through the dorsal body wall. A drop of sperm suspension, drawn up into a fine-mouthed pipette, should be diluted in 40 cc. of sea water.

C. Preparation of Cultures: When first shed, the egg contains a germinal vesicle, and fertilization at this time results in polyspermy and abnormal development. Allow the eggs to stand until microscopic examination shows that the germinal vesicles have ruptured and the eggs have reached the metaphase of the first maturation division (a matter of 10 to 30 minutes, depending on the temperature and the ripeness of the eggs). Now add one drop of freshly prepared, dilute sperm suspension. It is important to avoid over-insemination. The eggs remain fertilizable for as long as five hours after shedding.

The cultures should stand undisturbed for half an hour after insemination; then decant the upper layers of water and add a fresh supply of sea water. All cultures should be kept on the water table, at temperatures not exceeding 20° C.

When swimming larvae are formed, they should be decanted daily to fresh sea water. If they are to be followed through to metamorphosis, diatom feeding must be initiated after the first few days.

D. Methods of Observation: Eggs and larvae can be examined by mounting them in a drop of sea water under a supported coverslip. A very small amount of chloral hydrate added to the preparation will usually narcotize the swiftly moving larvae.

NORMAL DEVELOPMENT:

A. The Unfertilized Ovum: The egg is about 120 microns in diameter and is contained in a chorionic sac considerably larger than the egg itself. The egg is dark brown and opaque, due to the presence of large masses of radially arranged yolk globules. At one pole of the egg, and also in the overlying chorion, a small, nipple-like protrusion is present. This marks the point of former attachment to the ovarian wall, and lies immediately opposite the region where the polar bodies are extruded. The prominent germinal vesicle is often located somewhat excentrically, near the animal pole (Wilson, 1900).

When first shed, the eggs are surrounded by a transparent jelly-layer, but this soon dissolves upon contact with sea water. Each egg is surrounded by a thin chorion, which begins to lift from the surface immediately after shedding. This membrane is soft and can easily be cut away or removed by shaking. Ten to twenty minutes after shedding, the germinal vesicle breaks down and its substance flows toward the animal pole, appearing as a diffuse lighter area. The chromosomes become arranged on the first maturation spindle and remain at metaphase until fertilization.

B. Fertilization and Cleavage: The sperm are relatively large, and have a long, sickle-shaped head, and a long tail which propels them through the water with rather slow powerful strokes. While several sperm may penetrate the outer membrane of freshly inseminated eggs, only one normally will bore its way into the egg substance (Wilson, 1900). Apparently the entire sperm enters the egg (Yatsu, 1909). No fertilization cone or membrane is formed.

About 75 minutes after insemination the egg flattens slightly at the animal pole in preparation for polar body formation. During this interval the protrusion at the opposite pole slowly diminishes. This decrease continues throughout maturation and the lobe is usually completely withdrawn by the time the second polar body is given off. After the formation of the first polar body, the egg rounds up and becomes spherical, but again flattens when the second polar body is extruded, a process which occurs about 20 minutes later.

The egg continues to elongate in a direction perpendicular to the animal-vegetal axis. The first cleavage cuts through the egg along the axis marked by the polar bodies, dividing the ovum into two equal cells. The second cleavage furrow appears at right angles to the first. The third cleavage, which quickly follows, is horizontal, and, since it passes through the egg slightly below the equator, produces four large upper cells and four smaller lower cells. In spite of their larger size the upper cells are considered to be the first quartet of "micromeres," the lower cells being the "macromeres." This third cleavage is clearly dexiotropic. Following it, at least six quartets of micromeres are cut off by alternating laeotropic and dexiotropic divisions, faithfully following the pattern of spiral cleavage as seen in annelids and molluscs. (See figures in the paper by Wilson, 1900.)

The blastula is a nearly spherical, ciliated structure composed of a single layer of cells surrounding a large segmentation cavity. Although not visible in the living embryo, those cells which are destined to invaginate and become the endoderm are distinctly taller than those at the aboral pole. About the time when these cells start to invaginate, a small plate of cells near the aboral pole becomes conspicuous and, while a two-layered, pyramidal gastrula is forming, these cells sink in slightly and produce a cluster of cilia. The cilia elongate enormously and fuse to form an apical flagellum, which is probably sensory in nature. At the time of gastrulation, the mesodermal mother cells migrate inward from the region of the blastoporal lip. Towards the end of gastrulation, the prototroch appears as a band of long cilia encircling the oral surface of the larva. (See the paper by Wilson, 1900, for diagrams of these stages.)

C. Time Table of Development: The following schedule of development is compiled from the data of Wilson (1900). No temperature was recorded. Times are given from insemination.

Stage	Time
First polar body	75 minutes
Second polar body	95 minutes
First cleavage	135 minutes
Second cleavage	155 minutes
Third cleavage	170 minutes
Blastula	15 hours
Gastrula	20 hours
Hatching, young pilidium	38 hours
Well-formed pilidium	108 hours

D. Later Stages of Development and Metamorphosis: Pilidium larvae of three days have a characteristic helmet shape, due to the extension of the edges of the oral surface to form two large, rounded lappets bordered with powerful cilia. The apical organ and its associated flagella persist. Through the transparent outer ectoderm the inner organs are clearly visible. The mouth leads into a wide, ciliated oesophagus which is separated by a slight constriction from the globular stomach. Neither proctodeum nor intestine develops in the free-swimming larva. Spanning the internal cavity, which is the remnant of the old blastocoele, the developing muscle fibers can be seen, the most conspicuous being those which extend from the apical organ to the digestive tract and marginal lappets. Scattered mesenchyme cells are also present in the blastocoele cavity. See the diagrams of Wilson (1900) and Coe (1943) for further details of the structure of the pilidium.

Relatively few larvae reared in the laboratory reach metamorphosis. There is a free-swimming period of about 12 days before this remarkable metamorphosis sets in. When the future worm has differentiated, utilizing only the larval intestine and the material from four ectodermal invaginations which sink in and surround it, the larval ectoderm, prototroch, lappets and apical organ are cast away and the little worm sinks to the bottom. The cap-like larval rudiment swims about for a time and then, unable to feed and exhausted, it dies. (Further details can be found in the text-book by MacBride, 1914, pp. 118–127.)

REFERENCES:

CHAMBERS, R., 1933. The manner of sperm entry in various marine ova. *J. Exp. Biol.,* **10**: 130–141.

COE, W. R., 1895. On the anatomy of a species of Nemertean (*Cerebratulus lacteus* Verrill), with remarks on certain other species. *Trans. Conn. Acad. Arts and Sci.,* **9**: 479–514.

COE, W. R., 1899a. The maturation and fertilization of the egg of Cerebratulus. *Zool. Jahrb., abt. Anat. u. Ontog.,* **12**: 425–476.

COE, W. R., 1899b. On the development of the pilidium of certain nemerteans. *Trans. Conn. Acad. Arts and Sci.,* **10**: 235–262.

COE, W. R., 1937. Methods for the laboratory culture of nemerteans. *In:* Culture Methods for Invertebrate Animals, edit. by Galtsoff *et al.,* Comstock, Ithaca, pp. 162–165.

COE, W. R., 1943. Biology of the nemerteans of the Atlantic Coast of North America. *Trans. Conn. Acad. Arts and Sci.,* **35**: 129–327.

HÖRSTADIUS, S., 1937. Experiments on determination in the early development of *Cerebratulus lacteus. Biol. Bull.,* **73**: 317–342.

MACBRIDE, E. W., 1914. Text-Book of Embryology. Vol. I. Invertebrata. Macmillan and Co., Ltd., London, pp. 118–127.

WILSON, C. B., 1900. The habits and early development of *Cerebratulus lacteus* (Verrill). A contribution to physiological morphology. *Quart. J. Micr. Sci.,* **43**: 97–198.

WILSON, E. B., 1903. Experiments on cleavage and localization in the nemertine-egg. *Arch. f. Entw.,* **16**: 411–460.

YATSU, N., 1904. Experiments on the development of egg fragments in Cerebratulus. *Biol. Bull.,* **6**: 123–136.

YATSU, N., 1909. Observations on oökinesis in *Cerebratulus lacteus,* Verrill. *J. Morph.,* **20**: 353–401.

YATSU, N., 1910a. Experiments on cleavage in the egg of Cerebratulus. *J. Coll. Sci., Tokyo,* **27**: no. 10, pp. 1–19.

YATSU, N., 1910b. Experiments on germinal localization in the egg of Cerebratulus. *J. Coll. Sci., Tokyo,* **27**: no. 17, pp. 1–36.

ZELENY, C., 1904. Experiments on the localization of developmental factors in the nemertine egg. *J. Exp. Zool.,* **1**: 293–329.

BRYOZOA *

(ENTOPROCTA)

Barentsia laxa

LIVING MATERIAL:

The colonies of this form are tan or grey in color, and are composed of numerous pin-like individuals crowded together; the colonies are approximately one-half inch in height, and from one-half to one inch in extent. They are often found in association with Venus shells which are encrusted with the sponge, Cliona (Rogick, 1948), and are obtained by dredging in the Hole at Woods Hole, Mass. Barentsia is very similar to Pedicellina, but is larger, hardier, and easier to find.

BREEDING SEASON:

Rogick (1948) reports that free-swimming larvae and embryos in various stages of development were obtained between July and September, but that very probably they are also obtainable earlier and later during the summer. It is not certain whether Barentsia is sometimes hermaphroditic (Rogick, 1948), but in many instances, at least, the sexes are separate.

PROCURING AND HANDLING MATERIAL:

A. Care of Adults: The animals are hardy and easy to keep in the laboratory if they are supplied with running sea water. They do not require feeding.

B. Procuring Embryos: Embryos and larvae are found within the calyx of the adult; larvae are released through a channel opening into the atrial cavity in front of the anal opening (Rogick, 1948).

NORMAL DEVELOPMENT:

The development of this form is apparently very much like that of Pedicellina (Rogick, personal communication), except that the embryos, larvae and adults are easier to study. Calyx regeneration is a conspicuous phenomenon in Barentsia and one which, as Rogick points out, is probably worthy of detailed study.

REFERENCES:

OSBURN, R. C., 1910. The Bryozoa of the Woods Hole region. *Bull. U. S. Bur. Fisheries,* **30**: 205–266.

ROGICK, M. D., 1948. Studies on marine bryozoa. II. *Barentsia laxa* Kirkpatrick 1890. *Biol. Bull.,* **94**: 128–142.

(See, also, references for Pedicellina.)

* We are grateful to Dr. Mary D. Rogick for much of the information on which this and succeeding sections concerning bryozoan development are based.

BRYOZOA

(ENTOPROCTA)

Pedicellina cernua (P. echinata)

LIVING MATERIAL:

These colonial bryozoans are moderately common on shells and algae in shallow water. The zoids arise independently from a branched, creeping stolon, and have cup-shaped calyces and yellow-red stalks. Hyman (1951) reports that Pedicellina is sometimes hermaphroditic, sometimes dioecious.

BREEDING SEASON:

Although this has not been determined for the Woods Hole, Mass., region, it probably occurs during the summer months.

PROCURING AND HANDLING MATERIAL:

A. Care of Adults: The animals are moderately hardy in the laboratory, if they are supplied with running sea water.

B. Methods of Observation: Cleaving eggs and young larvae can be dissected from the egg capsules; older larvae will be released if fertile colonies are allowed to stand in fingerbowls of fresh sea water. Harmer (1887) states that the larvae will not attach in small amounts of water. He suggests placing the ripe colonies, together with the algae to which the colonies are attached, in glass jars covered with fine bolting silk. These jars are then suspended in live-boxes, and examined in about a day. At that time, a large number of attached and metamorphosing larvae should be present.

NORMAL DEVELOPMENT:

A. The Ovum: The ripe eggs measure 40 by 50 by 60 microns, the shortest axis being apico-vestibular.

B. Fertilization and Cleavage: There is some disagreement as to whether the colonies are bisexual or unisexual (see "Living Material" above). Marcus (1939) suggests that they are unisexual, although hermaphroditism occasionally occurs. Fertilization is internal, and at least the first maturation division occurs within the ovary. After its release from the ovary, the egg passes through a short vagina where it is enclosed in a soft shell with a long stalk. The shelled eggs are attached by means of the stalks to the floor of the brood-chamber, which consists of the walls of the vestibule between the tentacles and the vestibular groove. Cleavage is equal and spiral, closely resembling that of the annelids. Five quartets of micromeres and one quartet of macromeres are produced (Hyman, 1951). A hollow blastula is formed by the 67-cell stage. Gastrulation is by invagination and starts at about the 90-cell stage.

C. Later Stages of Development: Following gastrulation, there is an apical-oral elongation of the embryo, accompanied by closure of the slit-like blastopore. An apical plate, bearing cilia, develops at the aboral pole but invaginates by the time

the larva is set free.   Shortly after this organ is formed, the stomodeum and proctodeum invaginate on the oral surface, and the pre-oral or dorsal organ appears as
an invagination on the anterior side of the larva above the mouth.   At this time,
the egg shell vanishes and the larva is freed.   When released, the larva swims with
the aid of an oral ring of strong cilia, the corona.   The digestive tract is complete
and feeding occurs.   Shortly after release, a well-marked invagination appears
between the mouth and anus.   This is the vestibule or atrium; it is bordered by
the corona.   Both the mouth and the anus are borne on long projections called
the epistome and anal cone, respectively.

After about a day, the free-swimming larvae attach by means of the atrial surface, and undergo a complicated metamorphosis which involves a degeneration of
the apical plate and dorsal organ, and a complete upward rotation of the entire
larval body.   For further details concerning the larvae and metamorphosis, see
the papers by Harmer (1887), Cori (1933) and Hyman (1951).

REFERENCES:

CORI, C. J., 1933. Dritter Cladus der Vermes Amera. Kamptozoa. Allgemeines über den
     Cladus Kamptozoa. Erste und einzige Klasse des Cladus Kamptozoa; Kamptozoa =
     Bryozoa Entoprocta = Calyssozoa. *Kükenthal Handbuch d. Zool.*, **2**: Hft. 1 (5), 1–64.
HARMER, S. F., 1887. On the life-history of Pedicellina. *Quart. J. Micr. Sci.*, **27**: 239–263.
HATSCHEK, B., 1877. Embryonalentwicklung und Knospung der *Pedicellina echinata. Zeitschr.
     f. wiss. Zool.*, **29**: 502–549.
HYMAN, L. H., 1951. The Invertebrates: Acanthocephala, Aschelminthes, and Entoprocta.
     The Pseudocoelomate Bilateria. McGraw-Hill Book Co., Inc., New York.
MARCUS, E., 1939. Briozóarios Marinhos Brasileiros. III. *Bol. d. Fil. Ciên., e Let., Univ.
     de São Paulo, Zool.*, **3**: 111–291.

BRYOZOA

(ECTOPROCTA)

Bugula flabellata and B. turrita

LIVING MATERIAL:

Bugula flabellata is found on the lower surfaces and edges of horizontal submerged timbers in Eel Pond, at Woods Hole, Mass.; *B. turrita* is found in similar habitats in Vineyard Sound or on the rocks at Stony Beach. Colonies of *B. turrita* are about 30 cm. high, yellow in color, and composed of flat branches growing in spirals. The flesh-colored colonies of *B. flabellata* are slightly shorter and are composed of broad, flat branches, each of which contains three to seven rows of zooecia. Both species have stalked avicularia shaped like birds' heads. Ripe colonies can be recognized by the prominent ovicells.

BREEDING SEASON:

At Woods Hole, these animals have been found to release larvae from the first or second week of June until November 1 (Grave, 1930).

PROCURING AND HANDLING MATERIAL:

A. Care of Adults: The animals should be provided with running sea water.

B. Methods of Observation: Early stages of development can be obtained only by dissection of the ovicells, but larvae are easily obtained. Breeding colonies should be collected on the afternoon of the day previous to that on which they will be used. If they are placed in fingerbowls of sea water and left overnight in front of a window, the larvae will be released some time between 5 and 10 A.M. the next morning. If the fingerbowl is left in a dark-room during the night, the larvae will not be released at dawn, but will be retained until the colony is exposed to light. However, this release of larvae in response to light decreases after noon. The released larvae, which gather at the lighted side of the dish, can be pipetted to fingerbowls or other receptacles where they will attach. After attachment, the larvae should be transferred to vessels provided with running sea water, if further development is desired.

NORMAL DEVELOPMENT:

A. Early Stages of Development: Taxonomic confusion makes it uncertain whether the species *B. flabellata* found at Woods Hole is identical with *B. calathus,* studied by Vigelius (1886). If the two species are identical, the animals are hermaphroditic, and the internally fertilized eggs are transferred to ooecia where development occurs. The cleavages are regular and equal as far as the 32-cell stage, producing a flat, two-layered plate of cells. Gastrulation is probably by epiboly, and further development leads to the formation of a rather degenerate free-swimming larva.

B. Later Stages of Development: The ciliated larvae of the two species of Bugula found around Woods Hole are almost spherical and measure approximately

180 microns.   Larvae of both species have a stiff circle of cilia surrounding a convex apical organ on the pole which is carried foremost in swimming.   The opposite pole is depressed and bears a central invagination called the internal sac. This depression extends up one side of the larva to the equator in the form of a glandular groove.   At the apex of this groove is a tuft of long flagella (the vibratile plume).   The lateral groove and the plume make up the so-called "pyriform organ."   The larva of *B. turrita* has, in addition, four or six eyespots: two or four located on the anterior borders of the lateral groove, and two on the opposite side.   When they are first released, the larvae are strongly attracted by light, but after two or three hours, they gradually become negatively phototropic.   If they are left undisturbed, the larvae also show a moderate negative geotropism.

After a swimming period of four to six hours, the larva attaches.   A temporary attachment is first made by the lateral groove; then the internal sac is suddenly everted and fastened to the substrate.   About an hour after fixation, the larva begins to elongate, and in four to eight hours the body cavity is visible and the first polyp begins to form.   The primary zoid is completely formed in 24 hours. From this time on, secondary individuals are produced rapidly by asexual budding, until a large colony is formed.   Sexual maturity is attained about one month after attachment.

REFERENCES:

CORRÊA, D., 1948. A embriologia de *Bugula flabellata*. *Universidade de São Paulo Bol. d. Fac. Fil., Ciên., e Let., Zool.,* **13**: 7–73.

GRAVE, B. H., 1930. The natural history of *Bugula flabellata* at Woods Hole, Massachusetts, including the behavior and attachment of the larva. *J. Morph.,* **49**: 355–383.

GRAVE, B. H., 1937. *Bugula flabellata* and *B. turrita*. *In:* Culture Methods for Invertebrate Animals, edit. by Galtsoff *et al.,* Comstock, Ithaca, pp. 178–179.

HASPER, M., 1912. On a method of rearing larvae of Polyzoa. *J. Mar. Biol. Assoc.,* **9**: 435–436.

LYNCH, W. F., 1947. The behavior and metamorphosis of the larva of *Bugula neritina* (Linnaeus): Experimental modification of the length of the free-swimming period and the responses of the larvae to light and gravity. *Biol. Bull.,* **92**: 115–150.

LYNCH, W. F., 1952. Factors influencing metamorphosis of Bugula larvae. *Biol. Bull.,* **103**: 369–383.

LYNCH, W. F., 1955. Synergism and antagonism in the induction of metamorphosis of Bugula larvae by neutral red dye. *Biol. Bull.,* **109**: 82–98.

McDOUGALL, K. D., 1943. Sessile marine invertebrates of Beaufort, North Carolina. A study of settlement, growth, and seasonal fluctuations among pile-dwelling organisms. *Ecol. Monog.,* **13**: 321–374.

MAWATARI, S., 1951. The natural history of a common fouling bryozoan *Bugula neritina* (L.). Misc. Reps. Res. Inst. Natural Resources, Nos. 19–21, Keita Shibata Memorial Numbers, Feb., 1951, pp. 47–54.

MILLER, M. A., 1946. Toxic effects of copper on attachment and growth of *Bugula neritina*. *Biol. Bull.,* **90**: 122–140.

VIGELIUS, W. J., 1886. Zur Ontogenie der marinen Bryozoen. *Mitt. Zool. Stat., Neapel,* **6**: 499–541.

VIGELIUS, W. J., 1888. Zur Ontogenie der marinen Bryozoen. *Mitt. Zool. Stat., Neapel,* **8**: 374–376.

BRYOZOA

(Ectoprocta)

Crisia eburnea (Crisiella sp.)

LIVING MATERIAL:

This species grows in the form of upright, white, bushy tufts, 8 to 25 mm. high. The tube-like zooecia are arranged in two alternate rows. There is some question as to whether the species is dioecious or monoecious and protandrous. The conspicuous ovicells make the fertile "female" colonies easy to recognize. The form is common at Woods Hole, Mass.

BREEDING SEASON:

In San Francisco Bay, the animals breed from late February to May. The limits of the breeding season have not been investigated in the Woods Hole region, although Rogick and Croasdale (1949) report that they found embryos in the ovicells as late as August 8.

PROCURING AND HANDLING MATERIAL:

A. Care of Adults: The colonies may be kept in aquaria supplied with an adequate amount of running sea water.

B. Methods of Observation: Although the animals must be sectioned if early developmental stages are desired, both the primary embryo and the secondary embryos can be dissected from the ovicells with fine needles.

NORMAL DEVELOPMENT:

A. Early Stages of Development: The early development of the eggs occurs in ovicells, which are highly modified zooecia. These structures are usually the modified second or third zooecium of an internode, although they are not present in each internode. The ovicell is a vase-like structure, consisting of a narrow stalk, a bulging mid-region and a short neck. The neck contains an opening through which the free-swimming larvae are released. The opacity of the ovicells, and the minute size of the eggs and developing embryos, make it impracticable to study early development by methods other than histological.

The eggs, measuring 18 microns or less in diameter, become associated with young zoid buds which are transformed into gonozoids. Only one egg develops in each gonozoid. Fertilization is internal, but the details of maturation and fertilization are not known. The early cleavages are unusual, in that the small follicle cells, which apparently serve as food for the developing embryo, actually penetrate between the blastomeres and separate them completely. The follicle cells start to disappear in the 24-cell stage and by the 60- or 70-cell stage, the embryo consists of a solid ball of cells, measuring about 43 microns in diameter. The increase in cell number continues until the embryo contains about 200 cells.

B. Later Stages of Development: When the primary embryo reaches the 200-cell stage, it sends out processes which bud off as secondary embryos. When they are first formed, these secondary embryos are solid balls of cells, measuring between 25 and 35 microns in diameter. They develop into very degenerate free-swimming larvae, which leave the gonozoids through the open mouth. The larvae of *Crisia eburnea* have apparently not been described, but if they resemble those of *C. ramosa,* they are simple, ciliated, sac-like structures, consisting of an inner and an outer layer of cells. One surface bears a large invagination or sucker, by which attachment is effected; the opposite pole, which develops into the mouth cavity of the primary zoid, is flattened and non-ciliated. For a further description and figures of the larvae, see the papers of Barrois (1877) and Harmer (1893).

REFERENCES:

BARROIS, J., 1877. Recherches sur l'embryologie des Bryozoaires. Travaux de l'Inst. Zool. de Lille et de la Station Maritime de Wimereux. Monograph.

BORG, F., 1926. Studies on recent cyclostomatous Bryozoa. *Zool. Bidrag Från Uppsala,* **10**: 181–504.

HARMER, S. F., 1893. On the occurrence of embryonic fission in cyclostomatous Polyzoa. *Quart. J. Micr. Sci.,* **34**: 199–241.

ROBERTSON, A., 1903. Embryology and embryonic fission in the genus Crisia. *Univ. Calif. Pub. Zool.,* **1**: 115–156.

ROGICK, M. D., AND H. CROASDALE, 1949. Studies on marine bryozoa, III. Woods Hole region bryozoa associated with algae. *Biol. Bull.,* **96**: 32–69.

SILÉN, L., 1944. The anatomy of *Labiostomella Gisleni* . . . with special regard to the embryo chambers of the different groups of Bryozoa and to the origin and development of the bryozoan zoarium. *Kungl. Svenska Vetensk. Handlingar, Tredje ser.,* **21**: no. 6, pp. 3–111.

BRYOZOA

(Ectoprocta)

Electra (formerly *Membranipora*) *pilosa*

Living Material:

These animals form flat, encrusting colonies on sea-weeds and stones. They can be recognized by the ovate zooecia which are punctured by minute oval pores. The mouth of each zooecium is rimmed by a circle of from four to twelve short spines; a single, longer spine lies directly below the opening. The zoids are hermaphroditic and possibly protandrous. Breeding colonies can be recognized by the presence of eggs within the body cavity of the zoids.

Breeding Season:

This has not been determined for the Woods Hole, Mass., region. In European waters, the season lasts from June until December, with the peak in November.

Procuring and Handling Material:

A. Care of Adults: Colonies can be maintained easily in the laboratory, if an adequate supply of running sea water is provided.

B. Methods of Observation: Breeding colonies should be placed in fingerbowls of fresh sea water and examined at periodic intervals under the dissecting microscope, to ascertain whether shedding of eggs has begun. Since these eggs are small, they may not be visible to the unaided eye. Just (1934) warns that they are few in number and rather sensitive to environmental changes.

Normal Development:

A. The Unfertilized Ovum: Although the eggs are irregular in outline while they are in the body cavity, they soon round up after they are shed. When freshly shed, the eggs are greyish in color, and measure 79 microns in diameter.

B. Fertilization and Cleavage: Fertilization presumably occurs within the body cavity, before the eggs are shed. Although it is absent in body-cavity eggs, a membrane rises from the surface of shed eggs; when this membrane is fully formed, it is connected to the egg surface by fine radiating lines. The polar bodies are given off within a few minutes of shedding. The cleavages are regular and equal as far as the 16-cell stage. At this time, a bilateral symmetry becomes apparent, and by the 32-cell stage, the future ectoderm and endoderm cells are distinguishable and the cells are arranged in a flat plate. Gastrulation is by epiboly.

C. Later Stages of Development: The larva is a typical "cyphonautes," with a complete digestive tract. It is conical in shape, the broad end being termed the oral surface. At the aboral pole, a tuft of long cilia springs from the apical organ. The margin of the oral surface is rimmed with a circle of powerful cilia, forming the corona. A bivalve shell and a peculiar pyriform organ are formed soon after the free-swimming stage is reached; the internal sac seems to be associated solely with metamorphosis and appears late in development. Details and figures of the development of the eggs and larvae are given by Prouho (1892), Kupelweiser (1905) and MacBride (1914).

REFERENCES:

BONNEVIE, K., 1907. Untersuchungen über Keimzellen. II. Physiologische Polyspermie bei Bryozoen. *Jenaische Zeitschr. f. Naturw.,* **35**: 567–598.

JUST, E. E., 1934.   Fertilization in *Membranipora pilosa. Carnegie Inst. Year Book,* **33**: 268–270.

KUPELWEISER, H., 1905. Untersuchungen über den feineren Bau und die Metamorphose des Cyphonautes. *Zoologica,* **19**: Hf. 47, pp. 1–50.

MACBRIDE, E. W., 1914. Text-Book of Embryology. Vol. I. Invertebrata. Macmillan and Co., Ltd., London.

PROUHO, H., 1892.   Contribution à l'histoire des Bryozoaires. *Arch. de Zool. Exp.,* **20**: 557–656.

SILÉN, L., 1944.   The main features of the development of the ovum, embryo and ooecium in the ooeciferous Bryozoa Gymnolaemata. *Arkiv f. Zool., K. Svenska Vetenskap.,* **35A**: no. 17, pp. 1–34.

SIPUNCULIDA

Phascolosoma gouldi

LIVING MATERIAL:

The adults are found on sand flats, just below low tide level. They are abundant at Hadley Harbor, near Woods Hole, Mass. Animals covered with a mass of sea-weed will remain in good condition, even after several hours of transportation. The sexes are separate, but similar in appearance.

BREEDING SEASON:

The season probably extends from mid-June through September. Eggs have been obtained at Woods Hole in July, August and early September.

PROCURING AND HANDLING MATERIAL:

A. Care of Adults: Since there are no external criteria for distinguishing the sexes, it is best to wash several animals free of mud and place them together in a large fingerbowl. A gentle stream of water should flow through the dish, but a direct current of water on the worms is undesirable.

B. Procuring Gametes: Although body-cavity eggs of several European species of Phascolosoma are readily fertilized, artificial insemination rarely succeeds in *P. gouldi* (Just, 1939). Normally-shed eggs are sometimes procured from animals kept in the laboratory; the shedding of sperm acts as a stimulus to egg-laying. Spawning occurs in the evening and during the night from 8 P.M. to 5 A.M., usually on the first or second day after collection if at all; however, occasionally several days may pass before the ova are shed.

C. Preparation of Cultures: Inseminated eggs should be transferred as soon as possible to a fingerbowl of fresh sea water, to prevent over-insemination, and the culture stored on a sea water table. In about 12 hours the rotating trochophores should be transferred to a fresh container of sea water. The larvae can be reared through metamorphosis.

NORMAL DEVELOPMENT:

A. The Unfertilized Ovum: The mature ovum is red-brown in color and is spherical, measuring 150 to 180 microns in diameter. It is enclosed in a chitinous, highly refractive vitelline membrane, which is three to four microns thick. Through the perforated "zona radiata" extend a number of fine filaments. The ovum is shed after formation of the first maturation spindle.

B. Fertilization and Cleavage: The fine filaments extending through the "zona radiata" are withdrawn at the time of fertilization. Cleavage is unequal and spiral, producing a D cell that is perhaps five times as large as the A, B or C cells. The micromeres of the first quartet are exceptionally large. Gastrulation is by epiboly.

C. Rate of Development: Development is relatively rapid. Gerould (1907) obtained rotating embryos 10 hours after insemination; by 24 hours the trochophores were fully formed, and at 48 to 60 hours after fertilization metamorphosis occurred. The temperature was not recorded.

D. Later Stages of Development and Metamorphosis: The young trochophore is spherical and has a long apical tuft and a very wide prototroch. By 48 hours the digestive tract is well developed, two eyespots are present, and the pre-oral band of long cilia is conspicuous. At metamorphosis, the yolk membrane is cast off and the body elongates. Figures of larval stages may be found in two papers by Gerould (1903, 1907).

REFERENCES:

GEROULD, J. H., 1903. Studies on the embryology of the Sipunculidae. I. The embryonal envelope and its homologue. Mark Anniv. Vol., no. 22, pp. 437–452.

GEROULD, J. H., 1907. The development of Phascolosoma. (Studies on the embryology of the Sipunculidae II.) *Zool. Jahrb., abt. Anat. u. Ontog.,* **23**: 77–162.

JUST, E. E., 1939. Basic Methods for Experiments on Eggs of Marine Animals. P. Blakiston's Son and Co., Inc., Philadelphia, p. 33.

ANNELIDA

(Polychaeta)

Amphitrite ornata

Living Material:

These worms live in U-shaped, rather tough, mud tubes. The adults are fairly easy to obtain, but ripe individuals are never abundant. The best collecting grounds are at Barnstable, Mass., although some animals are found in Hadley Harbor. They should be collected during the day at low tide, washed free of mud, and placed immediately in a bucket of sea water. The sexes are separate, and may be distinguished by the darker abdominal segments of the females.

Breeding Season:

June, July and August, the peak being in July. Lunar periodicity is marked, and ripe individuals are most plentiful within two days of the new or full moon (Scott, 1909).

Procuring and Handling Material:

A. Care of Adults: In the laboratory the worms should be washed and isolated in separate dishes. Injured worms tend to release their sexual products; for this reason, care should be taken to handle them gently, especially during transportation.

B. Procuring Gametes: Eggs obtained by cutting open the body wall can rarely be fertilized. However, if ripe, the worms will shed spontaneously during the afternoon or evening of the day of collection (Scott, 1909). The period of egg-laying lasts 30 to 60 minutes, with large, immature eggs appearing toward the end of that time. The eggs remain fertilizable for as long as one hour after entering sea water.

C. Preparation of Cultures: Half an hour after insemination, the excess sperm should be washed off the eggs, and the cultures placed on a water table. When the larvae develop, they should be decanted daily to fresh sea water; from the fifth day on, those larvae which are metamorphosing should be kept in dishes with fresh Ulva (Mead, 1897).

Normal Development:

A. The Unfertilized Ovum: Under normal conditions the oöcyte is retained in the body cavity until the metaphase of the first maturation division (Scott, 1906). When it is released from the ovary into the body cavity, the germinal vesicle breaks down and the egg, which until that time was spherical, flattens at the polar region. It measures 100 microns in diameter and is very opaque. A thin, wrinkled membrane is present (Mead, 1899), but it is slightly thicker than that of Lepidonotus (compare Figures 1 and 89 in the paper by Mead, 1897). There is a noticeable perivitelline space.

B. Cleavage: Cleavage is unequal and spiral. No polar lobes are formed. Gastrulation is by invagination (Mead, 1897).

C. Rate of Development: The rate of development is rapid. Swimming forms are present four to five hours after insemination, and well-formed trochophores in 20 hours. Larval segmentation starts at 36 hours, and metamorphosis begins at about the fifth day, when five trunk segments are present. By 11 days, metamorphosis is completed.

C. Later Stages of Development and Metamorphosis: The trochophore has a wide prototroch, a neurotroch, and a paratroch. The frontal bodies and gland cells are prominent. Larval segmentation occurs early, and when the larvae have developed about five trunk segments, they cease to swim about freely, and, sinking to the bottom, begin to metamorphose. (See text figures 6, and 9–18, in the paper by Mead, 1897.)

REFERENCES:

JUST, E. E., 1939. Basic Methods for Experiments on Eggs of Marine Animals. P. Blakiston's Son and Co., Inc., Philadelphia.

MEAD, A. D., 1894. Preliminary account of the cell lineage of Amphitrite and other annelids. *J. Morph.,* **9**: 465–473.

MEAD, A. D., 1897. The early development of marine annelids. *J. Morph.,* **13**: 227–326.

MEAD, A. D., 1899. The cell origin of the prototroch. Biol. Lectures M. B. L., Wood's Holl, Mass., 1898, pp. 113–138.

SCOTT, J. W., 1906. Morphology of the parthenogenetic development of Amphitrite. *J. Exp. Zool.,* **3**: 49–97.

SCOTT, J. W., 1909. Some egg-laying habits of *Amphitrite ornata* Verrill. *Biol. Bull.,* **17**: 327–340.

SCOTT, J. W., 1911. Further experiments on the methods of egg-laying in Amphitrite. *Biol. Bull.,* **20**: 252–265.

TREADWELL, A. L., 1898. The cell lineage of *Podarke obscura.* Preliminary communication. *Zool. Bull.,* **1**: 195–203.

TREADWELL, A. L., 1899. Equal and unequal cleavage in annelids. Biol. Lectures M. B. L., Wood's Holl, Mass., 1898, pp. 93–111.

ANNELIDA

(POLYCHAETA)

Arenicola cristata

LIVING MATERIAL:

The burrows of these animals are exposed at low tide on the mud flats at Lagoon Pond and Hadley Harbor, near Woods Hole, Mass. The sexes are separate, the mature males being creamy white, the females pinkish-brown.

BREEDING SEASON:

The latter part of June, and July (Bumpus, 1898). There is a definite periodicity, associated with the neap tides (Okada, 1941).

PROCURING AND HANDLING MATERIAL:

A. Care of Adults: Several males and females should be kept together in an aquarium containing a layer of sand brought in from their natural habitat. A tank 60 cm. long, 55 cm. wide and 75 cm. high is recommended by Okada (1941); the sand layer should be about 20 cm. deep. A constant stream of sea water running through this aquarium keeps the water level at about 50 cm.

B. Procuring Gametes: The jellied egg-masses can be collected at the mouths of the burrows where they are deposited at nightfall. Okada (1941) has been successful in inducing these animals to shed eggs in laboratory aquaria.

NORMAL DEVELOPMENT:

A. The Unfertilized Ovum: The egg is spheroidal in shape. In the Japanese form, the polar axis measures approximately 120 microns, while the diameter in polar view is 150 microns (Okada, 1941). The egg is faintly pink in color, granular and almost opaque. It is homolecithal. Germinal vesicle breakdown occurs immediately after discharge into sea water (Okada, 1941). The eggs are embedded in large, irregular jelly-masses.

B. Fertilization and Cleavage: Fertilization occurs at the metaphase of the first polar division, and is followed by the lifting of a thick fertilization membrane and the formation of the first and second polar bodies (Okada, 1941). Cleavage is unequal and spiral, and the micromeres are relatively large. No polar lobes are formed. Gastrulation is by a combination of invagination and epiboly.

C. Rate of Development: The following time table of development at 23 to 25° C. is given by Okada (1941). Time is calculated from shedding of the eggs.

Stage	Time
First cleavage	7 hours
Second cleavage	7½ hours
Third cleavage	8 hours
Early blastula	15 hours
Gastrula	24 hours

Stage	Time
Young trochophore	2 days
Trunk segmentation, loss of capsule	3 days
Three to five pairs of setae (embryos hatching from jelly-mass)	4 days

D. Later Stages of Development: A trochophore is developed during late gastrulation. The free-swimming larvae within the jelly-mass are oval organisms, with a narrow prototroch and telotroch; a small ventral neurotroch and a posterior tuft of cilia are also present. At this time, there is a single pair of eyespots in the pre-trochal region. The hatched larvae have three to five pairs of setigerous segments and an additional pair of eyespots. Diagrams of the larvae can be found in the papers by Wilson (1882), Child (1900) and Okada (1941).

REFERENCES:

BUMPUS, H. C., 1898. The breeding of animals at Woods Holl during the months of June, July and August. *Science, 8:* 850–858.

CHILD, C. M., 1897. A preliminary account of the cleavage of *Arenicola cristata,* with remarks on the mosaic theory. *Zool. Bull., 1:* 71–94.

CHILD, C. M., 1898. The maturation and fertilization of the egg of *Arenicola marina. Trans. N. Y. Acad. Sci., 16:* 387–394.

CHILD, C. M., 1900. The early development of Arenicola and Sternaspis. *Arch. f. Entw., 9:* 587–723.

DOWNING, E. R., 1911. The formation of the spermatophore in Arenicola and a theory of the alternation of generations in animals. *J. Morph., 22:* 1001–1051.

NEWELL, G. E., 1948. A contribution to our knowledge of the life history of *Arenicola marina* L. *J. Mar. Biol. Assoc., 27:* 554–580.

OKADA, K., 1941. The gametogenesis, the breeding habits, and the early development of *Arenicola cristata* Stimpson, a tubicolous polychaete. *Sci. Rep. Tôhoku Imp. Univ., ser. 4, Biol., 16:* 99–146.

OKUDA, S., 1938. Notes on the spawning habit of *Arenicola claparedii* Levinsen. *Annot. Zool. Japon., 17:* 577–580.

WILSON, E. B., 1882. Observations on the early developmental stages of some polychaetous Annelides. *Stud. Biol. Lab., Johns Hopkins Univ., 2:* 271–299.

ANNELIDA

(Polychaeta)

Chaetopterus pergamentaceus

Living Material:

These worms live in parchment-like, U-shaped tubes in sand just below tide level; they can be dug only at low tide. The sexes are separate, and are distinguished by the parapodia on the posterior (sexual) segments. These parapodia are uniformly ivory white in the male, but in the female they contain yellow coils, which are the ovaries with their enclosed eggs.

Breeding Season:

June, July, and sometimes the first two weeks in August.

Procuring and Handling Material:

A. Care of Adults: When brought into the laboratory, the animals are often still in their leathery tubes, which can be slit with scissors so that the worms can be removed gently. The sexes should be segregated, with no more than two or three animals per large fingerbowl. The dishes should be placed on a water table, and supplied with a constant, gentle stream of sea water. One or two females and one ripe male will give an adequate supply of eggs and sperm for ordinary embryological experiments.

B. Procuring Gametes: Animals may be kept in the laboratory for several days and parapodia removed as needed.

Female gametes: Unless the sexes have been kept separate for at least two days, rinse the female for a few seconds under a gentle stream of fresh water, to kill any sperm which may have adhered to the mucous film on the body. Cut off one or two parapodia and transfer them to a double layer of cheesecloth (which has been rinsed well in fresh water and then in sea water), allowing the eggs to filter into a fingerbowl of freshly filtered sea water. The straining will remove debris and most of the mucous matrix around the eggs. The parapodia may be teased apart, if necessary, to release the eggs.

Male gametes: Scissors are used to remove a posterior parapodium from a male, the tip of the segment being held with forceps. Allow the sperm to flow into a stender dish containing 10 cc. of filtered sea water. A drop of this suspension examined microscopically should contain highly motile sperm. If large numbers of motionless sperm are present, the suspension should be discarded and the procedure repeated with another male.

C. Preparation of Cultures: Procure eggs as directed above, and about 10 minutes later prepare the sperm suspension. Fifteen minutes after they are obtained, the eggs should be inseminated with one drop of the sperm suspension. This allows time for germinal vesicle breakdown. Thirty minutes after insemination, the eggs should be transferred to a fingerbowl of fresh sea water and placed on a water table. The bowl should be covered and the water changed at least twice a day after trochophores develop.

D. Methods of Observation: No special technique is required for observing living Chaetopterus eggs, but it is often desirable to prepare permanent slides of various stages. For whole mounts, which are useful for determining stages of mitosis, fertilization, etc., see the paper by Henley and Costello (1957). For sectioning these eggs, consult the very complete directions given by Just (1939, p. 88).

NORMAL DEVELOPMENT:

A. The Unfertilized Ovum: This egg is rather dark and granular, from the contained yolk-spheres. It is slightly more than 100 microns in diameter, and is often not quite spherical. When taken from the female the oöcyte, like that of Nereis, contains a large, central, immature nucleus, the germinal vesicle. However, in the egg of Chaetopterus maturation proceeds spontaneously to the metaphase of the first polar division after exposure to sea water. At this stage development is arrested until activation or death (Lillie, 1906; Pasteels, 1935). The spindle cannot be distinguished as such in the living egg without considerable flattening; the relatively clear region containing it is located quite excentrically. The spindle is attached to the egg surface in the region where the first polar body subsequently will be given off.

B. Fertilization and Cleavage: A few sperm may be seen adhering to the eggs almost immediately after insemination. Within five to six minutes the vitelline membrane separates slightly from the egg surface, and may now be called the fertilization membrane. Membrane elevation is inconspicuous in the egg of Chaetopterus, and there is little or no change in the membrane itself at this time; thickening and hardening do not occur. Later, however, the membrane undergoes a series of wrinklings which are quite pronounced (Pasteels, 1950). Ten to twelve minutes after insemination, the eggs, which become almost spherical after fertilization, elongate along an axis perpendicular to the polar axis. This is preparatory to the formation of the first polar body. In this division the egg thus assumes approximately the shape of a blastomere, although the polar body which results is a vestigial cell. The egg now rounds up, but elongates again in the same manner to produce a second polar body, which is usually formed under the first, pushing it away from the egg surface. The egg rounds up again, and the egg pronucleus may sometimes be seen migrating toward the center of the egg; occasionally, the sperm nucleus may be detected. The clear zone extends from the polar region toward the equator of the egg. A typical "pear-shaped" stage is reached, with the polar bodies in a position corresponding to that of the stem attachment in a pear. The bulge which forms the polar lobe appears quite suddenly at the antipolar end of the egg, reversing its shape.

The first cleavage furrow begins at the animal pole and passes to one side of the polar lobe, which thus becomes incorporated into one of the two smooth, unequal blastomeres. Abnormal three-celled eggs, resulting from polyspermy, may be seen. The two blastomeres become closely apposed, and about 10 minutes later the second cleavage occurs. The large blastomere again forms a polar lobe, and a four-cell stage results, in which one blastomere is larger than the other three.

The four clear nuclei become visible, and shortly after this the third division takes place, forming four relatively large micromeres. A profile view shows the rotated displacement of the micromeres resulting from spiral cleavage, although this displacement is neither great nor conspicuous in the egg of Chaetopterus.

The polar bodies are larger than those of Nereis. The inequality of the first two cleavage blastomeres is due to two factors: 1) an inequality of the poles and asters of the first cleavage spindle, and 2) the addition of the polar lobe material to the CD blastomere (Mead, 1897; Lillie, 1906).

C. Time Table of Development: Chaetopterus eggs develop rapidly. If eggs are fertilized after the partial maturation in sea water has been completed, they develop as rapidly as eggs inseminated when first placed in sea water 12 to 15 minutes earlier. A rise in temperature increases the rate of development, but temperatures above 26° C. are not desirable.

The following table includes a summary of the development of many batches of Chaetopterus eggs, at temperatures of 22–23° C. and 24–26° C. The times are calculated from insemination, and represent the averages of data obtained over a period of several years.

| | Time at | |
Stage	22–23° C.	24–26° C.
First polar body	14 minutes	11 minutes
Second polar body	28 minutes	18 minutes
"Pear" stage	42 minutes	36 minutes
Polar lobe	47 minutes	41 minutes
First cleavage	51 minutes	42 minutes
Second cleavage	71 minutes	59 minutes
Swimming trochophore	22–24 hours	8–20 hours

D. Later Stages of Development: Chaetopterus larvae differ from typical trochophores in having no pre-oral prototroch. A prominent apical flagellum (single except in rare cases) is present. In slightly older larvae, a second band of cilia, the mesotroch, is found below the prototroch (Wilson, 1882, 1929).

In the late trochophore, two to six days old, there is a gradual disappearance of yolk. The various regions of the digestive tract can be identified: the wide, slit-like mouth on the ventral surface, which leads to a short, ciliated oesophagus; the large, clear, sac-like stomach, which is separated from the short intestine by a double fold of endoderm; the anus which opens on the dorsal side, just anterior to the terminal papilla or holdfast. The mesotroch of the early larva is replaced in the older animal by a pair of lateral flagella, and a second ciliated band, the paratroch, appears in the region of the posterior boundary of the intestine. In the anterior region (the head vesicle) the apical flagellum is retained and a pair of lateral eyespots is now visible. (See the paper of Wilson, 1882, and Figures 49 and 55 in the paper of Wilson, 1929).

REFERENCES:

GOLDSTEIN, L., 1953. A study of the mechanism of activation and nuclear breakdown in the Chaetopterus egg. *Biol. Bull.,* **105**: 87–102.

HENLEY, C., AND D. P. COSTELLO, 1957. The effects of x-irradiation on the fertilized eggs of the annelid, Chaetopterus. *Biol. Bull.,* **112**: 184–195.

JUST, E. E., 1939. Basic Methods for Experiments on Eggs of Marine Animals. P. Blakiston's Son and Co., Inc., Philadelphia.

LILLIE, F. R., 1902. Differentiation without cleavage in the egg of the annelid *Chaetopterus pergamentaceus*. *Arch. f. Entw.*, **14**: 477–499.

LILLIE, F. R., 1906. Observations and experiments concerning the elementary phenomena of embryonic development in Chaetopterus. *J. Exp. Zool.*, **3**: 153–268.

MEAD, A. D., 1897. The early development of marine annelids. *J. Morph.*, **13**: 227–326.

PASTEELS, J., 1935. Recherches sur le déterminisme de l'entrée en maturation de l'oeuf chez divers Invertébrés marins. *Arch. Biol.*, **46**: 229–262.

PASTEELS, J., 1950. Mouvements localisés et rythmiques de la membrane de fécondation chez des oeufs fécondés ou activés (Chaetopterus, Mactra, Nereis). *Arch. Biol.*, **61**: 197–220.

TITLEBAUM, A., 1928. Artificial production of Janus embryos of Chaetopterus. *Proc. Nat. Acad. Sci.*, **14**: 245–247.

TYLER, A., 1930. Experimental production of double embryos in annelids and mollusks. *J. Exp. Zool.*, **57**: 347–407.

WHITAKER, D. M., 1933. On the rate of oxygen consumption by fertilized and unfertilized eggs. IV. Chaetopterus and *Arbacia punctulata*. *J. Gen. Physiol.*, **16**: 475–495.

WILSON, E. B., 1882. Observations on the early developmental stages of some polychaetous Annelides. *Stud. Biol. Lab., Johns Hopkins Univ.*, **2**: 271–299.

WILSON, E. B., 1929. The development of egg-fragments in annelids. *Arch. f. Entw.*, **117**: 179–210.

ANNELIDA

(POLYCHAETA)

Cirratulis grandis

LIVING MATERIAL:

These worms live in muddy sand and are abundant in many locations at Woods Hole, Mass. The sexes are separate; mature males can be recognized by the bright orange body color which develops during the breeding season (Mead, 1898).

BREEDING SEASON:

The limits of the season have not been established for the Woods Hole region, but ripe individuals are available during July and at least the early part of August (Bumpus, 1898). Mead (1898) states that the height of the breeding season is early July, and that nearly ripe females were found as early as April 17.

PROCURING AND HANDLING MATERIAL:

A. Care of Adults: The worms should be washed free of mud and placed in a fingerbowl of sea water. It is best if the water is changed daily.

B. Preparation of Cultures: Spawning occasionally occurs in the laboratory. After it is completed, the adults should be removed and the eggs allowed to remain undisturbed for an hour or so. Then the inseminated eggs should be transferred to a fingerbowl of fresh sea water. Change the sea water daily.

NORMAL DEVELOPMENT:

A. The Unfertilized Ovum: The mature ovum measures approximately 104 microns in diameter. It is opaque and pale yellow-green in color. A conspicuous refractive membrane is present. The egg is probably shed in the germinal vesicle stage, but the oöcyte nucleus quickly ruptures and the egg proceeds spontaneously to metaphase of the first maturation division.

B. Cleavage: Although no details of cleavage are available in the literature, it is presumably spiral.

C. Rate of Development: Development is relatively rapid. A trochophore-like form, which never becomes an active swimmer, appears within about 24 hours, but it is rapidly converted into a three-segmented larva. Metamorphosis is well on its way by the fourth day after insemination.

D. Later Stages of Development: The vestigial trochophore has an apical tuft and a poorly developed prototroch. A three-segmented larva is formed.

SPECIAL COMMENTS:

Although this animal was at one time routinely used in the Embryology Course at Woods Hole, practically no details of its culture or embryology are recorded. Since it is quite abundant in the Woods Hole region, it merits further investigation.

REFERENCES:

BUMPUS, H. C., 1898. The breeding of animals at Woods Holl during the months of June, July and August. *Science,* **8**: 850–858.

MEAD, A. D., 1898. The breeding of animals at Woods Holl during the month of April, 1898. *Science,* **7**: 702–704.

ANNELIDA

(POLYCHAETA)

Cistenides (now Pectinaria) gouldi

LIVING MATERIAL:

The adults live in small tubes shaped like ice-cream cones, made of sand grains cemented together. They are found in muddy sand in shallow water, and can be collected readily by digging on sand flats around Woods Hole, Mass. The sexes are separate.

BREEDING SEASON:

The limits of the season have not been investigated, but it is possible to secure ripe animals at least during August.

PROCURING AND HANDLING MATERIAL:

A. Care of Adults: These worms are quite hardy and will survive in the laboratory if they are kept in dishes of running sea water, whether they are removed from their tubes or left in them.

B. Procuring Gametes: Eggs and sperm can be obtained by removing male and female animals from the tubes and pinching the bodies with a pair of fine forceps. When first released, the sperm are in packets, but these quickly break up into masses of free-swimming sperm when they come into contact with sea water.

C. Preparation of Cultures: Just (1922) reports that the larvae can be reared through metamorphosis, but without special feeding the trochophores die within a few days.

NORMAL DEVELOPMENT:

A. The Unfertilized Ovum: The mature ovum measures approximately 55 microns in diameter. It is pale yellow-green in color and very transparent, showing internal changes without staining. The egg contains a large germinal vesicle with a prominent nucleolus when shed, but the vesicle breaks down rapidly when the egg comes in contact with sea water.

B. Fertilization and Cleavage: A thin membrane is elevated at the time of fertilization. The formation of two polar bodies quickly follows. Cleavage is total, unequal and spiral; the D cell is markedly larger than the other macromeres, and the micromeres are usually large. Gastrulation is by invagination.

C. Time Table of Development: The following table shows the rate of development at 24° C. The time is recorded from insemination.

Stage	Time
Polar bodies formed	29 minutes
Fusion of pronuclei	40 minutes
First cleavage	54 minutes
Second cleavage	72 minutes

Stage	Time
Third cleavage	92 minutes
Free-swimming blastula	5 hours
Gastrula	10 hours
Well-formed trochophore	22 hours

D. Later Stages of Development: The trochophore is small and transparent. It has a long tuft of apical cilia and a well-developed prototroch. Ciliated lateral and anterior lips overhang the mouth like a hood. From one of the lower corners of the mouth a tuft of long cilia protrudes; it is particularly noticeable in side view. There are indications of a telotroch. The tri-partite digestive tract is well ciliated and contractile. The diagrams by Wilson (1936), illustrating the larvae of a European species of *Pectinaria,* show that these larvae are almost identical with those of *Cistenides gouldi.*

REFERENCES:

Just, E. E., 1922. On rearing sexually mature *Platynereis megalops* from eggs. *Amer. Nat.,* **56**: 471–478.

Wilson, D. P., 1936. Notes on the early stages of two polychaetes, *Nephthys hombergi* Lamarck and *Pectinaria koreni* Malmgren. *J. Mar. Biol. Assoc.,* **21**: 305–310.

ANNELIDA

(POLYCHAETA)

Clymenella torquata

LIVING MATERIAL:

This worm lives in a tube fashioned of sand grains; the tubes are in a vertical position, in the sand of inter-tidal regions, and at Beaufort, N. C., are often found in association with the similar tubes of *Axiothella mucosa,* another tubicolous annelid (Bookhout and Horn, 1949).

At times, the animals are abundant, but the number seems to fluctuate widely from year to year. · Since the breeding season apparently is very short, it is advisable to collect large numbers of the worms immediately before the onset of the breeding season.

Burbanck *et al.* (1956) report that Clymenella was regularly collected at Rand's Harbor, Mass., over a six-year period.

BREEDING SEASON:

According to Mead (1897), all mature individuals spawn during a restricted two- or three-day period which occurs between the latter part of April and the middle of May.

PROCURING AND HANDLING MATERIAL:

A. Care of Adults: Mature females have eggs which show through the body wall during the breeding season. The sexes should be segregated and the females placed in an aquarium which is supplied with sand. New tubes are rapidly built by the worms.

B. Procuring Gametes: Eggs are deposited on the surface of the sand, at the mouth of the tube. They may be left in sea water for several hours before insemination.

NORMAL DEVELOPMENT:

A. The Unfertilized Ovum: The egg measures 150 microns in diameter. It is practically spherical, and is very opaque because of the large amount of yellow yolk. A closely fitting, thin, smooth membrane is present (Mead, 1897).

B. Fertilization and Cleavage: The sperm enters after the first maturation spindle has formed, and the polar bodies remain to mark the animal pole (Mead, 1897). Cleavage is equal and spiral, and no polar lobes are formed. Gastrulation is probably by epiboly. In general, the development is very similar to that of Amphitrite, according to Mead; see Figures 65 to 88 in his paper (1897).

C. Rate of Development: No precise information is available.

D. Later Stages of Development: The larva is a free-swimming trochophore, reported to be similar to the trochophore of Amphitrite.

REFERENCES:

BOOKHOUT, C. G., AND E. C. HORN, 1949. The development of *Axiothella mucosa* (Andrews).
   J. Morph., **84**: 145–183.

BURBANCK, W. D., M. E. PIERCE AND G. C. WHITELEY, JR., 1956. A study of the bottom
   fauna of Rand's Harbor, Massachusetts: An application of the ecotone concept. *Ecol.
   Monog.,* **26**: 213–243.

MEAD, A. D., 1894. Preliminary account of the cell lineage of Amphitrite and other annelids.
   J. Morph., **9**: 465–473.

MEAD, A. D., 1897. The early development of marine annelids. *J. Morph.,* **13**: 227–326.

ANNELIDA

(POLYCHAETA)

Diopatra cuprea *

LIVING MATERIAL:

These are large worms (often 30 cm. long and 10 mm. wide), which live in dark grey parchment-like tubes embedded in hard-packed sand. The tubes are often encrusted with shells, algal particles and debris, and have a lateral vent (Hartman, 1945). Intact animals are not often obtained, since they tend to withdraw into their long tubes when disturbed. The animals are yellowish to dark brown in color, and the sexes are separate. Sexually mature males are white to yellowish in color; mature females are grey-green. It is very difficult to distinguish between the sexes (Allen, personal communication).

Sumner *et al.* (1911) state that Diopatra is "almost ubiquitous" in Woods Hole waters. North Falmouth and Hadley Harbor, Mass., are among the collecting grounds for this form.

BREEDING SEASON:

Bumpus (1898) reported that at Woods Hole the ova were "nearly ripe" in August; young larvae were obtained in tows at Beaufort, N. C. in July (Andrews, 1891a). Hartman (1945) found egg-strings exposed at low tide during June and July at Beaufort; she suggested that these egg-strings were probably deposited at night.

Allen (personal communication) has been successful in rearing embryos from the middle of June until the end of August, at Woods Hole. However, she has not found naturally-spawned egg-strings of Diopatra at Woods Hole any time during the period from April to the end of August.

PROCURING AND HANDLING MATERIAL:

A. Care of Adults: The animals do well, if they are left in their tubes and supplied with adequate amounts of running sea water. They are carnivorous and thrive if fed pieces of Mytilus every day or two (Allen, personal communication).

B. Procuring Embryos and Gametes: The naturally-fertilized eggs are surrounded by a gelatinous substance, and are deposited on the sand in long, slender, cylindrical egg-masses (Hartman, 1945). Various stages of embryonic development are contained within the jelly; when a freshly-laid string is placed in a culture tank, the larvae leave the jelly and seek the upper, light side of the container (Hartman, 1945). Ordinarily, however, they remain within the jelly-mass for a period of several days.

In the female, the ripe eggs are packed into the body cavity (Andrews, 1891b), apparently unattached to the ovary. The sperm are likewise found in masses in

* Much of the information on which this section is based was obtained from Dr. M. Jean Allen, to whom we are most grateful.

the body cavity of the male. Allen (personal communication) states that when
the adults are held with forceps, they readily pinch off posterior segments. Eggs
may be obtained from such isolated posterior sections by slitting the body wall;
sperm ooze out when the body wall at the base of a parapodium is pricked with a
dissecting needle.

C. Preparation of Cultures: Andrews (1891b) was not successful in obtaining
development of artificially-inseminated Diopatra eggs. However, Allen (1951,
1953) reported that eggs could be successfully inseminated *in vitro;* the percentage
of fertilization under such conditions is often not very high (Allen, personal communication). Just (1922) stated briefly (p. 477) that he was successful in artificially inseminating Diopatra eggs cut from the females.

After they are obtained, the eggs should be washed in a fingerbowl containing
sand-filtered sea water. Inseminate with several drops of milky sperm suspension
(in sand-filtered sea water); polyspermy should be avoided. It is probably best
to provide two or three changes of fresh, sand-filtered sea water within a few
minutes after insemination, and at least once daily thereafter.

NORMAL DEVELOPMENT:

A. The Unfertilized Ovum: The eggs of this form are produced in the ovary
by a remarkable process which was described by Andrews (1891b). The ovarian
tissue is composed of cell-strands which are thrown into loops, projecting into the
body cavity of the female. One of the cells at the apex of each loop becomes
enlarged and specialized, and gives rise to the ovum. The remaining cells (often
15 in number) of the loop continue to be attached to the ovum (even after it is
detached from the ovary and lies free in the body cavity) in the form of two long
strands. These strands are retained until the ovum is almost ripe; however,
Andrews suggests that the function of the "sister cells" is supportive rather than
nutritive. Their subsequent fate, after detachment from the ovum, is not known.

The ripe egg, free of the two strands, is ovoid in shape; it is approximately
235 microns high and 205 microns wide (Allen, 1951). A considerable amount
of yolk is present, rendering it heavy and opaque in the living condition. There
is a striking aggregation of green pigment, in an area which is near the large
nucleus (see Figure 4, Plate I, of the ripe egg of *D. magna,* in the paper by
Andrews, 1891b).

B. Fertilization and Cleavage: Fertilization is external and takes place at the
germinal vesicle stage (Allen, 1953). Two polar bodies are given off, and the
first cleavage results in the formation of two unequal blastomeres. Subsequent
divisions are of the spiral type (Allen, 1953), the four micromeres of the eight-cell
stage being polar in position and somewhat smaller than the macromeres. Within
three hours after insemination, functional cilia penetrate the egg membrane; anterior vacuolated cells form four plates, which surround a central mass (the source
of the future apical tuft of the larva, according to Allen, 1953). Gastrulation is
probably by epiboly.

C. Time Table of Development: The cleavage of Diopatra proceeds very rapidly (Allen, 1951). The following schedule is based on her data, at temperatures
of 22–24° C.; the times are recorded from insemination and represent approxi-
mations, only, inasmuch as egg-batches vary considerably.

Stage	Time
First (and sometimes the second) polar body	30 minutes
Two- to four-cells	40–60 minutes
Eight-cells	50–90 minutes
Mid- to late cleavage	90–120 minutes
Functional cilia	3 hours
Apical tuft	12 hours
Rotating trochophores	24 hours
Elongated larvae	2½ days

D. Later Stages of Development: The young larvae are spherical in shape, and provided with equatorial and terminal cilia, according to Andrews (1891b), which enable them to rotate within the jelly-mass. The egg membrane is apparently retained as a "cuticle" in the larva (Andrews, 1891b), and irregular patches of green pigment (presumably derived from the pigment of the egg) are scattered over the body.

Allen (1951, 1953, and personal communication) described the later stages of development in artificially-inseminated eggs as follows: An apical tuft forms within about eleven or twelve hours after insemination, and during the next 24 hours, elongated trochophores develop, which have a broad prototroch, a narrow telotroch, and red eyespots. These larvae continue to elongate, and by 60 hours have developed two or three sets of setae and a Y-shaped gut. Swimming is by a rotating movement. Allen (1951) reported that she was able to grow larvae in culture for as long as 21 days, by which time six sets of setae, pharyngeal muscle fibers, cerebral ganglion, tentacles, jaws and anal cirri were among the structures present.

SPECIAL COMMENTS:

Andrews (1891a) and Hartman (1951) comment on the fact that regeneration of the anterior end of Diopatra is a common phenomenon, and one which would be worthy of further study.

REFERENCES:

ALLEN, M. J., 1951. Observations on living developmental stages of the polychaete, *Diopatra cuprea* (Bosc). *Anat. Rec.,* **111**: 134.

ALLEN, M. J., 1953. Development of the polychaete, *Diopatra cuprea* (Bosc). *Anat. Rec.,* **117**: 572–573.

ANDREWS, E. A., 1891a. Report upon the Annelida Polychaeta of Beaufort, North Carolina. *Proc. U. S. Nat. Mus.,* **14**: 277–302.

ANDREWS, E. A., 1891b. Reproductive organs of Diopatra. *J. Morph.,* **5**: 113–124.

BUMPUS, H. C., 1898. The breeding of animals at Woods Holl during the months of June, July and August. *Science,* **8**: 850–858.

HARTMAN, O., 1945. The marine annelids of North Carolina. Duke Univ. Mar. Station, Bull. no. 2.

HARTMAN, O., 1951. The littoral marine annelids of the Gulf of Mexico. *Publ. Inst. Mar. Sci., Univ. of Texas,* **2**: 1–124.

JUST, E. E., 1922. On rearing sexually mature *Platynereis megalops* from eggs. *Amer. Nat.,* **56**: 471–478.

MONRO, C. C. A., 1924. On the post-larval stage in *Diopatra cuprea,* Bosc, a Polychaetous Annelid of the family Eunicidae. *Ann. Mag. Nat. Hist., ser. 9,* **14**: 193–199.

RENAUD, J. C., 1956. A report on some polychaetous annelids from the Miami-Bimini area. Amer. Mus. Novitates, No. 1812.

SUMNER, F. B., R. C. OSBURN AND L. J. COLE, 1911. A biological survey of the waters of Woods Hole and vicinity. Part 1. *Bull. U. S. Bur. Fisheries,* **31**: 1–544.

WILSON, E. B., 1882. Observations on the early developmental stages of some polychaetous Annelides. *Stud. Biol. Lab., Johns Hopkins Univ.,* **2**: 271–299.

ANNELIDA

(Polychaeta)

Harmothoë imbricata

LIVING MATERIAL:

These animals are found between tide levels, in pile scrapings and under stones. They may be distinguished from Lepidonotus, which is collected in the same localities, by having 15 rather than 12 pairs of scales. The sexes are separate.

BREEDING SEASON:

Mid-April through May. The season is about one week earlier than that of Lepidonotus (Bumpus, 1898).

PROCURING AND HANDLING MATERIAL:

Ripe females can be recognized by the bright pink color of the ventral surface. Eggs teased from the body cavity are easily fertilized, according to Mead (1898). Shedding of eggs may be induced by the methods suggested for Lepidonotus (p. 81).

NORMAL DEVELOPMENT:

A. The Unfertilized Ovum: The egg is pink and rather clear, with minutely granular yolk. It is small; Sars (1845) records 50 microns for the egg diameter of a European form of this species, and diameters ranging between 56 and 78 microns are reported by McIntosh (1900) at St. Andrews, N. B.

B. Cleavage: Cleavage is equal and spiral, and no polar lobes are present. Gastrulation is probably by invagination.

C. Rate of Development: No precise data are available, although Mead (1898) states briefly that the eight-cell stage was attained in less than two hours.

D. Later Stages of Development: Mead (1897) reports that the development of Harmothoë is very similar to that of Lepidonotus. The larval stages are well described and illustrated by McIntosh (1900) and Thorson (1946). Young trochophores are positively phototropic (McIntosh, 1900).

REFERENCES:

BUMPUS, H. C., 1898. The breeding of animals at Woods Holl during the month of May, 1898. *Science,* 8: 58–61.

MCINTOSH, W. C., 1900–1923. A monograph of the British Annelids, Pt. II. Polychaeta. Dulau & Co., Ltd., London. (Eight volumes.)

MEAD, A. D., 1897. The early development of marine annelids. *J. Morph.,* 13: 227–326.

MEAD, A. D., 1898. The breeding of animals at Woods Holl during the month of April, 1898. *Science,* 7: 702–704.

SARS, M., 1845. Zur Entwicklung der Anneliden. *Arch. f. Naturgesch., 11 Jahrg.,* 1: 11–19.

THORSON, G., 1946. Reproduction and larval development of Danish marine bottom invertebrates, with special reference to the planktonic larvae in the Sound (Øresund). *Medd. f. Komm. Danmarks Fiskeri. og Havunders., Ser. Plankton,* 4: (Nr. 1) 1–523.

ANNELIDA

(POLYCHAETA)

Hydroides hexagonus

LIVING MATERIAL:

Adults of *Hydroides hexagonus* live in white, twisting, calcareous tubes which they secrete on old mollusc shells, stones, or timbers which are dredged in abundance from the harbor. For a description of features which distinguish this worm from Sabellaria, see p. 93 of this manual. The sexes are separate, but similar in appearance.

BREEDING SEASON:

According to Grave (1933), this opens between June 10 and 15, and closes between October 1 and November 1. During the early part of the season, more than 50% of the shed eggs are immature and undersize; after the middle of July, nearly all the eggs are mature and fertilizable.

PROCURING AND HANDLING MATERIAL:

A. Care of Adults: If the worms are left in their tubes and placed in aquaria with a good supply of running sea water, they may be kept almost indefinitely in the laboratory.

B. Procuring Gametes: The gametes, which are carried in the coelomic cavity, will be released through the nephridiopores almost immediately after the worms are removed from their tubes. This is done by chipping away the tubes with forceps. Place each animal in a separate stender dish containing about 25 cc. of sea water, and observe shedding. Clouds of white sperm will flow from the male, while the female will release a large number of peach-colored eggs. This is a convenient way of distinguishing the sexes. Remove the male when the sea water is cloudy with sperm, and use this sperm suspension without dilution, as indicated below.

C. Preparation of Cultures: Eggs may be successfully fertilized as long as four hours after shedding. Sperm, once activated, remain viable for as long as eight hours. The sperm are inactive when first shed, but become activated slowly after dilution with sea water. For this reason it is best to delay insemination until at least half an hour after shedding. At this time examine a sperm sample under a compound microscope. If the sperm appear active, add five or six drops of the suspension to the eggs, which have been transferred to a stender dish of fresh sea water. Allow the inseminated eggs to stand undisturbed for about 30 minutes and then decant the upper layers of sea water, replacing it with fresh sea water. Cover the dish and place it on the water table. In ten hours or less, actively swimming gastrulae will be present; they should be decanted to a fingerbowl of fresh sea water. Discard the debris and the undeveloped eggs. The larvae are very hardy, and will develop for days without extra care, although if they are to be kept over long periods, they should be decanted daily to fresh sea water. They have been successfully reared through metamorphosis (about two weeks after hatching), but to do this, feeding with diatoms is necessary.

D. Methods of Observation: Since these eggs are small, they are best studied under high magnification, mounted on glass slides covered with unsupported cover-slips. The older, moving larvae can be temporarily quieted by adding a drop of very dilute Janus green solution (1:1000 in sea water) to the mount. This will also serve to indicate clearly details of the digestive tract.

NORMAL DEVELOPMENT:

A. The Unfertilized Ovum: The eggs are small (67–72 microns in diameter), peach-colored, and have a thick, refractive, vitelline membrane. They are spherical and very opaque, due to the presence of a considerable amount of yolk, but the outline of the large germinal vesicle can be seen.

B. Fertilization and Cleavage: Insemination is not immediately followed by any noticeable changes, no entrance cone nor fertilization membrane being formed. Colwin, Colwin and Philpott (1956b) report that a narrow perivitelline space is present, however, after fertilization. The outline of the germinal vesicle becomes irregular and lobulated, and 15 minutes after insemination, it ruptures completely. Although the maturation spindle is not visible (because of the opacity of the egg), it is forming and moving to the periphery of the egg.

Prior to the appearance of the first polar body, two changes may be seen to occur. The egg flattens at the animal pole, and the vitelline membrane rises from the surface in this vicinity to form a cap-like space into which the first polar body is elevated. This polar body usually divides once, soon after its formation. Following this division, the second polar body is produced. A second cap-like space is formed at the vegetal pole, by the separation of the egg surface from the membrane. This precedes the first cleavage, which is equal; the AB cell cannot be distinguished from the CD cell. The second cleavage divides the egg further, into four approximately equal blastomeres, and very shortly after this, a dexio-tropic, horizontal cleavage cuts off the first quartet of micromeres. Further cleavages follow the typical course of spiral cleavage, and produce a ciliated, moving blastula in about five hours. (See the paper by Shearer, 1911.)

C. Time Table of Development: The exact relationship between temperature and developmental rate has not been established in this form, but the following table will give an approximate chronology of stages observed at 24° to 25° C. The time is recorded from insemination.

Stage	Time
Germinal vesicle breakdown completed	14 minutes
First polar body	40 minutes
Second polar body	60–70 minutes
First cleavage	1 hour, 20 minutes
Second cleavage	1 hour, 36 minutes
Third cleavage	1 hour, 46–50 minutes
Swimming larva (blastula)	5–6 hours
Gastrula	9–12 hours
Well-formed trochophore	20 hours
Metamorphosis	12 days–2 weeks

D. Later Stages of Development and Metamorphosis: The process of gastrulation may be followed by observing embryos 6–10 hours after insemination. The vitelline membrane is not cast off when the cilia develop and the larvae start to swim; the cilia grow through it, and the membrane is not lost, eventually forming part of the cuticle of the worm body. In the young blastula, it is still possible to see the membrane raised from the surface in the polar area. The polar bodies, however, are no longer visible at this time. As gastrulation progresses, the elongated endodermal cells invaginate into the blastocoele to form the archenteron, which opens to the surface by way of the blastopore. In older gastrulae, the apical tuft and prototroch are well developed; they are therefore trochophores. (See the paper of Hatschek, 1886.)

Larval stage: The larva is a typical annelid trochophore. For details of structure, the excellent figures of Hatschek (1886) and Shearer (1911) may be consulted. The larvae show positive phototaxis, and gather on the illuminated side of the dish. Trochophores, three to five days old, can be mounted on a slide with a few shreds of lens paper to entangle them, or they can be quieted with a drop of dilute Janus green (1:1000 in sea water). The larvae are transparent, and proper illumination (obtained by adjusting the microscope mirror and condenser) will help to bring out the details of structure. The apical tuft and the anal vesicle are landmarks for the animal and vegetal poles, respectively; the mouth is on the ventral side, the eye on the right.

The following may be observed:

1. The shape of the trochophore, with pre-trochal and post-trochal regions.
2. Apical tuft; several long cilia probably functioning as a sense organ.
3. Apical organ, a thickening of the ectoderm at the animal pole; a nerve center and the primordium of the cerebral ganglion.
4. The prototroch, an equatorial band of large cilia. In older trochophores, two rows will be found, with a row of short cilia anterior to the large cilia.
5. The metatroch (paratroch), a circular band of cilia in the middle of the post-trochal hemisphere.
6. A ciliated groove on the mid-ventral line connecting the mouth and the anus. It marks the line of closure of the blastopore, the mouth being the remnant of the blastopore, the anus a secondary opening at the lower end of the blastoporal slit.
7. One eyespot (with red pigment) on the right side in the pre-trochal hemisphere.
8. Two statocysts on the ventral side.
9. The digestive tract, consisting of mouth opening, stomodeum or oesophagus (ectodermal), enlarged stomach (endodermal), narrow intestine (endodermal, with the exception of terminal, ectodermal proctodeum), and the anus, an opening dorsal to the vegetal pole. The whole tract is lined with cilia. The mechanism of food intake may be studied if the larvae are fed Chinese ink.
10. The anal vesicle, a large, vacuolated cell at the posterior end, not found in most other species of trochophores.
11. The cavity between the outer body wall and the intestine; not a true coelom but a primary body cavity, it is the persisting blastocoele.
12. The larval kidneys (paired), typical protonephridia with flame cells; they open near the anus, and appear as slender cords near the statocysts, extending between

oesophagus and anus. (Consult the figures in the papers by Hatschek and Shearer.)

13. Muscles. Two fine strands may be seen bifurcating at the upper end of the larval kidney. One of them can be traced to its insertion at the apical plate, the other at the oesophagus. These are longitudinal muscles. Other longitudinal muscles extend from the stomach to points in the upper hemisphere. A strong circular muscle is located near the metatroch; the constriction of the larva caused by its contraction will be frequently observed. There are circular, sphincter muscles in the digestive tract.

14. Undifferentiated ectomesodermal cells, single or in small groups, can be seen attached to the stomach, to the inner body wall, near the apical organ, etc.

15. The important entomesodermal cells (derivatives of the 4d teloblasts), which give rise to the mesodermal structures of the worm body, are difficult to distinguish. They are small groups of cells near the lower end of the larval kidney.

REFERENCES:

COLWIN, A. L., L. H. COLWIN AND D. E. PHILPOTT, 1956a. Sperm entry in *Hydroides hexagonus* (Annelida) and *Saccoglossus kowalevskii* (Enteropneusta). *Biol. Bull.,* 111: 289.

COLWIN, L. H., A. L. COLWIN AND D. E. PHILPOTT, 1956b. Electron microscope studies of the egg surfaces and membranes of *Hydroides hexagonus* (Annelida) and *Saccoglossus kowalevskii* (Enteropneusta). *Biol. Bull.,* 111: 289–290.

CONN, H. W., 1884. Development of Serpula. *Zool. Anz.,* 7: 669–672.

GRAVE, B. H., 1933. Rate of growth, age at sexual maturity, and duration of life of certain sessile organisms, at Woods Hole, Massachusetts. *Biol. Bull.,* 65: 375–386.

GRAVE, B. H., 1937. *Hydroides hexagonus. In:* Culture Methods for Invertebrate Animals, edit. by Galtsoff *et al.,* Comstock, Ithaca, pp. 185–187.

HARGITT, C. W., 1910. Observations on the spawning habits of *Hydroides dianthus. Amer. Nat.,* 44: 376–378.

HATSCHEK, B., 1886. Entwicklung der Trochophora von *Eupomatus uncinatus,* Philippi (*Serpula uncinata*). *Arbeit. Zool. Inst. Wien,* 6: 121–148.

SHEARER, C., 1911. On the development and structure of the trochophore of *Hydroides uncinatus* (Eupomatus). *Quart. J. Micr. Sci.,* 56: 543–590.

WILSON, E. B., 1890. The origin of the mesoblast-bands in annelids. *J. Morph.,* 4: 205–219.

ZELENY, C., 1905a. The rearing of serpulid larvae with notes on the behavior of the young animals. *Biol. Bull.,* 8: 308–312.

ZELENY, C., 1905b. Compensatory regulation. *J. Exp. Zool.,* 2: 1–102.

ZELENY, C., 1911. Experiments on the control of asymmetry in the development of the Serpulid, *Hydroides dianthus. J. Morph.,* 22: 927–944.

ANNELIDA

(Polychaeta)

Lepidonotus squamatus

LIVING MATERIAL:

These animals are relatively abundant, and can be found in pile scrapings and under stones at the tide level. The sexes are separate; the males are whitish and the females dark on the ventral surface (Mead, 1897; Bumpus, 1898).

BREEDING SEASON:

From the last of April to nearly the beginning of June (Mead, 1897; Bumpus, 1898).

PROCURING AND HANDLING MATERIAL:

A. Care of Adults: Males and females should be segregated in individual finger-bowls when brought into the laboratory, and supplied with running sea water.

B. Procuring Gametes: The animals shed during the evening of the day of collection, usually between 8 and 10 o'clock, although sometimes earlier. The shedding of eggs may be induced during this time by plunging the female into a dish of colder water and then placing the dish close to a lamp. The eggs can stand for several hours in sea water before insemination without impairing normal development (Mead, 1897).

NORMAL DEVELOPMENT:

A. The Unfertilized Ovum: The egg is irregular in shape when first shed, but soon becomes spherical. It measures 65 microns in diameter, and is rather opaque, although it contains a relatively small amount of yolk. A smooth, thin, closely fitting membrane is present.

B. Fertilization and Cleavage: There is apparently no information as to the time of sperm entrance. Cleavage is equal and spiral; no polar lobes are formed. Gastrulation is by invagination (Mead, 1897).

C. Rate of Development: In general, development proceeds rather slowly. Swimming forms are present 8 to 10 hours after insemination; gastrulation occurs in about 20 hours, well-formed trochophores by 48 hours. After this, there is little change for several days. The rate of development, however, is greatly increased with a rise in temperature (Mead, 1897).

D. Later Stages in Development: During the gastrula stage the trochophore assumes a remarkable shape: the membrane stands out from the body except in the regions of the apical tuft and the wide prototroch. The older trochophores are thin-walled and have a narrow, well-developed prototroch with longer cilia, and a neurotroch. An eyespot is present. (See text figures 19 and 20, and plate figure 104 in the paper by Mead, 1897.) The larvae show several interesting reversals of phototropic response during development according to Mead (1897).

81

REFERENCES:

Bumpus, H. C., 1898.　The breeding of animals at Woods Holl during the month of May, 1898.
　　Science, **8**: 58–61.
Mead, A. D., 1894.　Preliminary account of the cell lineage of Amphitrite and other annelids.
　　J. Morph., **9**: 465–473.
Mead, A. D., 1897.　The early development of marine annelids.　*J. Morph.,* **13**: 227–326.
Treadwell, A. L., 1898.　The cell lineage of *Podarke obscura.*　Preliminary communication.
　　Zool. Bull., **1**: 195–203.

ANNELIDA

(Polychaeta)

Nereis limbata

LIVING MATERIAL:

The heteronereis form of *Nereis limbata* lives in the mud of Eel Pond at Woods Hole, Mass., and also, in smaller numbers, in the Fisheries Basin and in Great Harbor. The sexes are separate. During certain phases of the lunar cycle (from full to new moon), these worms swarm at the surface, beginning about an hour after sunset. The males can be recognized by their smaller size, more active movements, and more vivid coloration— they are bright red, with white posterior segments. The larger, more sluggish females are a pale yellow-green in color.

It is convenient to collect the animals from the Eel Pond floating dock of the Supply Department, at Woods Hole. The light of a 100-watt lamp is used to attract the worms (the dock being wired with electricity for the collecting lamps). A long-handled net (having a flat, oval-shaped head, about 10 inches in length in the long axis, and with gauze stretched tightly over the framework) is used to scoop the worms from the water. On nights when there is a "run," a few males will appear first, swimming in wide circles. The females appear later; fewer in number and swimming more slowly than the males, they are first seen at the outer boundary of the circle of light. As a female spirals slowly towards the illuminated surface of the water, males which approach within a certain orbit will deviate from their original spiral paths to swim actively around her in rapidly narrowing circles, shedding sperm as they do so. This action is stimulated by substances which originate in the eggs and which are given off by the body of the ripe female. In turn, the presence of sperm in the water is a stimulus which induces the female to circle and shed. The females sink slowly to the bottom when they are spent. If females are to be collected before any shedding occurs, it is necessary to obtain them before they begin to circle.

Exceptions to the "dark of the moon" swarming are as follows: (1) In the first run of June, the animals may swarm every night until the full moon of July. (2) On stormy or windy nights, or nights following very cloudy days, Nereis may fail to appear. (3) In late September on cold nights they do not swarm even in the dark of the moon. (4) The curve of swarming is bimodal, with a depression several days before new moon.

Other striking examples of lunar periodicity have been described by Clark and Hess (1940a, 1940b), Hempelmann (1911), Izuka (1903), Just (1914), Mayer (1908) and Woodworth (1907).

BREEDING SEASON:

June through September, as discussed above (see, also, the paper by Lillie and Just, 1913).

PROCURING AND HANDLING MATERIAL:

A. Care of Adults: The animals should be collected one by one, and each female placed in a separate fingerbowl of sea water; several males may be kept together. It is best to prepare the fingerbowls in advance of the collection, placing a piece of Ulva (or a piece of paper towel, previously thoroughly soaked in clean sea water) in each dish, which is then half-filled with clean sea water. These dishes can be carried in a wooden tray to the collecting dock, and the animals placed directly in them. When they are brought back to the laboratory, the sea water should be changed and fingerbowls containing the animals should be covered and placed on a water table, surrounded by running sea water. *Do not keep the worms in a refrigerator.*

B. Procuring Gametes: An excess of sperm, which should be avoided, is usually obtained if the males and females are placed together in a dish, unless the male is removed as soon as it has shed its first cloud of sperm. Instead, gametes should be procured by pinching the animals with fine forceps, near the middle of the body; a single strong pinch should result in extrusion of the sex cells. The eggs from each female should be placed in a 250-ml. (or larger) fingerbowl, half-filled with clean sea water; no more than a single cell-layer of eggs should be present on the bottom of the dish, after the eggs have settled. "Dry" sperm are obtained by placing a male worm in a dry Syracuse dish and pinching the middle of the body. Adults should be removed from the dishes after shedding is completed.

Clipping the body with scissors is not a good practice, since it increases contamination of the gametes with coelomic fluid (which apparently adversely affects the normal fertilization reaction).

C. Preparation of Cultures: Add a few drops of dilute sperm suspension (one drop of "dry" sperm in 50 cc. of sea water) to the fingerbowl of eggs, and stir at once with a rapid circular movement of the dish. Care must be taken to avoid polyspermy, which results in interference with cleavage or in abnormal cleavage and development. In some forms, polyspermic eggs develop more rapidly than normally fertilized eggs, but those of Nereis usually fail to cleave.

To obtain later stages of development, allow the fingerbowl to remain undisturbed for about 30 minutes; then transfer the contents to a large dish and change the sea water. Keep the dish covered and on a sea water table, changing the water at least twice a day. After they leave the jelly, pour off the swimming trochophores to a clean dish of sea water; discard the jelly and dead eggs.

D. Methods of Observation: One or two minutes after insemination, place the eggs in a drop of thick Chinese ink suspension (made by rubbing a piece of the solid ink, wet with sea water, on a finely-ground glass surface). As the jelly is secreted by the eggs, it flows past the attached sperm, leaving a funnel-shaped cavity in which the ink particles remain, serving as an indicator of the point of sperm entrance.

Another method of studying sperm entrance is by the production of exaggerated entrance cones. Place a drop of eggs, inseminated 5 to 8 minutes earlier, in a stender dish containing 50 cc. of alkaline NaCl (pH 10.3–10.5) and mix rapidly and thoroughly. The vitelline membranes will elevate, due to a sudden inhibition of jelly release through the membrane, and a subsequent accumulation of the jelly in the perivitelline space (Costello and Young, 1939). The vitelline membrane remains permeable to water, which enters the perivitelline space as the jelly swells. The elevation of the membrane stretches out the sperm entrance cone between membrane and egg surface, forming a long filament which frequently causes a marked indentation of the membrane. It is sometimes necessary to use two or three changes of alkaline NaCl to obtain maximum exaggeration of the entrance cones. If the eggs (or the females from which they were obtained) have been kept in a refrigerator, they may become polyspermic when inseminated, and show numerous exaggerated entrance cones following this treatment. About ten minutes after treatment, the sperm head and middle piece may be seen moving across the perivitelline space to fuse with the egg surface. The membrane indentation is relaxed as soon as the sperm head has passed through. If the eggs are now carefully removed to sea water and washed several times, some will develop normally within the raised membranes. If they are left in the solution an optimum length of time before washing, and if the alkaline NaCl has been changed once or twice to remove most of the sea water, the eggs may be completely freed of their membranes. For further details of obtaining these denuded eggs, see the papers of Costello (1945a, 1949). For details of useful procedures for fixing, sectioning and staining Nereis eggs, consult the book by Just (1939b).

NORMAL DEVELOPMENT:

A. The Unfertilized Ovum: The egg of Nereis is approximately 140 microns in diameter and 100 microns high. Because of its shape, it tends to orient on a flat surface with the animal pole either above or below, only rarely to the side. It has a large germinal vesicle, with many small oil droplets and yolk spheres in the cytoplasm surrounding it. The egg has a cortex about seven microns thick, of jelly-precursor granules.

B. Fertilization and Cleavage: Very soon after insemination, a transparent jelly-layer is secreted by the egg, external to its vitelline membrane. This jelly arises from the cortical granules. In 20 minutes the zone of jelly will be as wide as the diameter of the egg it surrounds; its margin can often be observed with the aid of supernumerary spermatozoa or other particles (such as Chinese ink) at its edge or in the medium.

There is little visible change in the vitelline membrane at fertilization, although it is called the fertilization membrane after this event. However, a narrow perivitelline space is present shortly after insemination, resulting from the breakdown of the jelly-precursor granules and release of the jelly. The sperm entrance cone now becomes clearly visible, and is best seen in the profile view of an egg with a sperm at its periphery. In the course of the next 8 to 10 minutes, the vitelline membrane is indented slightly at its point of contact with the entrance cone, tending to obscure the sperm from view. About 20 minutes after insemination, the egg wrinkles, becoming distorted and almost amoeboid in appearance. The entrance cone has flattened considerably but is still present, and although the sperm is partially concealed from view, the entrance of its head into the egg is not completed until some time later (Just, 1912; Lillie, 1911, 1912). Its final penetration through the membrane (about 48 minutes after insemination) leaves the middle piece and tail outside.

The egg then rounds up, and elongates in a direction perpendicular to the polar axis, as the time approaches for the formation of the first polar body. The preparation should be shaken if no eggs lie so that the forming polar body is on the periphery. The polar body is given off into the space between the egg and the vitelline membrane, which is wider in the region of the animal pole than elsewhere. The second polar body forms under the first, thus lifting it away from the egg surface. The first polar body of Nereis rarely, if ever, divides.

The egg cleaves into two unequal blastomeres, and the second cleavage is also unequal. The third cleavage, from four to eight cells, produces four micromeres by spiral cleavage (Wilson, 1892; Costello, 1945a).

C. Time Table of Development: The following schedule is based on the development of 16 batches of eggs, at temperatures of 22–24° C.; times are calculated from insemination.

Stage	Time
Disappearance of membrane of germinal vesicle	10–15 minutes
First polar body	42 minutes
Sperm penetration	48 minutes
Second polar body	58 minutes
First cleavage	81 minutes
Second cleavage	108 minutes
Third cleavage	132 minutes
Fourth cleavage	162 minutes
Ciliated trochophore	8–10 hours
Pigmentation in trochophore	24–38 hours

There is a high temperature coefficient for the cleavage process; Lovelace (1949) gives data from which the following mean times have been calculated for first cleavage in 50% of the eggs in a given batch.

Mean temperature, ° C. (within a 1° range)	Time after insemination
20.0	97 minutes
21.3	86.9 minutes
22.1	84.2 minutes
23.1	77.3 minutes
24.1	70.8 minutes

D. Later Stages of Development and Metamorphosis: Gastrulation is by epiboly. The products of the first three quartets of micromeres overgrow the four large oil-bearing cells, 3A, 3B, 3C and 4D. These four endodermal cells, after giving off a few small cells, persist unchanged for a relatively long period. The four large oil droplets (which result from coalescence of the smaller oil droplets of the egg) may be used as a criterion of normal development, since those in the C and D quadrants are larger than those in the A and B quadrants. For further details, consult the papers of Wilson (1892, 1898) and Costello (1945a).

The trochophore larva metamorphoses into a segmented worm in about seven days. The trochophore is somewhat atypical, and there is an abbreviated, "telescoped" larval development. The first signs of the segmented adult organization appear very early. To study, mount the larvae on a slide, and either entangle them in a few shreds of lens paper or quiet them by adding a drop of very dilute (1:1000) Janus green solution.

Distinctive features of the trochophore larva at 40 hours (Wilson, 1892; Figure 84) include:

1. An equatorial prototroch consisting of 12 very large, ciliated cells, instead of the 16 typical of most annelidan and molluscan trochophores. There is the characteristic interruption in ciliation, in the mid-dorsal line. A narrow paratroch is present, near the vegetal pole.
2. Pigmentation, consisting of (a) a pair of red-pigmented eyespots in the pretrochal hemisphere; (b) orange-brown "prototrochal" pigment, in cells adjacent to the prototroch; (c) greenish-black anal pigment in the region of the proctodeum.
3. The four large macromeres (each still containing a single large oil drop) have not yet differentiated into the parts of the intestine. Short, blind ectodermal invaginations constitute stomodeum and proctodeum.

REFERENCES:

CLARK, L. B., AND W. N. HESS, 1940a. Swarming of the Atlantic Palolo worm, *Leodice fucata* (Ehlers). *Pap. Tortugas Lab.,* **33**: 21–70. (Carnegie Inst., Wash., Publ. no. 524.)

CLARK, L. B., AND W. N. HESS, 1940b. The reactions of the Atlantic Palolo, *Leodice fucata,* to light. *Pap. Tortugas Lab.,* **33**: 71–81. (Carnegie Inst., Wash., Publ. no. 524.)

COSTELLO, D. P., 1939. The volumes occupied by the formed cytoplasmic components in marine eggs. *Physiol. Zool.,* **12**: 13–20.

COSTELLO, D. P., 1940a. The cell origin of the prototroch of *Nereis limbata. Biol. Bull.,* **79**: 369–370.

COSTELLO, D. P., 1940b. The fertilizability of nucleated and non-nucleated fragments of centrifuged Nereis eggs. *J. Morph.,* **66**: 99–114.

COSTELLO, D. P., 1945a. Experimental studies of germinal localization in Nereis. I. The development of isolated blastomeres. *J. Exp. Zool.,* **100**: 19–66.

COSTELLO, D. P., 1945b. Segregation of oöplasmic constituents. *J. Elisha Mitchell Sci. Soc.,* **61**: 277–289.

COSTELLO, D. P., 1948. Oöplasmic segregation in relation to differentiation. *Ann. N. Y. Acad. Sci.,* **49**: 663–683.

COSTELLO, D. P., 1949. The relations of the plasma membrane, vitelline membrane, and jelly in the egg of *Nereis limbata. J. Gen. Physiol.,* **32**: 351–366.

COSTELLO, D. P., AND R. A. YOUNG, 1939. Mechanism of membrane elevation in egg of *Nereis limbata. Coll. Net,* **14**: 209, 214–215.

FOX, H. M., 1924. Lunar periodicity in reproduction. *Proc. Roy. Soc., London, ser. B,* **95**: 523–550.

HEMPELMANN, F., 1911. Zur Naturgeschichte von *Nereis dumerilii* Aud. et Edw. *Zoologica,* **25**: Hft. 62, 1–135.

HOADLEY, L., 1934. Pulsations in the Nereis egg. *Biol. Bull.,* **67**: 484–493.

IWANOFF, P. P., 1928. Die Entwicklung der Larvalsegmente bei den Anneliden. *Zeitschr. Morph. u. Okol.,* **10**: 62–161.

IZUKA, A., 1903. Observations on the Japanese Palolo, *Ceratocephale osawai,* n. sp. *J. Coll. Sci. Imp. Univ., Tokyo,* **17**: no. 11, 1–37.

JUST, E. E., 1912. The relation of the first cleavage plane to the entrance point of the sperm. *Biol. Bull.,* **22**: 239–252.

JUST, E. E., 1914. Breeding habits of the heteronereis form of *Platynereis megalops* at Woods Hole, Mass. *Biol. Bull.,* **27**: 201–212.

JUST, E. E., 1915. The morphology of normal fertilization in *Platynereis megalops. J. Morph.,* **26**: 217–233.

JUST, E. E., 1922. On rearing sexually mature *Platynereis megalops* from eggs. *Amer. Nat.,* **56**: 471–478.

JUST, E. E., 1930a. Hydration and dehydration in the living cell. III. The fertilization capacity of Nereis eggs after exposure to hypotonic sea-water. *Protoplasma,* **10**: 24–32.

JUST, E. E., 1930b. Hydration and dehydration in the living cell. IV. Fertilization and development of Nereis eggs in dilute sea-water. *Protoplasma,* **10**: 33–40.

JUST, E. E., 1939a. The Biology of the Cell Surface. P. Blakiston's Son & Co., Inc., Philadelphia.

JUST, E. E., 1939b. Basic Methods for Experiments on Eggs of Marine Animals. P. Blakiston's Son & Co., Inc., Philadelphia.

LILLIE, F. R., 1911. Studies of fertilization in Nereis. I. The cortical changes in the egg: II. Partial fertilization. *J. Morph.,* **22**: 361–393.

LILLIE, F. R., 1912. Studies of fertilization in Nereis. III. The morphology of the normal fertilization of Nereis. IV. The fertilizing power of portions of the spermatozoön. *J. Exp. Zool.,* **12**: 413–477.

LILLIE, F. R., AND E. E. JUST, 1913. Breeding habits of the heteronereis form of *Nereis limbata* at Woods Hole, Mass. *Biol. Bull.,* **24**: 147–168.

LOVELACE, R., 1949. The effects of precocious sperm entry on the egg of *Nereis limbata*. *J. Exp. Zool.,* **112**: 79–108.

MAYER, A. G., 1908. The annual breeding-swarm of the Atlantic Palolo. *Pap. Tortugas Lab.,* **1**: 107–112. (Carnegie Inst., Wash., Publ. no. 102.)

MEAD, A. D., 1897. The early development of marine annelids. *J. Morph.,* **13**: 227–326.

MORGAN, T. H., AND A. TYLER, 1930. The point of entrance of the spermatozoön in relation to the orientation of the embryo in eggs with spiral cleavage. *Biol. Bull.,* **58**: 59–73.

NOVIKOFF, A. B., 1939. Changes at the surface of *Nereis limbata* eggs after insemination. *J. Exp. Biol.,* **16**: 403–408.

PASTEELS, J., 1950. Mouvements localisés et rythmiques de la membrane de fécondation chez des oeufs fécondés ou activés (Chaetopterus, Mactra, Nereis). *Arch. Biol.,* **61**: 197–220.

WHITAKER, D. M., 1931. On the rate of oxygen consumption by fertilized and unfertilized eggs. III. *Nereis limbata*. *J. Gen. Physiol.,* **15**: 191–200.

WILSON, E. B., 1892. The cell-lineage of Nereis. A contribution to the cytogeny of the Annelid body. *J. Morph.,* **6**: 361–480.

WILSON, E. B., 1898. Considerations on cell lineage and ancestral reminiscence. *Ann. N. Y. Acad. Sci.,* **11**: 1–27.

VON WISTINGHAUSEN, C., 1891. Untersuchungen über die Entwicklung von *Nereis dumerilii*. Ein Beitrag zur Entwicklungsgeschichte der Polychaeten. *Mitt. Zool. Stat., Neapel,* **10**: 41–74.

WOLTERECK, R., 1904a. Wurm"kopf", Wurmrumpf, und Trochophora. Bemerkungen zur Entwicklung und Ableitung der Anneliden. *Zool. Anz.,* **28**: 273–322.

WOLTERECK, R., 1904b. Beiträge zur praktischen Analyse der Polygordius-Entwicklung nach dem "Nordsee-" und dem "Mittelmeertypus". I. Der für beide Typen gleichverlaufende Entwicklungsabschnitt: Vom Ei bis zum jüngsten Trochophora-Stadium. *Arch. f. Entw.,* **18**: 377–403.

WOLTERECK, R., 1905. Zur Kopffrage der Anneliden. *Verh. d. Deutsch Zool. Ges.,* **15**: 154–186.

WOODWORTH, W. McM., 1907. The Palolo worm, *Eunice viridis* (Gray). *Bull. Mus. Comp. Zool., Harvard,* **51**: 1–21.

ANNELIDA

(POLYCHAETA)

Platynereis megalops

LIVING MATERIAL:

Platynereis megalops may be found in Great Harbor and in Eel Pond at Woods Hole, Mass. The swarming heteronereis form is attracted to light and may conveniently be collected with the same type of flat net as is used to obtain *Nereis limbata*. The sexes are separate. The reddish males swim with rapid, jerky movements, rotating in spirals tangential to the surface of the water. The large females, pale yellow in color, swim slowly at a greater depth. They travel either in a straight line, or, with head bent at right angles to the body, describing a circle about the head (Just, 1914). The males are smaller than those of *Nereis limbata* (which swarm at the same times) and swim more rapidly. Although it may be somewhat difficult to distinguish these two species when swarming, they are easily differentiated when examined in the laboratory. The eyes of Platynereis are much larger and form conspicuous dark spots on the prostomium, which, unlike that of Nereis, lacks palps and protrudes anterior to the eyes as a transparent, oval lobe.

The animals rarely appear in large swarms, and as a rule, the number appearing during an evening can be easily counted.

BREEDING SEASON:

July, and the first three weeks in August. Platynereis shows a lunar periodicity, appearing in varying numbers from full to new moon. The frequency curve does not correspond precisely to that of *Nereis limbata*. See the paper of Just (1914) for details of swarming.

PROCURING AND HANDLING MATERIAL:

A. Care of Adults: The animals should be isolated in separate fingerbowls of sea water as soon as they are collected. As with Nereis, trays of bowls containing clean sea water and a piece of Ulva should be used. The water should be changed in the laboratory, and the dishes placed on the sea water table.

B. Procuring Gametes: It is imperative to obtain gametes by allowing males and females to mate. Just (1914) succeeded in artificially inseminating eggs only when he mixed "dry" eggs with "dry" sperm. Artificial insemination was not successful, when the eggs were diluted with more than an equal volume of sea water. Mating, fertilization and subsequent egg-extrusion will occur when a male and female are placed together. The mating habits, as described by Just (1914), are of special interest; polyspermy does not ordinarily occur.

C. Preparation of Cultures: The animals should be allowed to mate as soon as possible after collection and the adults removed immediately following shedding. After 20 minutes, decant the water from the dish of eggs and replace with fresh sea water. At the time of the first cleavage, gently break up the jelly-mass and distribute it equally among 7 to 10 fingerbowls of fresh sea water. After about

8 hours, the water should be changed again, and when the trochophores become free-swimming, they should be transferred daily to fresh sea water. The trochophores of this form are markedly sensitive to light, and if too many are kept in one dish, clumping and consequent smothering will occur. One way to prevent this is to keep the larvae in subdued light.

No feeding is necessary up to the three-somite stage, but as soon as all the endodermal oil drops are absorbed, diatom feeding should be initiated (Just, 1922).

NORMAL DEVELOPMENT:

A. The Unfertilized Ovum: The oöcyte from the body cavity is compressed and irregular. After they are shed, the few uninseminated eggs round up and become nearly spherical, although the polar axis remains slightly shorter than the diameter of the equator. The egg diameter varies somewhat, the largest measuring between 180 and 200 microns. The egg is almost perfectly transparent (much more so than the egg of *Nereis limbata*), with an equatorial ring of oil drops and a well-marked, clear cortex containing very fine granules and striations.

B. Fertilization and Cleavage: Insemination follows the curious copulation phenomenon (see the paper by Just, 1914), and is internal; therefore, although the egg is shed in the germinal vesicle stage, it usually has a sperm attached, and a jelly layer and perivitelline space are forming at this time. No sharply defined fertilization cone is present. Sperm penetration is completed about 30 minutes after egg-extrusion; the middle and tail piece are left outside the egg (Just, 1915b). Development is very similar to that of *Nereis limbata*.

C. Rate of Development: No detailed information is available. Well-formed, swimming trochophores are present in 24 hours; by the seventh day the larvae have three setigerous segments bearing parapodia. After this time, at least one new segment is added daily.

D. Later Stages of Development: The larvae resemble those of *Nereis limbata*.

REFERENCES:

JUST, E. E., 1914. Breeding habits of the heteronereis form of *Platynereis megalops* at Woods Hole, Mass. *Biol. Bull.,* **27**: 201–212.

JUST, E. E., 1915a. An experimental analysis of fertilization in *Platynereis megalops. Biol. Bull.,* **28**: 93–114.

JUST, E. E., 1915b. The morphology of normal fertilization in *Platynereis megalops. J. Morph.,* **26**: 217–233.

JUST, E. E., 1922. On rearing sexually mature *Platynereis megalops* from eggs. *Amer. Nat.,* **56**: 471–478.

JUST, E. E., 1929. Effects of low temperature on fertilization and development in the egg of *Platynereis megalops. Biol. Bull.,* **57**: 439–442.

JUST, E. E., 1939. The Biology of the Cell Surface. P. Blakiston's Son & Co., Inc., Philadelphia.

ANNELIDA

(POLYCHAETA)

Podarke obscura

LIVING MATERIAL:

These animals are relatively abundant at Woods Hole, Mass. They may be obtained during the day from the bottom or vegetation of Eel Pond, or during the evening, between 7:30 and 9:30, when the mature worms are swarming at the surface. They are attracted by the light of the Nereis-collecting lamps. The sexes are separate, and when the animals are ripe, they may be distinguished by the color of the gametes seen through the semi-transparent body wall; the females are seal-brown, the males cream color.

BREEDING SEASON: July and August.

PROCURING AND HANDLING MATERIAL:

A. Care of Adults: Transferred to clean dishes, with an occasional change of sea water, these worms will live indefinitely in the laboratory. It is best to segregate the sexes.

B. Procuring Gametes: Swarming animals usually will shed when taken. Females procured during the day shed eggs from 7:30 to 9 P.M. on the second or third, but rarely on the first, night after collection (Treadwell, 1901). The eggs sink to the bottom of the dish where they may be collected with a pipette. A simpler method of collecting them is to strain the water through a fine cloth which allows the eggs to pass through, but retains the spent adults.

C. Preparation of Cultures: Fertilized eggs may be obtained either by placing several males and females in a fingerbowl and allowing them to shed, or by inseminating naturally-shed eggs from isolated females with sperm from the body cavity of the males (Treadwell, 1901).

NORMAL DEVELOPMENT:

A. The Unfertilized Ovum: The eggs are slightly irregular when first shed, but soon become spherical. The average diameter is about 63 microns, and a thin, smooth membrane is present. Upon shedding, the egg proceeds spontaneously to the metaphase of the first maturation division and remains in this condition until fertilized (Treadwell, 1901).

B. Fertilization and Cleavage: There is no visible alteration of the egg membrane at fertilization. Cleavage is equal and spiral with especially large entomeres; no polar lobes are formed. Gastrulation is by invagination (Treadwell, 1898, 1901).

C. Rate of Development: Swimming forms appear five hours after insemination; well-formed trochophores are present in cultures 24 hours old.

D. Later Stages of Development: The trochophores are small, thin-walled and active. They have a large enteron; the intestinal portion of it seems to be almost severed from the remainder by a circular "shelf" of tissue. There is no paratroch, but the neurotroch, prototroch, apical tuft, and an additional anterior tuft are well developed. Two ventral eyespots and five frontal bodies are present (Treadwell, 1899). (See Figure 12 in the paper of Treadwell, 1899, and Figure 60 of Treadwell, 1901.)

REFERENCES:

JUST, E. E., 1939. Basic Methods for Experiments on Eggs of Marine Animals. P. Blakiston's Son & Co., Inc., Philadelphia.

TREADWELL, A. L., 1898. The cell lineage of *Podarke obscura*. Preliminary communication. *Zool. Bull.*, **1**: 195–203.

TREADWELL, A. L., 1899. Equal and unequal cleavage in annelids. Biol. Lectures M. B. L., Wood's Holl, Mass., 1898, pp. 93–111.

TREADWELL, A. L., 1901. The cytogeny of *Podarke obscura* Verrill. *J. Morph.*, **17**: 399–486.

TREADWELL, A. L., 1902. Notes on the nature of "artificial parthenogenesis" in the egg of *Podarke obscura*. *Biol. Bull.*, **3**: 235–240.

ANNELIDA

(POLYCHAETA)

Sabellaria vulgaris

LIVING MATERIAL:

These tube-dwelling, polychaete worms are common at Woods Hole, Mass.; they live on old shells, stones, etc., which are dredged from the harbor bottom. The worms may be distinguished from Hydroides, which occurs in the same localities at Woods Hole, by their tubes and certain other adult features. The tubes of Sabellaria, often brown or pinkish in color, are formed by sand grains and are moderately soft and crumbly; those of Hydroides, greenish-gray or white in color, are calcareous and hard. The gill filaments of Sabellaria are filiform in general appearance, the "barbules" being very inconspicuous. Those of Hydroides, however, are much more brilliant, and may vary from purplish (sometimes striped) to brilliant scarlet in both males and females; each one has small "barbules" coming off the central shaft. Sabellaria has a tail-like abdomen which has no parapodia and which folds back on the thorax. The setae are more prominent than in Hydroides.

The sexes are separate. They are externally recognizable after the individuals have been removed from their tubes, but only if the worms are fully mature, containing large numbers of gametes. In these animals, the abdominal segments are swollen and appear opaque and white in the male, pink in the female. Individuals showing neither color distinctly may, however, shed abundantly. The sex of such animals can be ascertained by placing them in a few drops of sea water until shedding starts. Sperm will pour forth from the male in dense clouds, but egg masses will break up into small clumps on contact with water.

BREEDING SEASON:

Sabellaria is said to spawn naturally in May and June, but ripe individuals may be obtained throughout the summer months (Waterman, 1934).

PROCURING AND HANDLING MATERIAL:

A. Care of Adults: If worms are left in their tubes and placed in aquaria with a good supply of running sea water, they will produce normally developing eggs for as long as nine weeks.

Uninjured animals are most easily obtained by removing the sand tubes from the substrate, chipping away enough of the tube to expose the head and tail of the worm, and then gently forcing out the animal by inserting a blunt probe into the anterior end of the tube— the animal slowly withdraws, hind-end foremost, from the tube (Novikoff, 1939).

B. Procuring Gametes:

Female gametes: Place a female in a fingerbowl containing 200 cc. of sea water, in which it will shed if ripe. After it has shed for a few seconds, move it to a new spot and allow it to continue shedding. The eggs first shed should be discarded, as they may have been exposed to air when the worm was out of water. Since the eggs are expelled by active contractions of the body, it is easy to tell when shedding has ceased; the female should be removed and discarded at this time.

Male gametes: Sperm may be obtained by placing a male in a dish containing four drops of sea water. When shedding is completed, remove and discard the worm.

C. Preparation of Cultures: Allow the eggs to stand in sea water for about 15 minutes after shedding. Toward the end of this period, prepare a dilute sperm suspension as follows: Add one drop of concentrated sperm suspension to four drops of sea water, and add one drop of this diluted sperm suspension to a finger-bowl of sea water. To this fingerbowl add the eggs, using a narrow-mouth pipette to transfer them. This method of insemination prevents polyspermy and its accompanying abnormalities. If only small amounts of eggs and sperm are available, however, culturing can be done in stender dishes instead of fingerbowls. Allow the culture to stand undisturbed for an hour; then change the water, cover, and place on a water table. After 24 hours, decant the upper layers of water, which contain the more normal, top-swimming trochophores, to a clean fingerbowl. Repeat this procedure at least once a day, adding water each time. After a day or so, larvae should be fed on a pure culture of Nitzschia.

D. Methods of Observation: Because of the small size of these eggs, they are best examined using a high magnification (440 ×). The eggs are too opaque to reveal internal changes other than the breakdown of the germinal vesicle. The ciliation of the early larvae can best be seen with dark-field illumination. A very dilute solution of Janus green (1:1000 in distilled water) will partially inactivate older swimming forms.

E. Removal of Membranes: It is sometimes desirable for study or experimental work to obtain Sabellaria eggs without their tough vitelline membranes. The method devised by Hatt (1931), and modified by Novikoff (1939), consists of treating the eggs with alkaline NaCl. The details of this method, as described by Costello (1945a) for the egg of Nereis, are given on p. 84 of this manual. Sabellaria eggs from which the membranes have been removed may still retain some of the perivitelline jelly; this can be demonstrated readily by placing the eggs in a suspension of Chinese ink in sea water.

NORMAL DEVELOPMENT:

A. The Unfertilized Ovum: When first shed, the egg is very irregular in shape; usually it has a particularly deep indentation directly opposite the animal pole. This crater coincides with the point of former ovarian attachment. The small egg has a large, rather excentrically placed germinal vesicle, and a considerable amount of yolk distributed through the cytoplasm, making it appear opaque. A conspicuous vitelline membrane is very closely applied to the egg surface (Waterman, 1934).

A few minutes after shedding, a series of pre-maturation changes occurs. The germinal vesicle breaks down and its contents flow to one side of the egg, to form a clear, hyaline cap at the future animal pole. The first maturation spindle extends across not quite half the diameter of the egg. The egg rounds up, becoming spherical, and the vitelline membrane rises from the egg surface, leaving a perivitelline space about 12 microns wide. The surface changes accompanying this can best be observed in the thin cytoplasm at the edge of the large, crater-like indentation. As the vitelline membrane elevates, a thin, transparent, hyaline plasma layer appears on the egg surface, presumably outside the egg's plasma membrane. The vitelline membrane and hyaline plasma membrane remain connected with one another by means of numerous fine, granule-free protoplasmic strands, which stretch across the perivitelline space. Elevation is due to the swelling of a transparent, dense jelly which is located between the membrane and the surface of the egg (Hatt, 1931). At first the membrane is smooth, but as it elevates and stretches further, it becomes wrinkled. An interesting series of cortical changes accompanies membrane elevation. Upon contact with sea water, the small, refringent spherules lying just beneath the vitelline membrane disappear, leaving a granule-free surface. It is this layer of hyaline material which is pulled out to form the radiating filaments. As elevation continues, many of the deeper cortical granules move toward the egg periphery and disappear, increasing the width of the cortical hyaline layer, the outer boundary of which becomes conspicuous (Waterman, 1936; Novikoff, 1939).

At the end of the pre-maturation stage, the egg is approximately 60 microns in diameter (Waterman, 1934).

The pre-maturation changes are very rapid, and are usually completed within ten minutes after shedding. To observe them, eggs should be transferred to a slide immediately after they are shed.

B. Fertilization and Cleavage: The phenomena of insemination uncomplicated by pre-maturation changes may be seen in eggs which have been allowed to stand in sea water for 15 minutes or longer. Except for the formation of an entrance cone and the withdrawal of the radiating filaments, the ovum is not visibly changed by insemination. No additional fertilization membrane is formed, and the cortical zone and existing membranes remain the same. When a spermatozoon attaches to the vitelline membrane, a large, rounded, hyaline entrance cone rises from the egg surface and pushes out toward the membrane. Novikoff (1939) and Waterman (1934, 1936) fail to agree on all details of sperm penetration, and those interested in the minor discrepancies are referred to the papers cited. According to Novikoff's account, when the entrance cone contacts the sperm, the head and middle piece separate from the tail and pass through the membrane. The discarded tail twitches a few times, and, after freeing itself from the membrane, may swim about with a rapid, whip-like motion for some time. The cone recedes, carrying the sperm head down into the egg cytoplasm. The filaments are withdrawn at this time, so that within 11 minutes of insemination, the egg surface is again smooth.

The formation of the first polar body occurs about twenty minutes after insemination, preceded by a distinct flattening of the egg in the polar region. The egg rounds up, but again flattens before the second polar body is produced. The egg then becomes spherical and remains in this condition until shortly before the first cleavage. At this time a large, first polar lobe is formed. A little more than an hour after insemination the first cleavage is completed, and the egg assumes a trefoil shape. Since the first cleavage plane passes just to one side of the polar bodies, the cleavage is slightly unequal. The polar lobe is soon resorbed into the larger CD blastomere. Soon a smaller second polar lobe is given off at the anti-polar region of this cell, and the second cleavage follows. At the completion of this division, the lobe flows into the D cell. The first quartet of micromeres (which are almost as large as the macromeres) is given off by the usual dexiotropic division. During this division, a third polar lobe forms in the D cell, and afterwards it is incorporated into the larger basal 1D macromere. The later cleavages presumably follow the normal pattern of spiral cleavage, as exemplified by Nereis.

C. *Time Table of Development:* The exact relationship of temperature and developmental rate has not been worked out in detail. The following schedule is approximate for laboratory temperatures varying between 19° and 25° C. (Novikoff, 1937). Times are recorded from insemination.

Stage	Time
First polar body	19–23 minutes
Second polar body	28–34 minutes
First polar lobe	50–55 minutes
First cleavage	65–70 minutes
Second polar lobe and cleavage	80–85 minutes
Swimming larva	5½ hours
Apical tuft and prototroch	8 hours
Metamorphosis	7 weeks

D. *Later Stages of Development and Metamorphosis:* Consult the papers by Novikoff (1938a) and Wilson (1929) for details of development, and for illustrations of larvae 5 to 29 hours old. The larvae of Sabellaria are interesting because they show very long bristles which have probably both a suspensory and a protective function.

In Sabellaria trochophores two days old and older, some of the distinctive features include:

1. Stiff cilia in the apical region, which develop before the disappearance of the apical tuft (Novikoff, 1938a).
2. The prototroch, consisting of three rows of cilia with a gap on the dorsal side.
3. The neurotroch in the mid-ventral line.
4. One eye on the left side; more eyespots develop later.
5. Very long bristles with a fine structure, which develop in seta sacs. Ten pairs are formed, one after another. At metamorphosis they are replaced by ordinary setae.
6. The digestive tract, which is internally ciliated.

REFERENCES:

Fauré-Fremiet, E., 1924. L'oeuf de *Sabellaria alveolata* L. *Arch. d'Anat. Micr.,* **20**: 211–342.

Harris, J. E., 1935. Studies on living protoplasm. I. Streaming movements in the protoplasm of the egg of *Sabellaria alveolata* (L.). *J. Exp. Biol.,* **12**: 65–79.

Hatt, P., 1931. La fusion expérimentale d'oeufs de "*Sabellaria alveolata* L." et leur développement. *Arch. Biol.,* **42**: 303–323.

Hatt, P., 1932. Essais expérimentaux sur les localisations germinales dans l'oeuf d'un Annélide (*Sabellaria alveolata* L.). *Arch. d'Anat. Micr.,* **28**: 81–98.

Novikoff, A. B., 1937. *Sabellaria vulgaris.* In: Culture Methods for Invertebrate Animals, edit. by Galtsoff *et al.,* Comstock, Ithaca, pp. 187–191.

Novikoff, A. B., 1938a. Embryonic determination in the annelid, *Sabellaria vulgaris.* I. The differentiation of ectoderm and endoderm when separated through induced exogastrulation. *Biol. Bull.,* **74**: 198–210.

NOVIKOFF, A. B., 1938b. Embryonic determination in the annelid, *Sabellaria vulgaris*. II. Transplantation of polar lobes and blastomeres as a test of their inducing capacities. *Biol. Bull.*, **74**: 211–234.

NOVIKOFF, A. B., 1939. Surface changes in unfertilized and fertilized eggs of *Sabellaria vulgaris*. *J. Exp. Zool.*, **82**: 217–237.

NOVIKOFF, A. B., 1940. Morphogenetic substances or organizers in annelid development. *J. Exp. Zool.*, **85**: 127–155.

WATERMAN, A. J., 1934. Observations on reproduction, prematuration, and fertilization in *Sabellaria vulgaris*. *Biol. Bull.*, **67**: 97–114.

WATERMAN, A. J., 1936. The membranes and germinal vesicle of the egg of *Sabellaria vulgaris*. *Biol. Bull.*, **71**: 46–58.

WILSON, D. P., 1929. The larvae of the British Sabellarians. *J. Mar. Biol. Assoc.*, **16**: 221–268.

ANNELIDA

(Polychaeta)

Sthenelais leidyi

LIVING MATERIAL:

The adults are rather flattened, elongate worms, covered with flat scales which alternate anteriorly with dorsal cirri. The body color is grey, with a mid-dorsal stripe; the head is brown with a central red spot, two pairs of eyes, and a single tentacle. The worms have been collected at Hadley Harbor, near Woods Hole, Mass., but are not abundant. They can be obtained by sand-sieving.

BREEDING SEASON:

The limits of the season have not been determined; however, mature animals have been obtained during the middle and latter parts of August (Bumpus, 1898).

PROCURING AND HANDLING MATERIAL:

A. Care of Adults: The worms should be isolated in fingerbowls of sea water when brought into the laboratory.

B. Procuring Gametes: Mature animals usually shed a few hours after collection. Body-cavity eggs, obtained by cutting up a female, do not develop as well as those which are spawned normally. The males and females should be removed from their respective dishes as soon as shedding is completed.

C. Preparation of Cultures: Only one or two drops of dilute sperm suspension should be added to a fingerbowl of eggs; over-insemination results in abnormal cleavage. The embryos may be raised through the trochophore stage. Swimming larvae should be decanted to bowls of fresh sea water daily.

NORMAL DEVELOPMENT:

A. The Unfertilized Ovum: The egg is approximately 110 microns in diameter, very opaque, and flattened and triangular in shape when shed. It has not been ascertained whether the germinal vesicle breaks down before shedding, or whether this occurs soon after contact with sea water.

B. Fertilization and Cleavage: The eggs in which germinal vesicle breakdown has occurred can be fertilized. As soon as fertilization occurs, a wrinkled fertilization membrane rises from the egg surface. Cleavage is spiral and almost equal; gastrulation is probably by invagination.

C. Time Table of Development: The following schedule indicates the development of an egg batch at a temperature of 23° to 24° C. Times are given from insemination.

Stage	Time
Polar bodies formed	30 minutes
First cleavage	40–45 minutes
Second cleavage	60 minutes
Third cleavage	85 minutes
Free-swimming embryos	3½ hours
Trochophores	17 hours

D. Later Stages of Development: The larva is a large, plump trochophore which swims with a peculiar end-over-end motion. When fully formed, it has a long, stiff, apical tuft, and a telotroch. In addition, a long tuft of cilia projects from the lower left corner of the mouth. A pair of eyespots and prototrochal pigment appear during development. The stomach is very large and vesicular; the intestine and oesophagus are small.

REFERENCES:

BUMPUS, H. C., 1898. The breeding of animals at Woods Holl during the months of June, July and August. *Science,* **8**: 850–858.

MOLLUSCA

(AMPHINEURA)

Chaetopleura apiculata

LIVING MATERIAL:

Chitons are usually found clinging to shells or rocks dredged from Vineyard Sound at Woods Hole, Mass.; they are quite abundant. The sexes are separate, but there is no way of distinguishing them externally.

BREEDING SEASON:

The breeding season begins about June 20 and continues to the end of September, reaching its height from about July 10 to August 20. There is evidence of a lunar periodicity; and although the eggs are obtainable at any time during the breeding period, they are shed most abundantly between full moon (or a few days before) and third quarter (Grave, 1932).

PROCURING AND HANDLING MATERIAL:

A. Care of Adults: When brought into the laboratory, the chitons should be removed from the shells and rocks to which they cling, and placed in large fingerbowls (25 to 30 animals per dish) supplied with running sea water. Ripe animals seem to shed most abundantly during their second evening in the laboratory, with a pronounced decrease during subsequent nights. For this reason, it is advisable to obtain fresh animals after about three days.

B. Procuring Gametes: If naturally-inseminated eggs are desired, toward evening wash the adults free of sediment and replace them in a large fingerbowl. Half-fill it with fresh sea water, and allow to stand undisturbed. The males extrude sperm at about 8 P.M., and about half an hour later a few females may spawn. Shedding by the males seems to have a stimulating effect on the females, although isolated females do shed. Unfertilized eggs and sperm may be collected separately by isolating the animals at dusk, in small fingerbowls half-filled with sea water (Grave, 1937).

C. Preparation of Cultures: If the animals were isolated before spawning, several pipettes-ful of sperm suspension may be added to a fingerbowl of eggs. Many of the eggs remain fertilizable for as long as 24 to 48 hours after shedding (Grave, 1932). The inseminated eggs should be left undisturbed for 30 minutes, and the sea water then changed. When spawning is completed, naturally-inseminated eggs can be collected in a pipette and transferred to fingerbowls of fresh sea water.

All cultures should be kept covered on the water table. Decant the upper layers of sea water and refill the dishes several times during the first 24 hours. The larvae, which hatch in about 25 to 30 hours, should be transferred twice daily to fresh sea water, using a pipette to collect them. Since they are well supplied with yolk, there is no need to feed the larvae, although diatom feeding, initiated on the sixth day of larval life, often hastens the onset of metamorphosis.

Young metamorphosed chitons can be kept indefinitely if sea water is allowed to flow through their dishes for a part of each day. Special feeding is not necessary, and if they are occasionally washed free of sediment, the young animals will thrive.

D. Methods of Observation: Because of the size and opacity of the egg, the early development is best studied by mounting egg samples in depression slides. A dilute solution of Janus green will slow down the moving larvae.

NORMAL DEVELOPMENT:

A. The Unfertilized Ovum: The egg is spherical and measures 180 to 190 microns in diameter. It is opaque, due to its high yolk content and to the chorion which surrounds it (Grave, 1932); the chorion is tough, ornate and bristly. When the eggs emerge from the oviduct, they are embedded in a viscid, jelly-like secretion which spreads over the bottom of the dish in a thin film. Although it cannot be seen in the living egg, sections show that the ovum is usually developing the first maturation spindle when it is shed.

B. Fertilization and Cleavage: There are no visible changes at the time of fertilization; no fertilization membrane is elevated and the egg does not change shape. Two transparent polar bodies are formed, but no polar lobes. The first noticeable change occurs shortly before first cleavage when there is a slight flattening of the egg at the animal pole.

The first cleavage furrow usually divides the egg into two equal blastomeres, but in a small percentage of eggs one blastomere is perceptibly larger. The second cleavage is at right angles to the first, and again in some cases the D cell is slightly larger than the others. The cells of the first quartet of micromeres, given off by the dexiotropic third cleavage, are distinguishable from the larger macromeres. Further divisions follow the regular pattern of spiral cleavage. Four quartets of micromeres are produced. The first three give rise to ectoderm, nervous system and stomodeum, while the fourth quartet, except for 4d, becomes part of the endoderm, along with the macromeres; the 4d cell gives rise to mesoderm and to some endoderm.

C. Time Table of Development: The following schedule, based on a batch of eggs developing at 23° to 24° C., is offered as an approximate outline of developmental rate. Metamorphosis seemed to occur early in this particular batch, the usual time being 6 to 10 days (Grave, 1932). The times are recorded from insemination.

Stage	Time
First polar body	30 minutes
Second polar body	55 minutes
First cleavage	1 hour, 30 minutes
Second cleavage	2 hours
Third cleavage	2 hours, 40 minutes
Gastrulation	About 13 hours
Beating cilia	14 hours
Rotation within capsule	20 hours
Hatching	36 hours
Free-swimming trochophores	2½ to 3 days
Metamorphosis	4 days

D. Later Stages of Development and Metamorphosis: The young trochophore (40 to 60 hours old) is propelled rapidly through the water by a band of powerful cilia, the prototroch.   The larva rotates on its longitudinal axis, following a spiral path.   Crowning the pre-trochal hemisphere (the head vesicle) is a clump of very long cilia, the apical tuft, which is apparently sensory in function.   There are two lateral, reddish-brown eyes; the mouth lies just below the prototroch.   Other regions of the digestive tract are obscured by the yolk mass.

As the larva develops, there is an elongation of the body, especially of the post-trochal hemisphere.   By three to four days, the mouth and archenteron are visible, due to reduction in the quantity of yolk.   An anus is formed, and the shell segments begin to appear on the dorsal surface, gradually extending anteriorly to the region of the head vesicle.   A contractile foot develops on the ventral surface, just posterior to the mouth.   The larvae are still propelled by the prototrochal cilia, although slightly older stages may creep along by means of the foot.

Metamorphosing larvae are found on the bottoms of the culture dishes.   The prototroch and the apical cilia are lost during metamorphosis.   There is a sudden dorso-ventral flattening of the body, and the larva now creeps about by the well-developed foot.   The shell plates increase in number, although at this time, the full adult set is not complete.   The mantle, a fold of the body wall, develops just dorsal and lateral to the foot.

REFERENCES:

GRAVE, B. H., 1922.   An analysis of the spawning habits and spawning stimuli of *Chaetopleura apiculata* (Say).   *Biol. Bull.,* **42**: 234–256.

GRAVE, B. H., 1932.   Embryology and life history of *Chaetopleura apiculata. J. Morph.,* **54**: 153–160.

GRAVE, B. H., 1937.   *Chaetopleura apiculata. In:* Culture Methods for Invertebrate Animals, edit. by Galtsoff *et al.,* Comstock, Ithaca, pp. 519–520.

HEATH, H., 1899.   The development of Ischnochiton.   *Zool. Jahrb., abt. Anat. Ontog. Thiere,* **12**: 567–656.

KOWALEVSKY, A. O., 1879.   Ueber die Entwickelung der Chitonen.   *Zool. Anz.,* **2**: 469–473.

KOWALEVSKY, A. O., 1882.   Weitere Sudien [*sic*] über die Entwickelung der Chitonen.   *Zool. Anz.,* **5**: 307–310.

KOWALEVSKY, M. A., 1883.   Embryogénie du *Chiton polii* (Philippi) avec quelques remarques sur le développement des autres Chitons.   *Ann. Mus. Hist. Nat., Marseilles,* **1**: (Mém. 5) pp. 1–46.

LOVÉN, S., 1856.   Ueber die Entwickelung von Chiton.   *Arch. f. Naturgesch., 22 Jahrg.,* **1**: 206–210.

METCALF, M. M., 1893.   Contributions to the embryology of Chiton.   *Stud. Biol. Lab., Johns Hopkins Univ.,* **5**: 249–267.

MOLLUSCA

(Pelecypoda)

Callocardia convexa *

(Syn. *Pitar morrhuana* Gould)

LIVING MATERIAL:

These small white bivalves are found with *Venus mercenaria,* burrowing on muddy or sandy flats near the lower part of the intertidal zones, and also in deeper waters. Although somewhat similar to Venus in appearance, Callocardia is much smaller and, unlike Venus, does not have a crenulated shell-margin. The species is moderately plentiful at Woods Hole, Mass., and may be collected by digging or dredging. The sexes are separate and similar in appearance.

BREEDING SEASON:

Although the limits of the breeding season have not been ascertained, it is known that mature animals are available during the early part of July at Woods Hole. Loosanoff (personal communication) states that animals brought from their natural beds in Long Island waters during the month of January were apparently ripe.

PROCURING AND HANDLING MATERIAL:

A. Care of Adults: Adults may be kept on a water table or in large fingerbowls supplied with a continuous stream of sea water.

B. Procuring Gametes: Open the valves and excise the visceral mass, discarding the gills and mantle. After rinsing in running sea water, place the visceral mass in a stender dish filled with about 25 cc. of sea water. If mature, the gametes will ooze from the gonads which are located dorsal to the foot, on either side of the liver. The testis is light yellow in color; the ovary is creamy-white (Loosanoff, personal communication). The eggs appear as tiny flecks, the sperm as a milky suspension. Using a pipette, transfer the eggs to a large fingerbowl of sea water. They are very fragile and can stand neither rapid changes of temperature nor high temperatures.

Loosanoff (personal communication) states that he and his associates have been unsuccessful in all attempts to induce spawning in these animals, nor has he observed spontaneous spawning of Callocardia in the laboratory.

C. Preparation of Cultures: When a microscopical examination reveals that the eggs have become spherical, inseminate them by adding two or three drops of sperm suspension. Place the culture on a water table, and leave for about 15 to 17 hours. At the end of this time, use a mouth-pipette to remove the free-swimming larvae to a fresh dish of sea water; this procedure should be repeated daily.

This culture method has yielded veligers which lived for a week or more. It

* We are indebted to Dr. V. L. Loosanoff for some of the information reported here.

should be noted, however, that only a very small percentage of the inseminated eggs developed.

Loosanoff (1954) has described another method for culturing older larvae, by rearing the embryos in large (five-gallon) earthenware jars; the cultures are left undisturbed until swimming larvae are present. Then the water is changed every day or two, by passing it through fine sieves which hold back the larvae. Older larvae should be fed; it is convenient to use mixed plankton for this purpose.

NORMAL DEVELOPMENT:

A. The Unfertilized Ovum: The egg is small, measuring from 49 to 60 microns in diameter, and is surrounded by a thick jelly-hull. It contains prominent yolk granules and a large germinal vesicle, which breaks down after entrance of the sperm. When first shed, the ovum often has a protrusion at one side (undoubtedly the remnant of the ovarian attachment), but after standing in sea water, it soon rounds up.

B. Cleavage: Cleavage is unequal and spiral, and gastrulation is probably by invagination. The early development of Callocardia is almost identical to that of other pelecypods (Loosanoff, personal communication).

C. Time Table of Development: The developmental rate of naturally-shed eggs has not been determined. Those eggs which have been artificially procured from the gonads seem to be slow in maturation and rather irregular in cleavage. The speed of development is apparently dependent to a large extent on the temperature (Loosanoff, personal communication). Loosanoff observed the following schedule of events at room temperatures; times are recorded from insemination.

Stage	Time
Polar bodies	30–45 minutes
Ciliated swimming larvae	6–8 hours
Late trochophores	18 hours
Straight-hinge larvae	24 hours
Setting	About 14 days

D. Later Stages of Development: The larvae are quite small; Loosanoff reports (personal communication) that normal straight-hinge larvae measure approximately 78 × 64 microns. The trochophores are top-shaped, and have a long apical flagellum. Typical bivalve veligers are formed, similar in structure to those of Mactra and Pecten, but smaller and more opaque. After setting, the young clams grow quite well, according to Loosanoff.

REFERENCES:

LOOSANOFF, V. L., 1954. New advances in the study of bivalve larvae. *Amer. Sci.,* **42**: 607–624.

SULLIVAN, C. M., 1948. Bivalve veliger larvae of Malpeque Bay, P. E. I. Bull. Fish. Res. Bd., Canada, no. 77, pp. 1–36.

MOLLUSCA

(Pelecypoda)

Crassostrea virginica

(Formerly *Ostrea virginica*)

(Syn. *O. virginiana* Gould)

LIVING MATERIAL:

The American oyster is found in shallow and brackish water and may be collected at West Falmouth, Rand's Harbor, and Hadley Harbor, Mass. The animals are raised commercially at Cotuit, Mass. The species is protandrous in these northern waters, but in one-year-old animals the sexes are essentially separate, although externally similar in appearance.

BREEDING SEASON:

Mid-June to mid-August in the North Atlantic states (Galtsoff, 1937), provided that the temperature is 20 to 21° C. or above. Loosanoff and Davis (1952) state that in Long Island Sound, spawning begins at the end of June or early in July. They also demonstrated that animals could be induced to spawn at temperatures as low as 15° C.

PROCURING AND HANDLING MATERIAL:

A. Care of Adults: These animals will live indefinitely in aquaria provided with running sea water. If they are to be kept for any period of time, the sexes should be segregated, since the presence of members of the opposite sex acts as a stimulus to spawning. To ascertain the sex of an adult, one can drill a small hole in the anterior portion of one of the shell valves, and pinch off a small piece of the gonad for microscopic examination. This procedure does not seem to disturb the animal (Galtsoff, 1937), and the eggs or sperm are easily recognized in such a preparation.

B. Procuring Gametes: Galtsoff (1937) gives several methods for procuring gametes and fertilizing the eggs of the oyster. The following account is abstracted from his article.

Remove one of the shells and locate the gonads which, in a ripe animal, appear as a creamy-white layer surrounding the visceral mass. Cut out a portion of an ovary and shake it gently into a fingerbowl of filtered sea water. As soon as the requisite number of eggs are released, the gonad should be removed. Sperm can be obtained by cutting up 0.5 gram of testes into 50 cc. of sea water.

C. Preparation of Cultures: One or two cc. of sperm suspension is sufficient to inseminate a fingerbowl of eggs. According to Brooks (1880), the sperm retain their full vitality for several hours; the eggs, however, should be fertilized immediately after they are released. Mix the eggs and sperm, allow the eggs to settle and then decant the top layers, containing superfluous sperm. Fill the fingerbowl with fresh, filtered sea water. In about four to six hours the larvae will rise to the surface. They should be transferred by means of a wide-mouthed pipette to

105

a large battery jar of fresh sea water, and left undisturbed on a water table until the following day. Sea water filtered through coarse filter paper will contain enough microplankton to feed the larvae, but will be free of predators and competing species. The sea water should be changed every day. The larvae may be concentrated by the use of filter paper or bolting silk. For details of culture methods for older larvae consult the papers of Prytherch (1937) and Loosanoff (1954).

D. *Extension of the Breeding Season:* After the natural breeding season, oysters pass into an "indifferent" stage. This is followed by sex differentiation and then by a winter inactive stage which normally persists until April or May. Precocious gonad development may be induced in mid-winter during the inactive stage. The following conditioning method has been developed by Loosanoff (1945, 1954) : The animals are brought in from water in which the surface layer is frozen or nearly frozen, and placed in trays of sea water maintained at 7–8° C.; the temperature is gradually increased by several degrees per day, until it reaches 20–22° C. (after two to three weeks). Then the animals are removed from the conditioning trays and placed in small glass dishes (containing sea water) which, in turn, are set in a large tray into which warm water is poured. This procedure rapidly increases the temperature of the sea water in the small dishes, and the animals are induced to spawn. The fertilized eggs are freed of debris by passing them through a series of fine screens; they are then transferred to large (five-gallon) earthenware jars containing sea water, and left undisturbed until they reach the swimming larva stage (Loosanoff, 1954).

NORMAL DEVELOPMENT:

A. *The Unfertilized Ovum:* When first shed, the egg is irregular, hexagonal or pear-shaped, but on exposure to sea water it quickly becomes spherical, measuring 45 to 54 microns in diameter. It is somewhat opaque. The ovum is shed in the germinal vesicle stage.

B. *Fertilization and Cleavage:* The germinal vesicle breaks down shortly after insemination and two polar bodies are quickly formed by two maturation divisions. A thin fertilization membrane is present. Cleavage is unequal and spiral, with large polar lobes forming during the first two divisions. Gastrulation is accomplished chiefly by invagination, preceded by epibolic movements (Brooks, 1880).

C. *Time Table of Development:* The following schedule of development at 18 to 21° C. is given by Amemiya (1926). The time is calculated from insemination.

Stage	Time
First polar body	40 to 50 minutes
Second polar body	45 to 60 minutes
First cleavage	75 to 90 minutes
Second cleavage	80 to 120 minutes
Rotating blastula	6½ hours
Free-swimming gastrula	8 hours
Trochophore	24 hours
Shell well developed	52 hours
Feeding begins	60 hours

At 20° C. the free-swimming stage lasts about 17 days; according to Galtsoff (1937), the free-swimming stage is reached in 4½ to 5 hours at 23°–25° C.

  D. *Later Stages of Development and Metamorphosis:* A rounded trochophore is formed, with an aboral circle of cilia. It rapidly develops into a veliger by the expansion of the prototroch into a round, flat velum and by formation of a shell, bivalved from the time of its origin. The straight-hinge larva is a delicate pink in color. This color darkens to reddish-brown in the older veliger, which has a prominent foot, digestive tract and gills before metamorphosis. Diagrams and further details of the younger forms are given by Brooks (1880) and of later developmental stages by Stafford (1909).

REFERENCES:

AMEMIYA, I., 1926. Notes on experiments on the early developmental stages of the Portuguese, American and English native oysters, with special reference to the effect of varying salinity. *J. Mar. Biol. Assoc.,* **14**: 161–175.

BROOKS, W. K., 1880. Development of the American oyster (*Ostrea virginiana* List.). *Stud. Biol. Lab., Johns Hopkins Univ.,* **1**: no. 4, 1–81.

CLELAND, K. W., 1950. Respiration and cell division in developing oyster eggs. *Proc. Linn. Soc., N. S. Wales,* **75**: 282–295.

COE, W. R., 1936. Environment and sex in the oviparous oyster *Ostrea virginica. Biol. Bull.,* **71**: 353–359.

DAVIS, H. C., 1953. On food and feeding of larvae of the American oyster, *C. virginica. Biol. Bull.,* **104**: 334–350.

GALTSOFF, P. S., 1937. Spawning and fertilization of the oyster, *Ostrea virginica. In:* Culture Methods for Invertebrate Animals, edit. by Galtsoff *et al.,* Comstock, Ithaca, pp. 537–539.

LOOSANOFF, V. L., 1945. Precocious gonad development in oysters induced in midwinter by high temperature. *Science,* **102**: 124–125.

LOOSANOFF, V. L., 1954. New advances in the study of bivalve larvae. *Amer. Sci.,* **42**: 607–624.

LOOSANOFF, V. L., AND H. C. DAVIS, 1952. Temperature requirements for maturation of gonads of northern oysters. *Biol. Bull.,* **103**: 80–96.

PRYTHERCH, H. F., 1937. The cultivation of lamellibranch larvae. *In:* Culture Methods for Invertebrate Animals, edit. by Galtsoff *et al.,* Comstock, Ithaca, pp. 539–543.

STAFFORD, J., 1909. On the recognition of bivalve larvae in plankton collections. *Contr. Canadian Biol.,* 1906–1910, pp. 221–242.

MOLLUSCA

(PELECYPODA)

Cumingia tellinoides

LIVING MATERIAL:

This small, thin-shelled bivalve formerly was found on certain sandy mud bottoms, usually in the vicinity of eel grass; it was collected by digging at low tide. Formerly abundant at Woods Hole, Mass., it has not been available in this region in appreciable numbers since the severe winter of 1934–35, although the population is now slowly increasing.

The sexes are separate and can be distinguished by the color of the gonads which can be seen through the thin shell; the testes are white, the ovaries salmon-pink.

BREEDING SEASON:

Mid-June to mid-September. There is a critical water temperature (about 20° C.) below which the species does not spawn. At Woods Hole, eggs were usually abundant until about August 20, following which there was a lull lasting until the beginning of September, or until the next full moon. Details of this lunar periodicity can be found in a paper by Grave (1927a).

PROCURING AND HANDLING MATERIAL:

A. Care of Adults: The animals should be transported to the laboratory as quickly as possible after collection, kept barely damp in moist sand, and protected from high temperatures. While it is desirable to use them on the day they are collected, they will survive for one or two days in cool, moist sand. They must be kept *away from sea water,* to prevent shedding of gametes.

B. Procuring Gametes: Wash the adults free of all sediment and isolate them in small stender dishes half-filled with sea water. If mature, both sexes will shed 30 minutes to one hour after being placed in sea water. Grave (1927a) believes this spawning reaction in the laboratory is induced by shock. Collect the eggs as they are shed, and transfer them to a fingerbowl containing about 200 cc. of sea water. After shedding, remove the adults from the stender dishes. They should then be returned to their normal habitat.

C. Preparation of Cultures: Allow the eggs to stand for about 15 minutes (so that they may advance to the metaphase of the first maturation division) and then inseminate by adding one or two drops of dilute sperm suspension. Polyspermy occurs if too much sperm is used. Allow to stand for about 30 minutes, and then change the sea water several times to remove excess sperm and body fluids. Cover the culture dish and store on the sea water table.

About 12 hours after insemination, pour the upper layers of water, containing the normal, top-swimming larvae, into a large battery jar, and fill it with sea water. Repeat this procedure in about four hours, and then leave undisturbed for one or two days. At this time, the veligers tend to settle and lie quiescent on the bottom.

They are readily collected with a pipette and should be transferred once a day to fresh dishes of sea water until they metamorphose. During this time they must be fed diatoms, preferably Nitzschia. It is advisable to employ some device for gently agitating the water.

D. Methods of Observation: Early stages may be mounted on vaselined slides or on slides with the coverslips supported in some other manner. The jelly which surrounds the eggs is rendered visible if they are placed in a suspension of Chinese ink. Older moving larvae may be trapped in shredded lens paper or lightly anaesthetized with a dilute solution of chloral hydrate in sea water, and mounted in a Chinese ink suspension.

NORMAL DEVELOPMENT:

A. The Unfertilized Ovum: The egg is small; measurements of the diameter vary from 61 to 65 microns, but the majority measure 62 or 63 microns. It is surrounded by a tough vitelline membrane and a thick jelly-envelope. The egg is transparent and contains yolk granules which give it a faintly pink cast. It is shed in the germinal vesicle stage and, on contact with sea water, proceeds spontaneously to metaphase of the first maturation division.

B. Fertilization and Cleavage: The vitelline membrane is not elevated perceptibly at fertilization. The polar body is relatively enormous and seems to round up before reaching the surface of the egg. Two polar bodies are formed, the first usually remaining undivided. The living egg is sufficiently clear for the approach and association of the pronuclei to be observed. Cleavage is spiral and very closely resembles that of Dreissensia (see the paper by Meisenheimer, 1901). The late blastula becomes ciliated.

C. Time Table of Development: The rate of development varies considerably with the temperature. A table showing developmental rates at different temperatures is presented by Grave (1927b). The following schedule was observed at 20 to 21° C.; times are recorded from fertilization.

Stage	Time
First polar body	12–15 minutes
Second polar body	28–35 minutes
First cleavage	60–70 minutes
Second cleavage	90–102 minutes
Blastula	5–6 hours
Gastrula	7–10 hours
Trochophore	12–18 hours
Fully-formed veliger	2–24 days
Metamorphosis	16–24 days

D. Later Stages of Development and Metamorphosis: The early gastrula develops a prototroch and swims vigorously. The trochophore stage is of short duration (less than 10 hours). Yolk obscures the internal organs of this larval form. When first formed, the typical veliger settles temporarily to the bottom, swimming less and less frequently until metamorphosis. A pair of semi-circular valves develops, and extending from the straight hinge line to the ciliated velum are several strands of muscle fibers. The digestive tract is ciliated and consists

of oesophagus, stomach and intestine.   The mouth and anal openings have formed.
Late veligers rarely swim, and the velum appears to have become more and more
an accessory feeding organ (Grave, 1927b).

REFERENCES:

COSTELLO, D. P., 1934.   The hyaline zone of the centrifuged egg of Cumingia.   *Biol. Bull.,* **66:**
   257–263.
GRAVE, B. H., 1927a.   An analysis of the spawning habits and spawning stimuli of *Cumingia
   tellinoides.   Biol. Bull.,* **52:** 418–435.
GRAVE, B. H., 1927b.   The natural history of *Cumingia tellinoides.   Biol. Bull.,* **53:** 208–219.
HEILBRUNN, L. V., 1920.   Studies in artificial parthenogenesis.   III. Cortical change and the
   initiation of maturation in the egg of Cumingia.   *Biol. Bull.,* **38:** 317–339.
MEISENHEIMER, J., 1901.   Entwicklungsgeschichte von *Dreissensia polymorpha* Pall.   *Zeitschr.
   f. wiss. Zool.,* **69:** 1–137.
MORGAN, T. H., 1910.   Cytological studies of centrifuged eggs.   *J. Exp. Zool.,* **9:** 593–655.
WHITAKER, D. M., 1931.   On the rate of oxygen consumption by fertilized and unfertilized
   eggs.   II. *Cumingia tellinoides.   J. Gen. Physiol.,* **15:** 183–190.
WHITAKER, D. M., 1939.   The effect of fertilization on the rate of staining of Cumingia eggs.
   Growth, **3:** 153–158.

MOLLUSCA

(Pelecypoda)

Ensis directus

LIVING MATERIAL:

Razor clams are found burrowing in muddy sand habitats, which are also suitable for collecting Mya. They are procured by rapid digging at low tide. One of the best collecting grounds in the Woods Hole region is Barnstable Harbor, Mass., and another is Rand's Harbor, Mass. The sexes are separate, but cannot be distinguished externally.

BREEDING SEASON:

Little is known of the breeding season of this species, but according to Just (1939), mature animals are found at Woods Hole during July. It is probable that spawning begins before this, since in the colder waters at Prince Edward Island, larvae have been found in the plankton throughout June (Sullivan, 1948).

PROCURING AND HANDLING MATERIAL:

A. Care of Adults: In the laboratory, the animals should be kept in wet sand in an aquarium, protected from increases in temperature.

B. Procuring Gametes: Fertilization is internal, but it is possible to obtain fully mature, unfertilized eggs. Best results are obtained with adults over five inches long. Such animals isolated in large fingerbowls will, according to Just (1939), shed naturally. Gametes may also be obtained directly from the gonads. To do this, remove one valve, exposing the gonads (white irregular masses) which lie on and around the dark brown digestive gland, just anterior to the heart. Remove the gonads with forceps or a pipette, and isolate in a watch glass. The gametes will ooze out, and when this extrusion has ceased, the gonads should be removed. The eggs are relatively clean, and require little washing. They remain fertilizable for five hours, but with a decreasing percentage of fertilization.

C. Preparation of Cultures: If fertilization has already taken place, eggs may be found in various stages of development. Unfertilized eggs may be inseminated by adding several pipettes-ful of sperm suspension. After a short time, change the sea water, in order to remove excess sperm. The cultures should be kept in a large amount of water and stored on a water table. The sea water in the cultures should be changed at least once a day. Loosanoff (1954) describes a method for culturing older larvae of this form.

NORMAL DEVELOPMENT:

A. The Unfertilized Ovum: The egg of Ensis may be quite irregular in shape; it is enclosed in a thin vitelline membrane and surrounded by a narrow perivitelline space. The ovum is light yellowish-brown in color. It is rather granular, but moderately transparent, and has a large germinal vesicle.

B. The Spermatozoon: The sperm are green in color, and relatively large, the

111

head measuring 2.8 microns in width and 5.6 microns in length. They have a very long tail.

C. *Fertilization and Cleavage:* Shortly after insemination, the egg rounds up and the germinal vesicle breaks down. The egg now measures 65 to 67 microns in diameter. Two polar bodies are given off, and prominent polar lobes are formed prior to each of the first two cleavages. Since the eggs are relatively transparent, the phases of spindle formation in cell division are readily distinguished. Cleavage is unequal and spiral. A ciliated blastula is formed, which hatches and swims in a clockwise circular manner at the surface. Gastrulation is by epiboly and invagination.

D. *Time Table of Development:* The following schedule represents a range of times observed in cultures developing at laboratory temperatures ranging from 27 to 30° C. Times are recorded from insemination.

Stage	Time
Germinal vesicle breakdown	3 to 5 minutes
First polar body	15 to 20 minutes
Second polar body	25 to 30 minutes
First polar lobe	30 to 35 minutes
First cleavage	42 to 46 minutes
Second polar lobe	50 to 60 minutes
Second cleavage	58 to 65 minutes
Third cleavage	75 to 85 minutes
Morula	$2\frac{1}{2}$ hours
Free-swimming blastula	$3\frac{3}{4}$ to 4 hours
Gastrula	10 hours
Early trochophore	11 hours
Early veliger	27 hours

E. *Later Stages of Development:* The ciliated gastrula is bell-shaped, with a prominent flagellum. It transforms rapidly into a typical trochophore, oval in shape. At the end of one day, the shell gland can be seen and the early veliger soon develops. The shell increases in size and has a long straight hinge. By the end of the second day, many of the veligers have lost their flagella. The velums are reduced in size. The viscera appear as an amorphous, coarse, granulated mass. The larvae are pale yellow throughout their development, darkening only just before settling to the bottom. The larval life seems to be of relatively short duration (Sullivan, 1948).

REFERENCES:

JUST, E. E., 1939. Basic Methods for Experiments on Eggs of Marine Animals. P. Blakiston's Son and Co., Inc., Philadelphia, pp. 33–34.

LOOSANOFF, V. L., 1954. New advances in the study of bivalve larvae. *Amer. Sci.,* **42**: 607–624.

SULLIVAN, C. M., 1948. Bivalve larvae of Malpeque Bay, P. E. I. Bull. Fish. Res. Bd., Canada, no. 77, pp. 1–36.

MOLLUSCA

(Pelecypoda)

Mactra (now *Spisula*) *solidissima*

LIVING MATERIAL:

These clams are found on sandy bottoms in shallow water, and may be collected by digging at low tide. Large individuals are obtainable at Barnstable, Mass. The sexes are separate, but are similar in appearance.

BREEDING SEASON:

Ripe animals can be secured at least throughout the summer months (Schechter, 1941). They have been collected off the New Jersey coast as late as December (Heilbrunn, personal communication), and Allen (1953) reports that eggs are obtainable from animals collected in New Jersey waters at any time from early spring until late autumn. In the Woods Hole region, Allen (1953) describes the season as beginning late in May and extending into September.

PROCURING AND HANDLING MATERIAL:

A. Care of Adults: Clams kept in large aquaria, with a good supply of running sea water, will retain their gametes in a viable condition for several weeks. It is advisable to segregate the sexes. Dead or dying individuals should be removed immediately.

The sex of an individual may be ascertained, without injury, as follows: Place a wooden peg between the open valves to keep them slightly apart. Now insert, as near the hinge as possible, a hypodermic needle (2½-inch, 20-gauge), attached to a syringe containing a small amount of sea water. Inject a few drops into the region of the gonad (anterior to, and below, the pedal retractor muscle), and then draw the fluid back into the syringe. If the animal is mature, this withdrawn material will contain either eggs or sperm, which are readily identifiable.

B. Procuring Gametes: Both male and female gametes may be procured by either of the following methods: 1) Select an animal, rinse it in fresh water and dry. In a few seconds, the valves will gape slightly and a strong, sharp scalpel can be introduced to cut the adductor muscles. Remove the animal from the shell and excise the gonad (which lies beneath the gills, mantle and heart). Eggs should be strained through several thicknesses of cheesecloth (previously washed in fresh water and then saturated with sea water) into a large volume of filtered sea water. When the eggs have settled, decant the supernatant fluid and replace it with fresh filtered sea water (Allen, 1953); this process of washing should be repeated at least three times, in order to remove all blood and body fluids, which apparently have a deleterious effect on fertilization. 2) Sometimes the animals shed spontaneously when they are removed from the shell.

C. Preparation of Cultures: Inseminate a fingerbowl of eggs with four or five drops of sperm suspension and gently rotate the dish once. Allow it to stand undisturbed for about 30 minutes; then change the water and cover the dish with a glass plate. Place the culture on a water table, and after about 10 hours, decant

113

the upper layers of water containing the vigorous top-swimming larvae to a clean fingerbowl. Add fresh sea water to the decanted larvae, and repeat this procedure at least once a day. After two or three days, diatoms should be added to the culture. Details for the maintenance of larval cultures are given by Prytherch (1937) and by Loosanoff (1954).

D. Methods of Observation: Nuclei will stand out very sharply if the eggs are placed on an ordinary slide, covered with a coverslip, and flattened slightly by removing some of the water. Both eggs and swimming larvae can be observed on depression slides, with or without coverslips. The larvae may be quieted by adding a few drops of dilute Janus green to the preparations. This paralyzes the cilia, and the animals, although living, are held motionless.

NORMAL DEVELOPMENT:

A. The Unfertilized Ovum: When freshly shed, the egg is irregular in shape due to pressure within the ovary, but on standing it soon becomes spherical. It is small, measuring 53 to 56 microns in diameter. The center of the egg is almost completely filled by an enormous germinal vesicle (30 microns in diameter), containing a prominent nucleolus. There is a thin layer of clear cortical protoplasm, surrounding some densely packed yolk. The eggs will retain this appearance for many hours, unless inseminated.

B. Fertilization and Cleavage: Within a few minutes after insemination, the germinal vesicle begins to break down, and soon only a light area in the center of the egg marks its former position. A thin fertilization membrane is elevated a very short distance from the egg surface. The first polar body forms shortly after germinal vesicle breakdown, and the second polar body is extruded directly beneath it. Their position marks the plane of the first cleavage.

The male and female pronuclei become visible, approach each other and fuse. Cleavage occurs soon after; it is unequal, and the first two blastomeres differ greatly in size. The second cleavage follows and, in the case of the larger cell, is again unequal, producing one large cell and three smaller ones. The subsequent cleavages are rapid. They are of a spiral type, but because of the size differences of the blastomeres, this is more difficult to follow than in Crepidula. The small, rapidly dividing ectodermal cells spread over the larger, yolk-filled endodermal cells, leaving an uncovered region, the blastopore. Thus, gastrulation is by epiboly; a swimming gastrula is formed.

C. Time Table of Development: There is considerable variation in developmental rate, depending on temperature and other environmental factors; however, the following schedules (which are obviously discrepant) give some idea of the chronology at 21° C. (Allen, 1953) and 25° C. (Schechter, 1941). Times are recorded from insemination.

Stage	Time (21° C.)	Time (25° C.)
Germinal vesicle breakdown	6–7 minutes	10 minutes
Formation of polar bodies	29 minutes	30 minutes
Pronuclei visible	50 minutes	50 minutes
First cleavage	74 minutes	65 minutes
Second cleavage	99 minutes	95 minutes
Swimming forms	Within 24 hours	5 hours

D. Later Stages of Development and Metamorphosis: The young swimming larva (5–6 hours after insemination) has on the future dorsal side a plate of large cells, the primordium of the shell gland. Internally, two large dark cells, the mesodermal teloblasts, are often visible. By 9 hours, the embryos have lost their somewhat barrel-shaped appearance and are pyramidal trochophores. The expanded base of the pyramid is the region in which the velum will form. The cilia are not markedly visible at this time. On the ventral side a small indentation marks the blastopore, and on the dorsal surface the invagination of the shell gland appears as a conspicuous concavity. By 14 hours the shell gland has evaginated, and this hollow cannot be seen. The cilia of the velum and the apical flagellum are well developed.

The young veliger (18–19 hours) has a well-developed bivalved shell, with a straight hinge line. On the side opposite the apical flagellum a telotroch has formed. The stomodeal invagination lies just below the velum, but as yet there is no proctodeal invagination. The internal structures are obscured by a mass of undifferentiated endodermal and mesodermal cells which fills most of the post-velar area.

The two-day larva has both mouth and anal openings, and clearly defined oesophagus, stomach, intestine and liver. The movements of the digestive tract and the cilia which develop along its entire length are easily observed. Three groups of retractor muscles converge dorsally, and the *anlage* of the anterior adductor muscle can be seen as a small clump of cells anterior and dorsal to the stomach.

In about five days the velum gradually disappears, giving place to a slender, active foot (Belding, 1910). This functions first as a swimming and later as a crawling organ. The young clam is now ready to settle to the bottom.

The development of Dreissensia is very similar to that of Mactra; it has been described and figured by Meisenheimer (1901).

REFERENCES:

ALLEN, R. D., 1953. Fertilization and artificial activation in the egg of the surf-clam, *Spisula solidissima. Biol. Bull.,* **105**: 213–239.

BELDING, D. L., 1910. The growth and habits of the sea clam, *Mactra solidissima.* Ann. Rep. Comm. Fish and Game, Massachusetts, 1909, pp. 26–41.

KOSTANECKI, K., 1902. Ueber künstliche Befruchtung und künstliche parthenogenetische Furchung bei Mactra. Bull. de l'Acad. des Sci., Cracovie, Cl. des Sci. Math. et Natur., Juillet, 1902, pp. 363–387.

KOSTANECKI, K., 1904. Cytologische Studien an künstlich parthenogenetisch sich entwickelnden Eiern von Mactra. *Arch. f. mikr. Anat.,* **64**: 1–98.

KOSTANECKI, K., 1908. Zur Morphologie der künstlichen parthenogenetischen Entwicklung bei Mactra. *Arch. f. mikr. Anat.,* **72**: 327–352.

KOSTANECKI, K., 1911. Experimentelle Studien an den Eiern von Mactra. Bull. de l'Acad. des Sci., Cracovie, Cl. des Sci. Math. et Natur., sér. B, Mars, 1911, pp. 146–161.

LOOSANOFF, V. L., 1954. New advances in the study of bivalve larvae. *Amer. Sci.,* **42**: 607–624.

MEISENHEIMER, J., 1901. Entwicklungsgeschichte von *Dreissensia polymorpha* Pall. *Zeitschr. f. wiss. Zool.,* **69**: 1–137.

PRYTHERCH, H. F., 1937. The cultivation of lamellibranch larvae. *In:* Culture Methods for Invertebrate Animals, edit. by Galtsoff *et al.,* Comstock, Ithaca, pp. 539–542.

SCHECHTER, V., 1936. Comparative hypotonic cytolysis of several types of invertebrate egg cells and the influence of age. *Biol. Bull.,* **71**: 410.

SCHECHTER, V., 1937. Calcium and magnesium in relation to longevity of Mactra, Nereis and Hydroides egg cells. *Biol. Bull.,* **73**: 392.

SCHECHTER, V., 1941. Experimental studies upon the egg cells of the clam, *Mactra solidissima,* with special reference to longevity. *J. Exp. Zool.,* **86**: 461–477.

SCLUFER, E., 1955. The respiration of Spisula eggs. *Biol. Bull.,* **109**: 113–122.

MOLLUSCA

(Pelecypoda)

Mya arenaria

LIVING MATERIAL:

The soft-shell clam is found between tide lines and in shallow water, on mud flats and under stones. It may be collected in many such areas around Woods Hole, Mass. (including Rand's Harbor), but is not abundant. The sexes are separate; however, they cannot be distinguished unless the gonads are cut open and the sexual products examined.

BREEDING SEASON:

Spawning begins when the sea water temperature rises above 10 to 12° C. (Nelson, 1928), and, according to Just (1939), extends throughout the summer. Observations by Bumpus (1898), Kellogg (1899), and Mead (1901), however, limit it to May and June. Belding (1915) recorded spawning in June and July, but we have seen only spent females at the beginning of July. The discrepancy might be explained if there is a second peak of gamete production in late summer, as suggested by Battle (1932) and, more recently, by Sullivan (1948). The latter observed an increase of young larvae at the beginning of August in plankton taken at Prince Edward Island.

PROCURING AND HANDLING MATERIAL:

A. Care of Adults: The adults must be kept in clean aquaria and occasionally allowed to lie exposed. Foul water and continuous submergence are unfavorable (Kellogg, 1899).

B. Procuring Gametes: Mature animals of both sexes have a firm, hard foot and large creamy gonads, surrounding the digestive tract. It is probably best to use naturally-shed gametes obtained from isolated mature individuals. Eggs and sperm obtained by cutting open the gonads in sea water will, upon insemination, produce only about 10 to 20 per cent normal development (Mead, 1901); Belding (1915) also reported that artificial insemination is not very successful.

C. Preparation of Cultures: Inseminate a fingerbowl of eggs by adding two or three cc. of sperm suspension. Leave for about 15 minutes and then decant the supernatant fluid and replace with filtered sea water. In about 12 hours the upper layers of water, containing free-swimming larvae, should be poured off into a large battery jar. Fill the container with sea water filtered through coarse filter paper, and aerate. The sea water should be changed every second day and a small quantity of mixed microplankton should be added daily. Old shells will provide surfaces for attachment as the time for metamorphosis approaches. Prytherch (1937) and Loosanoff (1954) give details for mass culture of larvae.

NORMAL DEVELOPMENT:

A. The Unfertilized Ovum: The egg is almost spherical; measurements of the diameter vary from 58 by 62 microns (Stafford, 1901) to 80 microns (Battle, 1932). Belding (1915) recorded 62.5 microns as the average diameter. The

117

ovum is surrounded by a vitelline membrane enclosing a thin perivitelline space, and a jelly-case is often seen. A considerable amount of yolk is present, and the egg is grey. It is shed in the germinal vesicle stage.

B. Cleavage: The unequal, spiral cleavage resembles that of Pecten and Venus. A ciliated blastula is formed, and gastrulation is by invagination, probably preceded by epibolic movement.

C. Developmental Rate: The blastulae develop in about 9 hours, and trochophores by 12 hours after insemination. The veliger larvae may be seen in about 36 hours. In Massachusetts waters, the larvae spend about two weeks at the swimming stage, before settling to the bottom as spat (Ayers, 1956).

D. Later Stages of Development and Metamorphosis: As the trochophore forms, the body becomes elongated and the cilia become confined to the anterior part of the body. A primitive mouth is present, and opposite it the shell gland develops. The 24-hour larva is a typical lamellibranch veliger with a transparent, bivalved, hinged shell, an apical flagellum, and a round, ciliated velum. In the older veliger, the velum degenerates and is replaced by the foot as an organ of locomotion. Mantle, gills, heart and a pair of otocysts develop prior to metamorphosis. Figures of the older larvae and fixation stages may be found in papers by Kellogg (1899), Mead (1900) and Stafford (1909).

REFERENCES:

AYERS, J. C., 1956. Population dynamics of the marine clam, *Mya arenaria. Limn. and Oceanog.,* 1 : 26–34.

BATTLE, H. I., 1932. Rhythmic sexual maturity and spawning of certain bivalve mollusks. *Contr. Canadian Biol. and Fish.,* 7 : 255–276.

BELDING, D. L., 1915. A report upon the clam fishery. 50th Ann. Rep., Comm. Fish and Game, Massachusetts, pp. 93–234.

BUMPUS, H. C., 1898. The breeding habits of animals at Woods Holl during the months of June, July and August. *Science,* 8: 850–858.

JUST, E. E., 1939. Basic Methods for Experiments on Eggs of Marine Animals. P. Blakiston's Son & Co., Inc., Philadelphia.

KELLOGG, J. L., 1899. Special report on the life-history of the common clam, *Mya arenaria.* 29th Ann. Rep., Comm. Inland Fish., Rhode Island, 1898, pp. 78–95.

LOOSANOFF, V. L., 1954. New advances in the study of bivalve larvae. *Amer. Sci.,* 42: 607–624.

MEAD, A. D., 1900. Observations on the soft-shell clam. 30th Ann. Rep., Comm. Inland Fish., Rhode Island, 1899, pp. 20–42.

MEAD, A. D., 1901. Observations on the soft-shell clam. 31st Ann. Rep., Comm. Inland Fish., Rhode Island, 1900, pp. 21–44.

MEAD, A. D., 1902. Observations on the soft-shell clam. 32nd Ann. Rep., Comm. Inland Fish., Rhode Island, 1901, pp. 20–33.

MEAD, A. D., AND E. W. BARNES, 1903. Observations on the soft-shell clam (*Mya arenaria*). 33rd Ann. Rep., Comm. Inland Fish., Rhode Island, 1902, pp. 29–48.

MEAD, A. D., AND E. W. BARNES, 1904. Observations on the soft-shell clam. 34th Ann. Rep., Comm. Inland Fish., Rhode Island, 1903, pp. 29–68.

NELSON, T. C., 1928. On the distribution of critical temperatures for spawning and for ciliary activity in bivalve molluscs. *Science,* 67: 220–221.

PRYTHERCH, H. F., 1937. The cultivation of lamellibranch larvae. *In:* Culture Methods for Invertebrate Animals, edit. by Galtsoff *et al.,* Comstock, Ithaca, pp. 539–543.

STAFFORD, J., 1901. The clam fishery of Passamaquoddy Bay. Contr. Canadian Biol., 1901, pp. 19–40.

STAFFORD, J., 1909. On the recognition of bivalve larvae in plankton collections. Contr. Canadian Biol., 1906–1910, pp. 221–242.

SULLIVAN, C. M., 1948. Bivalve larvae of Malpeque Bay, P. E. I. Bull. Fish. Res. Bd. Canada, no. 77, pp. 1–36.

MOLLUSCA

(PELECYPODA)

Mytilus edulis

LIVING MATERIAL:

The edible mussel is found attached by byssus threads to other mussels, to rocks and to piles, between tide lines and in shallow water. At Woods Hole, Mass., it is common and may be collected off docks and at Penzance Point and Pine Island. The sexes are separate but cannot be distinguished externally.

BREEDING SEASON:

Spawning individuals have been obtained in the Woods Hole region from early June to mid-September (Bumpus, 1898; Field, 1922). Nelson (1928) noted that spawning of this species begins at temperatures of 10 to 12° C., which indicates the possibility of an earlier season than has been recorded. His findings are supported by the recent work of Sullivan (1948) at Prince Edward Island; Sullivan obtained larvae from late May to early August, when temperatures ranged from 10 to 24° C. Battle (1932) offers some evidence of a lunar periodicity for this species.

PROCURING AND HANDLING MATERIAL:

A. Care of Adults: The animals may be kept on a sea water table or in aquaria provided with running sea water. The sexes may be identified by examining the gonads, which completely fill the mantle folds of mature animals. The testes are orange-pink in color, the ovaries deep maroon; spent gonads are transparent.

B. Procuring Gametes: Field (1922) states that rough handling, such as shaking in a bucket or stirring rapidly in a dish of sea water, will induce spawning within an hour. This method has not proved successful in our experience. Gametes can be obtained, however, by removing the valves of an individual and placing the mantle folds in a small fingerbowl containing about 100 cc. of sea water. If the gonads are fully ripe, the gametes will ooze from them. The eggs should be strained through cheesecloth (previously washed and rinsed in sea water) to a bowl of fresh sea water. Berg and Kutsky (1951) report that they obtained Mytilus gametes by placing the animals in separate bowls of sea water and allowing natural spawning to occur. Their animals were stored for periods as long as one week at 4° C. before spawning occurred.

C. Preparation of Cultures: As soon as a microscopical examination of the eggs reveals germinal vesicle breakdown, they may be inseminated by the addition of four or five drops of active sperm suspension. Artificial insemination is not successful unless the eggs are readily released, the sperm very active, and germinal vesicle breakdown prompt. The eggs remain fertilizable for about three or four hours. Larvae may be cultured through metamorphosis; a method is described by Loosanoff (1954).

119

NORMAL DEVELOPMENT:

A. The Unfertilized Ovum: The egg is almost spherical, measuring 70 microns in diameter, and is enclosed by a vitelline membrane about one micron thick. It is pale brownish-pink in color, but when viewed in transmitted light, has a yellowish color. Although shed in the germinal vesicle stage, the ovum rapidly proceeds to metaphase of the first maturation division, becoming somewhat oval in shape meanwhile. It remains in this condition for three to four hours and then, unless fertilized, it dies (Field, 1922).

B. Fertilization and Cleavage: The head of the sperm enters, enlarges and moves toward the center of the ovum, which assumes a spherical form. Two polar bodies are given off in fairly rapid succession, the second directly below the first. Prominent polar lobes are formed prior to the first two cleavages. Cleavage is unequal and spiral, and gastrulation is by epiboly followed by invagination (Rattenbury and Berg, 1954). Figures of these early stages may be found in a paper by Field (1922).

C. Time Table of Development: The following schedule of development at 20° C. was observed by Field (1922). The time is recorded from insemination.

Stage	Time
First polar body	18 to 20 minutes
Second polar body	30 minutes
Polar lobe formation, fusion of pronuclei	50 minutes
First cleavage	70 minutes
Second cleavage	80 minutes
Free-swimming blastula	4½ to 5 hours
Gastrulation, young trochophore	20 hours
Shell appears	43 hours
Well-formed veliger	69 hours
Metamorphosis	1½ weeks

D. Later Stages of Development and Metamorphosis: The young trochophore is a top-shaped organism with an extremely long apical flagellum and an equatorial circle of long cilia. About 40 hours after insemination, the shell gland appears as an invagination on the dorsal side of the larva; the apical flagellum is lost as the velar cilia develop (Rattenbury and Berg, 1954). The intestine is well developed, and the mouth, stomach and proctodeum are distinguishable. Within a few hours, the shell is formed, first as a single structure but soon becoming bivalved. It grows rapidly until it encloses the viscera. A conspicuous statocyst is present in the foot, which develops a "heel," enclosing the opening of the byssus gland. It also has a pair of eyespots. At metamorphosis, the larva, now asymmetrically shaped, settles to the bottom and becomes attached by byssus threads. The velum disintegrates, and the valves develop a blue rim as they increase in size. Stafford (1909) and Rattenbury and Berg (1954) present further details and diagrams of late larvae and metamorphosing forms.

SPECIAL COMMENTS:

Since this species is abundant at Woods Hole and the female furnishes an adequate supply of ova, it should be more frequently utilized as embryological research material. The eggs resemble those of Cumingia and Ensis.

REFERENCES:

BATTLE, H. I., 1932. Rhythmic sexual maturity and spawning of certain bivalve molluscs. *Contr. Canadian Biol. and Fish.*, **7**: 255–276.

BERG, W. E., 1950. Lytic effects of sperm extracts on the eggs of *Mytilus edulis*. *Biol. Bull.*, **98**: 128–138.

BERG, W. E., AND P. B. KUTSKY, 1951. Physiological studies of differentiation in *Mytilus edulis*. I. The oxygen uptake of isolated blastomeres and polar lobes. *Biol. Bull.*, **101**: 47–61.

BUMPUS, H. C., 1898. The breeding of animals at Woods Holl during the months of June, July and August. *Science*, **8**: 850–858.

FIELD, I. A., 1922. Biology and economic value of the sea mussel *Mytilus edulis*. *Bull. U. S. Bur. Fish.*, **38**: 127–259.

LOOSANOFF, V. L., 1954. New advances in the study of bivalve larvae. *Amer. Sci.*, **42**: 607–624.

MATTHEWS, A., 1913. Notes on the development of *Mytilus edulis* and *Alcyonium digitatum* in the Plymouth laboratory. *J. Mar. Biol. Assoc.*, **9**: 557–560.

MEVES, F., 1915. Über den Befruchtungsvorgang bei der Miesmuschel (*Mytilus edulis* L.). *Arch. f. mikr. Anat.*, **87**: A, 2, pp. 47–62.

NELSON, T. C., 1928. On the distribution of critical temperatures for spawning and for ciliary activity in bivalve molluscs. *Science*, **67**: 220–221.

RATTENBURY, J. C., AND W. E. BERG, 1954. Embryonic segregation during early development of *Mytilus edulis*. *J. Morph.*, **95**: 393–414.

STAFFORD, J., 1909. On the recognition of bivalve larvae in plankton collections. Contr. Canadian Biol., 1906–1910, pp. 221–242.

SULLIVAN, C. M., 1948. Bivalve larvae of Malpeque Bay, P. E. I. Bull. Fish. Res. Bd. Canada, no. 77, pp. 1–36.

WHITE, K. M., 1937. Mytilus. Liverpool Mar. Biol. Comm. Mem., vol. 31, pp. 1–117.

MOLLUSCA

(PELECYPODA)

Nucula proxima truncula

LIVING MATERIAL:

This species burrows on muddy bottoms and can sometimes be obtained by dredging in Hadley Harbor or the Fisheries Basin at Woods Hole, Mass. It is not very commonly found at present. The sexes are separate and cannot be distinguished externally.

Another member of this genus, *N. delphinodonta,* is found in the localities mentioned above, but it is smaller than *N. proxima,* and usually inhabits shallower waters. Various sub-species of *N. proxima* occur at intervals along the Atlantic Coast. The eggs of *N. delphinodonta* are retained in a brood-pouch attached to the shell, until the embryos have undergone metamorphosis. Neither eggs nor larvae of this species will develop outside the brood-pouch.

BREEDING SEASON:

Although it has not been investigated in the Woods Hole region, Drew (1901) indicated that in Maine waters, this species spawns during the summer.

PROCURING AND HANDLING MATERIAL:

A. Care of Adults: Adults may be kept in large fingerbowls supplied with running sea water.

B. Procuring Gametes: It is not known whether eggs removed from the gonads can be successfully fertilized. Drew (1901) reported that in the laboratory, the animals will shed in fingerbowls of sea water, but he did not describe his methods in detail.

C. Preparation of Cultures: Naturally-inseminated eggs have been cultured through metamorphosis by Drew (1901). The larvae are well supplied with yolk, and do not require any special feeding.

NORMAL DEVELOPMENT:

A. The Unfertilized Ovum: The mature ovum is yolky, and measures 90 microns in diameter. There is some evidence that maturation is completed in sea water, even if the egg is not inseminated.

B. Cleavage: Cleavage is total and spiral, but has not been described in detail. If the cleavage pattern resembles that of *N. delphinodonta,* it is unequal, and polar lobes are formed before both the maturation divisions and first cleavage. Gastrulation is probably by epiboly (Drew, 1899).

C. Rate of Development: Development is very rapid. By 25 hours, the larvae are swimming and possess a well-marked shell gland and intestine. Metamorphosis occurs at about 60 hours.

D. Later Stages of Development and Metamorphosis: The free-swimming larva is similar to that of Yoldia, but is smaller and rounder in shape. The embryo develops within an external test, formed of five rather indistinctly arranged rows of ciliated ectodermal cells. As in Yoldia, the cilia of three of these rows are long and concentrated into bands; there are indications occasionally of a fourth banded row, which is not characteristic of Yoldia. There is a prominent apical tuft and a well-marked stomodeum, leading into an elongate midgut. Close to the stomodeal opening on the dorsal side, there is an opening in the test which probably represents a region where the test failed to grow over the shell gland. At metamorphosis, the test is cast away, and the embryos lie helpless for several days while the foot develops. Diagrams of the larvae may be found in the papers by Drew (1899, 1901).

REFERENCES:

DREW, G. A., 1899. Some observations on the habits, anatomy, and embryology of members of the Protobranchia. *Anat. Anz.,* **15**: 493–519.

DREW, G. A., 1901. The life-history of *Nucula delphinodonta* (Mighels). *Quart. J. Micr. Sci.,* **44**: 313–391.

MOLLUSCA

(Pelecypoda)

Pecten irradians

(Syn. *Gibbus borealis* Say)

Living Material:

The common scallop inhabits the shallow waters of protected bays with sandy mud bottoms. It may be collected at Cotuit or from the Eel Pond at Woods Hole, Mass. The species is hermaphroditic and apparently self-fertile, but in nature the eggs and sperm of an individual are shed into the sea at different times.

Breeding Season:

Belding (1910) states that the breeding season at Wools Hole lasts from mid-June to mid-August, and in Buzzard's Bay is advanced about two weeks. There is some evidence that spawning begins when the ocean temperature rises to 15 to 16° C. (Belding, 1910; Nelson, 1928). However, at Beaufort, N. C., the season is reported to extend from the end of July, when the water temperature must be well above this critical temperature, to January, reaching its peak during the fall (Gutsell, 1930).

Procuring and Handling Material:

A. Care of Adults: It is convenient to keep the scallops in large aquaria, supplied with running sea water.

B. Procuring Gametes: Mature individuals can be selected by prying open their valves and inspecting the gonads. These organs are found in the lower portion of the visceral mass, and are covered by glossy black pigment during the breeding season. The testis is a narrow, elongated, cream-colored structure, ventral to the liver. It extends along the lateral border of the ovary, which in a ripe animal is distended and bright orange-pink in color. Both glands are small and pale after spawning.

The animals normally spawn between 8 A.M. and 4:30 P.M. The optimum spawning temperature, according to Belding (1910), lies between 24.5 and 29° C. In the laboratory, the frequency of spawning may sometimes be increased, but not always successfully, by raising the temperature of the sea water in which a previously washed, mature adult is placed. Belding's method was to expose the animal to the sun, in a small jar of sea water over dark paper; after a period, the animal might spawn. Gutsell (1930) raised the temperature of the sea water from 25 to 32° C., and on cooling, the animal occasionally spawned.

Since eggs and sperm are usually shed separately, the animals can be removed, rinsed in fresh water, and placed in fresh sea water after each discharge. In this way, the eggs and sperm can be collected separately. Spawning ceases when the animals are returned to cold water, so that specimens may be used repeatedly.

It is also possible to obtain gametes by cutting up the gonads in sea water, but

124

eggs obtained by this method are not as favorable as those which are naturally shed (Belding, 1910).

C. *Preparation of Cultures:* Inseminate the eggs with four or five drops of sperm suspension; when they have settled, decant the supernatant fluid and fill the container with fresh sea water. Store the culture on a sea water table. In about 12 hours, decant the upper layers of sea water, containing the swimming larvae, into a large battery jar. Fill the jar with sea water filtered through coarse filter paper; this will contain enough microplankton and other minute particles to feed the larvae, but will eliminate competing forms. The sea water should be changed once a day. The larvae may be concentrated by the use of filter papers or No. 25 bolting silk. For further details, consult the paper of Prytherch (1937).

NORMAL DEVELOPMENT:

A. *The Unfertilized Ovum:* The egg is pale orange in color and opaque, due to the presence of numerous yolk granules. It is surrounded by a thin membrane, which does not elevate upon insemination, and an outer, thin jelly-hull. Although one axis may be slightly longer than the other, the ovum is almost spherical, and measures about 63 microns in diameter (Belding, 1910). The germinal vesicle of the mature egg probably breaks down either before or immediately after it is released.

B. *Fertilization and Cleavage:* The fertilization membrane is not well marked. Some time after insemination, two polar bodies are formed; the second pushes out of the egg directly beneath the first. They remain attached to the egg. Cleavage is unequal and spiral. The yolk lobe is very prominent and a marked trefoil stage is present during first cleavage. Gastrulation is by epiboly followed by invagination. The ciliated gastrula rotates through the water.

C. *Rate of Development:* The following schedule was published by Belding (1910). The temperature was not recorded; time is calculated from insemination.

Stage	Time
First polar body	33 minutes
First yolk lobe	43 minutes
First cleavage	46 minutes
Second cleavage	67 minutes
Third cleavage	81 minutes
Blastula	9 hours
Ciliated gastrula	10 hours
Trochophore	12–14 hours
Straight-hinge veliger	17–40 hours
Late veliger	5 days

In cultures developing at 25° C., Gutsell (1930) obtained trochophores in one to two days, and straight-hinge veligers in 42 to 48 hours.

D. *Later Stages of Development and Metamorphosis:* The early trochophore is top-shaped, with a long apical flagellum and a ciliated anterior pole. It is propelled through the water, rotating about its longitudinal axis. The shell appears about 14 hours after insemination, and grows rapidly, forming a straight hinge in the young veliger. This has a simple, three-part digestive tract, an inconspicuous mantle, and one adductor muscle (the anterior one). The larva is propelled through the water by a conspicuous ciliated velum. In late veligers (four days old), the degenerating velum is replaced by a well-developed foot. Gill filaments and the posterior adductor muscle are present, and the mantle has now become conspicuous. The digestive tract has developed palps and a coiled intestine. At metamorphosis, the larva settles and becomes temporarily attached by the byssus, and the velum disintegrates. Diagrams of larval stages can be found in the paper by Belding (1910).

REFERENCES:

AMIRTHALINGHAM, C., 1928. On lunar periodicity in reproduction of *Pecten opercularis* near Plymouth in 1927–28. *J. Mar. Biol. Assoc.,* **15**: 605–641.

BELDING, D. L., 1910. A report upon the scallop fishery of Massachusetts, including the habits, life history of *Pecten irradians,* its rate of growth and other factors of economic value. Special Rep., Comm. Fish. and Game, Massachusetts, 1910, pp. 1–150.

DAKIN, W. J., 1909. Pecten. The edible scallop. *Proc. Trans. Liverpool Biol. Soc.,* **23**: 333–468.

DREW, G. A., 1906. The habits, anatomy, and embryology of the giant scallop (*Pecten tenuicostatus,* Mighels). Univ. of Maine Stud., no. 6, pp. 3–71.

GUTSELL, J. S., 1930. Natural history of the bay scallop. *Bull. U. S. Bur. Fish.,* **46**: 569–632.

NELSON, T. C., 1928. On the distribution of critical temperatures for spawning and for ciliary activity in bivalve molluscs. *Science, 67*: 220–221.

PRYTHERCH, H. F., 1937. The cultivation of lamellibranch larvae. *In:* Culture Methods for Invertebrate Animals, edit. by Galtsoff *et al.,* Comstock, Ithaca, pp. 539–543.

RISSER, J., 1901. Habits and life history of the scallop (*Pecten irradians*). 31st Ann. Rep., Comm. Inland Fish., Rhode Island, 1900, pp. 47–55.

MOLLUSCA

(PELECYPODA)

Teredo navalis

LIVING MATERIAL:

The shipworm normally attacks permanent wooden structures, such as wharf piles; it is therefore difficult to obtain large numbers of these animals without making advance preparations. Turner (1947) recommends the use of a laminated collecting board. It is made of six or more layers of soft, straight-grained wood $12' \times 6'' \times \frac{1}{2}''$, with brass or galvanized iron washers separating the layers to produce cracks large enough so that the animals will not cross from one layer to the next. The borers form long straight tubes and, as the wood is very thin, may be easily extracted. The board should be suspended vertically in the region of most severe attack, which is usually near the mud-line, and weighted so that it will remain in place. If this is done in July or August, the boards will be infested with shipworms by the following summer. Another device for collection is described by Lasker and Lane (1953); it is somewhat less cumbersome than that recommended by Turner.

The animal is abundant at Woods Hole, Mass.

In the adult, the sexes are separate and cannot be distinguished externally. Young animals, however, are potentially hermaphroditic and pass through alternating uni-sexual phases during their development. Details of this may be found in papers by Coe (1936, 1941) and Grave (1942). The species is viviparous, releasing larvae at an advanced veliger stage; certain other related species of shipworms (*T. dilitata* and *Bankia* (*Xylotria*) *gouldii*), not found in the Woods Hole region, are oviparous.

BREEDING SEASON:

These animals breed at Woods Hole from the first or second week of May until mid-October. Spawning begins when the water temperature rises above 11 to 12° C. (Grave, 1928).

PROCURING AND HANDLING MATERIAL:

A. Care of Adults: The animals should be left in the collecting board and supplied with running sea water until required for study or experimentation, at which time they may be dissected out with ease.

B. Procuring Gametes: Active sperm are expelled by sexually mature males when they are removed from their burrows. However, eggs of this species which are artificially inseminated will not develop beyond the third or fourth cleavage.

C. Preparation of Cultures: Various developmental stages can be obtained by dissecting open the gill chamber of a ripe female. (Sigerfoos, 1908, presents a diagram showing the anatomy of the adult, and the location of this brood chamber.) The tightly packed embryos are arranged in two parallel rows on either side of the elongate body. Three developmental stages are usually present in each mature

127

female; the oldest, which are grey in color, are located in the most anterior region (Hatschek, 1880). The eggs and younger stages are white in color; they will not live for more than a very short period outside the gill chamber. However, late trochophores and veligers can readily be cultured in fingerbowls of sea water. The veligers are very hardy and may be kept for about three weeks with a minimum of care, provided they are fed regularly with diatoms (Grave, 1937).

NORMAL DEVELOPMENT:

A. The Unfertilized Ovum: The egg is small, measuring 55 to 60 microns in diameter. It is surrounded by a delicate membrane and contains a large germinal vesicle. The animal pole is distinguishable from the darker vegetal pole, even in the unfertilized condition. The ovum is white in color.

B. Fertilization and Cleavage: There is apparently no observation recorded concerning the state of the ovum at fertilization. Cleavage is markedly unequal and undoubtedly spiral. Gastrulation is by epiboly and invagination. The embryo is about 250 microns in diameter when it is released from the maternal gill (Lane *et al.,* 1954).

C. Rate of Development: Since the eggs of this species cannot be reared outside the parent, the developmental rate has been estimated, only, using indirect methods. Grave (1928) suggested that the entire developmental period from insemination to metamorphosis lasts about five weeks, with at least half this time spent within the gill chamber of the mother. Lane *et al.* (1954) state that the normal free-swimming period does not exceed four days. The young animal reaches sexual maturity about six weeks after metamorphosis.

D. Later Stages of Development and Metamorphosis: The early trochophore is top-shaped and measures 59 by 60 microns. Although the alimentary tract appears solid and dark, a recognizable stomodeum is present. The prototroch is either very poorly developed or absent. In older trochophores the cilia, which previously covered the entire body surface, are limited to the region of the velum. The appearance of the shell gland coincides with, or slightly precedes, velum formation. The newly-formed shell is single, but it soon becomes bivalved. Older veligers are actively motile, even within the branchial chambers. The velum in these larvae is well developed and the pre-trochal hemisphere is tipped with an apical tuft of cilia. The complex digestive tract consists of stomach, intestine and liver, and has mouth and anal openings. Traces of kidney and muscles are also present. Diagrams of the stages developing in the brood chambers can be found in a paper by Hatschek (1880).

During the free-swimming period, the larva develops siphons, gills and a well-marked foot with byssus threads. The nervous and muscular systems continue to differentiate. As it grows older, the color of the larva changes from grey to yellow-green, and finally to olive green. After attachment, the young Teredo undergoes a remarkably rapid metamorphosis, during the course of which the velum is cast off and eaten. For details of metamorphosis and diagrams of the young attachment stages, see the paper by Sigerfoos (1908).

REFERENCES:

COE, W. R., 1933. Sexual phases in Teredo. *Biol. Bull.,* **65**: 283–303.
COE, W. R., 1934. Sexual rhythm in the pelecypod mollusk Teredo. *Science,* **80**: 192.

Coe, W. R., 1936. Sequence of functional sexual phases in Teredo. *Biol. Bull.,* **71**: 122–132.
(Also in Coll. Pap., Osborn Zool. Lab., Yale Univ., vol. 18.)

Coe, W. R., 1941. Sexual phases in wood-boring mollusks. *Biol. Bull.,* **81**: 168–176.

Grave, B. H., 1928. Natural history of shipworm, *Teredo navalis,* at Woods Hole, Massachusetts. *Biol. Bull.,* **55**: 260–282.

Grave, B. H., 1933. Rate of growth, age at sexual maturity, and duration of life of certain sessile organisms, at Woods Hole, Massachusetts. *Biol. Bull.,* **65**: 375–386.

Grave, B. H., 1937. Rearing *Teredo navalis. In:* Culture Methods for Invertebrate Animals, edit. by Galtsoff *et al.,* Comstock, Ithaca, pp. 545–546.

Grave, B. H., 1942. The sexual cycle of the shipworm, *Teredo navalis. Biol. Bull.,* **82**: 438–445.

Grave, B. H., and J. Smith, 1936. Sex inversion in *Teredo navalis* and its relation to sex ratios. *Biol. Bull.,* **70**: 332–343.

Hatschek, B., 1880. Ueber Entwicklungsgeschichte von Teredo. *Arb. Zool. Inst., Wien,* **3**: 1–44.

Lane, C. E., J. Q. Tierney and R. E. Hennacy, 1954. The respiration of normal larvae of *Teredo bartschi* Clapp. *Biol. Bull.,* **106**: 323–327.

Lasker, R., and C. E. Lane, 1953. The origin and distribution of nitrogen in *Teredo bartschi* Clapp. *Biol. Bull.,* **105**: 316–319.

Sigerfoos, C. P., 1908. Natural history, organization, and late development of the Teredinidae, or ship-worms. *Bull. U. S. Bur. Fish.,* **27**: 191–231.

Turner, R., 1947. Collecting ship-worms. Spec. Publ. Limnological Soc. of Amer., no. 19.

MOLLUSCA

(Pelecypoda)

Venus mercenaria

LIVING MATERIAL:

Venus mercenaria, the hard-shell clam, is also known as the "little-neck" or quahog. It burrows in mud or sand flats near the lower part of the intertidal zone. The quahog is common at Woods Hole, Mass., and can be dug from the mud off Devil's Foot Island. Another clam, Callocardia, obtained in the same areas, is similar in appearance, but has a smooth margin to its shell; it is considerably smaller than the mature Venus.

Venus is "partially hermaphroditic," but is never self-fertile. It is usually protandrous until the second year, when the animal either remains male or reverses its sex (see the paper by Loosanoff, 1937b, for details).

BREEDING SEASON:

Mid-June to mid-August, with a peak period extending from late June through early July. Individual batches of animals will shed for about 20 days only (Belding, 1911). The temperature of the sea water must be above the critical level of 23 to 25° C. (Loosanoff, 1937b).

PROCURING AND HANDLING MATERIAL:

A. Care of Adults: These animals will remain in good condition indefinitely in the laboratory, if they are kept in large aquaria provided with flowing sea water.

B. Procuring Gametes: Since all attempts to prepare cultures by cutting up the gonads have proved unsuccessful, it is necessary to use naturally-shed gametes. Animals kept in the laboratory have been known to spawn three different times during a single season, extruding the gametes through the excurrent siphon in a fine stream. Belding (1911) stated that mature quahogs spawn at night when the water temperature reaches 24.5° C., and do best when they are not covered with sand. To induce shedding, place a beaker containing an adult into a water-bath, raising the temperature rapidly to 32–33° C. Spawning usually occurs when the animal is cooled slowly. If the normal sea water temperature is above 20° C., the procedure is not effective until the animal has been pre-treated by chilling in an ice box for 24 to 36 hours (Zinn, personal communication).

C. Preparation of Cultures: The ova should be inseminated immediately. Add four or five cc. of sperm suspension to a fingerbowl of eggs and mix well. In a few minutes pour the contents through a #80 stainless steel sieve with 177-micron openings, into a fingerbowl of sea water. This will remove large debris. Repeat, using a finer sieve, which will retain the eggs and allow excess sperm and other small particles to be eliminated. Place the eggs in large battery jars of sea water and aerate continuously. Leave them undisturbed until the early veliger stage, then change the sea water every second day. Add a small quantity of mixed microplankton to the cultures daily; shells should be added to older cultures, to provide surfaces for attachment at metamorphosis. Using this method, Loosanoff and Davis (1950) reared cultures through metamorphosis without difficulty.

D. Extension of the Breeding Season: Loosanoff and Davis (1950) have conditioned quahogs so that they spawn in winter. They are taken from their natural beds at a temperature of about 0° C., and placed in trays of running sea water having a temperature of approximately 5 to 7° C. At intervals of three to five days, the temperature is increased by several degrees, up to 20 to 22° C. This conditioning period takes about three weeks. Actual spawning may now be induced by the method outlined above. Not all egg batches will have the same vitality, but with experience, poor batches can be recognized and eliminated.

NORMAL DEVELOPMENT:

A. The Unfertilized Ovum: Due to pressure within the ovary, the newly-shed egg is often irregular in shape, and one axis may be longer than the other. When spherical, the egg measures about 70 to 73 microns in diameter (Loosanoff and Davis, 1950). It is surrounded by a gelatinous membrane which swells markedly on contact with sea water; the diameter across this membrane measures 167 to 170 microns. The ovum is very yolky and appears white and opaque. It is shed in metaphase of the first maturation division. The germinal vesicle apparently will not break down in sea water (Loosanoff and Davis, 1950).

B. Fertilization and Cleavage: A fertilization membrane is formed; cleavage is spiral and unequal. Poorly defined polar lobes are developed. Gastrulation is by epiboly, followed by invagination.

C. Time Table of Development: The following schedule of development at about 22° C. is presented by Loosanoff and Davis (1950). Time is calculated from insemination.

Stage	Time
First cleavage	45 minutes
Second cleavage	90 minutes
Ciliated blastula	6 hours
Early gastrula	9 hours
Trochophore	12 hours
Straight-hinge veliger	24–36 hours
Fully-formed veliger	32–44 hours
Mature larva, ready to set	12 days

D. Later Stages of Development and Metamorphosis: The gastrula elongates to form a top-shaped trochophore, which has no apical flagellum, but which is propelled through the water in a spiral direction by a crown of cilia at its anterior end. A mouth and shell gland are formed. The shell of the early veliger is bivalved and has a straight hinge line. Two adductor muscles are present. The mouth, stomach and small intestine are clearly visible, but the mantle is inconspicuous. The velum is elliptical and well ciliated. In older veligers, the velum degenerates and is replaced by a prominent ciliated foot, with its associated byssus gland. The digestive tract becomes increasingly complex, developing a liver, palps, and a long, coiled intestine. A well-formed mantle is present. At metamorphosis, the larva settles and becomes temporarily attached by the byssus.

Diagrams and further details of the larval stages can be found in papers by Stafford (1909), Belding (1911), Loosanoff and Davis (1950) and Loosanoff, Miller and Smith (1951).

REFERENCES:

BELDING, D. L., 1911.   The life history and growth of the quahaug (*Venus mercenaria*).   Ann. Rep., Comm. Fish and Game, Massachusetts, 1910, pp. 18–128.

LOOSANOFF, V. L., 1937a.   Spawning of *Venus mercenaria* (L.).   *Ecology,* **18**: 506–515.

LOOSANOFF, V. L., 1937b.   Development of the primary gonad and sexual phases in *Venus mercenaria* Linnaeus.   *Biol. Bull.,* **72**: 389–405.

LOOSANOFF, V. L., 1937c.   Seasonal gonadal changes of adult clams, *Venus mercenaria* (L.).   *Biol. Bull.,* **72**: 406–416.

LOOSANOFF, V. L., 1949.   Method for supplying a laboratory with warm sea water in winter.   *Science,* **110**: 192–193.

LOOSANOFF, V. L., AND H. C. DAVIS, 1950.   Conditioning *V. mercenaria* for spawning in winter and breeding its larvae in the laboratory.   *Biol. Bull.,* **98**: 60–65.

LOOSANOFF, V. L., W. S. MILLER AND P. B. SMITH, 1951.   Growth and setting of larvae of *Venus mercenaria* in relation to temperature.   *J. Mar. Res.,* **10**: 59–81.

STAFFORD, J., 1909.   On the recognition of bivalve larvae in plankton collections.   Contr. Canadian Biol., 1906–1910, pp. 221–242.

MOLLUSCA

(Pelecypoda)

Yoldia limatula

LIVING MATERIAL:

This bivalve may be found burrowing in sandy mud or swimming in shallow coves and inlets. At Woods Hole, Mass., it is easily obtained by dredging in Eel Pond or Hadley Harbor; the pollution of Eel Pond, however, is not conducive to the development of prime individuals.

The sexes are separate and are easily recognized during the breeding season. The ripe gonads are very extensive and surround the visceral mass just above the foot; in mature females, they are chocolate brown in color, in males they are yellow.

BREEDING SEASON:

Probably during the early summer months. However, the season has not been determined for the Woods Hole area.

PROCURING AND HANDLING MATERIAL:

A. Care of Adults: Adults may be kept in aquaria or in large fingerbowls supplied with running sea water.

B. Procuring Gametes: It is not known whether eggs removed from the gonads can be artificially inseminated. Mature animals, however, will spawn spontaneously in the laboratory.

C. Preparation of Cultures: Naturally-inseminated eggs may be reared through metamorphosis. No special feeding is necessary, as the larvae are well supplied with yolk. They are free-swimming and should be decanted daily to fresh sea water.

NORMAL DEVELOPMENT:

A. The Unfertilized Ovum: The mature egg measures approximately 150 microns in diameter, and is free of membranes (Drew, 1897). It is chocolate brown in color and very opaque, containing a large amount of yolk. Two polar bodies are extruded and lost shortly after the ovum is shed.

B. Cleavage: Cleavage is total, unequal and spiral. Gastrulation is by epiboly.

C. Rate of Development: Development is fairly rapid. The first cleavage occurs about two hours after insemination. By 36 hours, the swimming embryo has a developing shell gland and cerebral ganglion, and by 80 to 105 hours it metamorphoses.

D. Later Stages of Development and Metamorphosis: The early barrel-shaped larva is marked by a unique structure: a ciliated outer covering which is discarded at metamorphosis. The ectodermal cells which form this covering, or test, are arranged in five distinct rows. The two end rows are covered with short, evenly distributed cilia, and each of the intervening rows bears a band of longer, powerful cilia. A very long apical tuft is visible at one pole, and at the opposite pole is the

133

blastopore. Close to this, on one side, there is a small invagination, the stomodeum. Beneath the test, another ectodermal layer is formed, that of the embryo proper.

At metamorphosis, the animals settle to the bottom, the apical cilia shrivel, and the test cells disintegrate. The young animal which emerges has a pair of straight-hinged shell valves, otocysts containing otoliths, and a well-developed foot which becomes active within a few hours. There are rudimentary gills and a complex rudimentary digestive tract. Further details, and illustrations of the development of this animal, may be found in the papers by Drew (1897, 1899a, 1899b).

REFERENCES:

DREW, G. A., 1897. Notes on the embryology, anatomy, and habits of *Yoldia limatula*, Say. *Johns Hopkins Univ. Circ.*, **17**: 11–14.

DREW, G. A., 1899a. The anatomy, habits, and embryology of *Yoldia limatula*, Say. *Mem. Biol. Lab., Johns Hopkins Univ.*, **4**: no. 3, 1–37.

DREW, G. A., 1899b. Some observations on the habits, anatomy and embryology of members of the Protobranchia. *Anat. Anz.*, **15**: 493–519.

MOLLUSCA

(Gastropoda)

Busycon carica (formerly *Fulgur carica*)
and *B. canaliculatum* (formerly *Sycotypus canaliculatum*)

LIVING MATERIAL:

Busycon carica is rare at Woods Hole, Mass.; *B. canaliculatum* can often be purchased from lobstermen in the vicinity. The egg-strings of *B. canaliculatum* (which have a single-keeled edge, according to Johnson, 1903) are sometimes found cast up on beaches in the Woods Hole-Falmouth area, but they are not very common.

BREEDING SEASON:

Conklin (1907) states that the breeding season of *B. canaliculatum* occurs in late August and early September. The season for *B. carica* is apparently earlier; at Beaufort, N. C., the animals deposit their egg-strings in May and June.

PROCURING GAMETES:

The eggs and larvae do not live very long when brought into the laboratory, and the eggs are unsuitable for experimental purposes because they flatten out when they are removed from the protective jelly.

NORMAL DEVELOPMENT:

A. Egg Characteristics: The eggs of both species are laid in parchment-like, disc-shaped capsules attached to a long central cord; in both forms, the first few capsules of a cord may be small and empty. Within each of the subsequent capsules there are 10–20 eggs, embedded in a gelatinous matrix. The eggs of both species are very large and yolky; the average diameter of the egg of *B. carica* is approximately 1700 microns, while that of *B. canaliculatum* is about 1000 microns. There is no fertilization membrane present on either egg.

B. Cleavage and Gastrulation: The development of *B. carica* has been studied by Conklin (1907) and by McMurrich (1886, 1896); presumably, that of *B. canaliculatum* is similar. The following description applies to *B. carica*. Cleavage is spiral and almost equal, closely resembling that of Crepidula until the 56- to 60-cell stage. Small yolk lobes are formed during the first two cleavages; the micromeres are small and yolk-free. Cleavage in Busycon shows a transition between the holoblastic and meroblastic types. The mitotic figures of at least the first few divisions are very small, in relation to the size of the cells.

C. Rate of Development: In *B. carica* this is known to be slow; a period of about 13 months is apparently spent within the capsules.

D. Later Stages of Development: Due to the enormous supply of yolk, the closure of the blastopore occurs very slowly, and the larval organs appear on the upper surface of the yolk mass long before closure is completed. Shell gland, mantle, ganglia and velum are well formed before the blastopore closes. The foot, intestine, gills, larval kidney and heart appear during later development. For details and diagrams, see the papers of McMurrich (1886) and Conklin (1907).

REFERENCES:

CONKLIN, E. G., 1907. The embryology of Fulgur: A study of the influence of yolk on development. *Proc. Acad. Nat. Sci., Philadelphia,* **59**: 320–359.
CONKLIN, E. G., 1912. Cell size and nuclear size. *J. Exp. Zool.,* **12**: 1–98.
JOHNSON, C. W., 1903. Some notes on the genus Fulgur. *The Nautilus,* **17**: 73–75.
MCMURRICH, J. P., 1886. A contribution to the embryology of the prosobranch gasteropods. *Stud. Biol. Lab., Johns Hopkins Univ.,* **3**: 403–450.
MCMURRICH, J. P., 1896. The yolk-lobe and the centrosome of *Fulgur carica. Anat. Anz.,* **12**: 534–539.

MOLLUSCA

(Gastropoda)

Crepidula fornicata and *C. plana*

LIVING MATERIAL:

The greenish-brown, boat-shaped *C. fornicata* adults pile one on top of another to form "chains" of individuals; the colony is attached to a stone, shell or other solid object by the bottom limpet. This species can be collected at Vineyard Haven Harbor, Mass. Another species common to the Woods Hole area, *C. plana,* is found within whelk or moonsnail shells inhabited by large hermit crabs, and can be obtained at Cotuit. This species has a flat, whitish shell and is considerably smaller than *C. fornicata.*

Both species are potentially protandric hermaphrodites. The active males are small, whereas the mature females are the large, older individuals; all sizes and sexual conditions can be found in any colony.

BREEDING SEASON:

C. fornicata breeds from mid-June until mid-August. *C. plana* has a longer season; it breeds through the first week in September (Bumpus, 1898). Sexual activity is reduced to a minimum at sea water temperatures below 15 to 16° C. (Gould, 1950).

PROCURING AND HANDLING MATERIAL:

A. Care of Adults: These limpets may be kept indefinitely in aquaria or finger-bowls provided with a current of flowing, unfiltered sea water. *C. plana* will readily attach itself to glass when it is removed from the hermit crab shell. Unless they are already in the adult female phase, these animals eventually differentiate into males and females.

B. Procuring Fertilized Ova: The animals can be detached with a heavy knife. If eggs have been deposited, they are found in a transparent capsule, attached to the substrate or to the foot of the female. Mature females which have not yet deposited eggs may be isolated in glass dishes supplied with running sea water. After a few hours (preferably in the early morning), pour off the water and ex-amine the ventral surfaces of the females through the glass. In this way females can be found in the process of oviposition, and the first stages of development can be obtained. Transfer the capsule to a Syracuse dish of sea water and tease it open with needles to release the eggs (Conklin, 1937).

C. Preparation of Cultures: Eggs removed from the mantle cavity of the female do not develop normally for more than one or two days. However, a complete series of embryos can be obtained by selecting a number of capsules. The young stages appear bright yellow through the capsule, while older embryos are brown.

D. Methods of Observation: Details of the living eggs and larvae are more dis-tinct against a dark background. Swimming larvae can be mounted on vaselined slides or on slides with supported coverslips. They are usually quite active, but can be tangled in a few shreds of lens paper or lightly anaesthetized with a dilute solution of chloral hydrate. Due to the opacity of the living eggs, the details of maturation, fusion of the germ nuclei, and cleavage are best studied from prepared whole-mounts.

E. Preparation of Slides:

Sections: In preparing sections it is advisable to fix, embed, and section eggs while they are still in the capsules.

Whole mounts: Fixation. Obtain decapsulated eggs as outlined above. After freeing the eggs, agitate them by gentle rotary rinsing with a pipette, in order to wash them and concentrate them in the center of the dish. Change the water two or three times. Concentrate the eggs and, using a pipette, transfer them to a vial three-quarters filled with Kleinenberg's picro-sulfuric fixative. Fix the eggs for 15 minutes.

Remove the fixative using a pipette of small diameter, and then fill the vial with 70% alcohol. Wash in 70% alcohol until the eggs are white; it is advisable to avoid a prolonged washing, since the stain employed is best when it does not penetrate the macromeres. The latter should therefore be left slightly acid. Thus, the eggs are removed from 70% alcohol immediately after the last wash which removes no picric acid from them, hydrated in 50% and 35% alcohols and washed thoroughly in two or three changes of water.

Staining. After washing with water, fill the vial with undiluted Mayer's haemalum, and stain for 5 to 10 minutes. For the polar body stages, a staining time of 5 to 7 minutes is usually sufficient. After staining, wash thoroughly in water, dehydrate, and clear in xylol. Remove the xylol used in clearing and replace it with a small amount of thin damar.

Mounting. Coverslips must be supported. For this purpose it is convenient to use paper squares the size of $7/8$-inch coverslips. A hole is punched in the center of each square with a paper punch. In mounting, the squares are cleared in xylol, and fixed to the center of the slides by adding three or four drops of thin damar before the xylol evaporates. When the paper mounts have dried, the eggs are removed from the vial, in which they are stored, by the use of a pipette drawn out to a long taper and having a small diameter at its tip. The eggs are allowed to settle toward the tip of the pipette, and one drop of the egg-damar suspension is placed in the center depression of each paper mount. The damar is allowed to dry to the point of formation of a thin film, in order that the eggs may remain dispersed and with the macromere quartet adjacent to the slide when mounted. Apply thick damar to the edge of the paper mount, immerse a #0 coverslip in xylol and apply it to the slide over the paper mount.

An alternative method:

1. Fix for 30 to 120 minutes in Mayer's picro-sulfuric fixative.
2. Wash in 35%, 50% and 70% alcohols; leave in the latter until the yellow color ceases to come out.
3. 50% and 35% alcohols, to water—5 minutes in each.
4. Stain in Conklin's haematoxylin (one part Delafield's haematoxylin in four or five volumes of distilled water, to which is added one drop of the picro-sulfuric fixative for each ten cc. of the diluted stain) : 5 to 10 minutes.

5. Wash in water, dehydrate 5 minutes in each alcohol; 10 minutes in 95% alcohol; two changes of absolute alcohol; xylol.

6. Mount in thick balsam or damar with supported coverslips.

NORMAL DEVELOPMENT:

A. The Ovum: The unsegmented ovum of both species is nearly spherical. It contains a small quantity of yolk granules which are more concentrated, and larger, at the vegetal pole. There is no egg membrane. The ovum of *C. fornicata* measures approximately 182 microns in diameter, that of *C. plana* about 136 microns. The eggs are deposited in transparent capsules (about 240 eggs per capsule for *C. fornicata,* and between 64 and 176 per capsule for *C. plana*), before maturation begins.

B. Cleavage: Two polar bodies are extruded and remain attached for some time. The pronuclei associate, but do not fuse, and the separate maternal and paternal portions of the zygote nucleus remain distinct at least until the 69-cell stage. Crepidula thus illustrates clearly the condition known as gonomery.

Cleavage is spiral and regular, and similar in all four quadrants as far as the 24-cell stage. Gastrulation is by epiboly, which is not accompanied by invagination. The mouth appears near the mid-ventral surface soon after the blastopore closes at this point (Conklin, 1897). Further details and illustrations of these early stages can be found in two papers by Conklin (1897, 1902).

C. Rate of Development: Development proceeds slowly. Not less than four hours elapse between fertilization and first cleavage. In both species, hatching of the fully-formed veliger takes about four weeks. The free-swimming period of *C. fornicata* probably lasts about two to three weeks (Conklin, 1897).

D. Later Stages of Development and Metamorphosis: There is no typical trochophore stage; the gastrula transforms directly into a veliger larva. The veliger has a bilobed, ciliated velum which develops purple pigment along its margin. The mouth and foot, containing a pair of statocysts, are on the ventral side. The head vesicle, the pair of pigmented eyes with lenses, the heart and oesophagus are dorsal. The digestive tract is well developed; stomach, liver and intestine can be seen. The anus lies on the right side, and the external kidneys are lateral to the foot. At metamorphosis, the head vesicle decreases rapidly in size, the velum is largely, if not entirely, absorbed, the foot becomes enlarged, and the shell, which during the veliger stage was of the spiral type, takes on the form characteristic of the adult. Consult the paper by Conklin (1897) for further details and illustrations of the larval stages of these species. A good description of organogenesis in *C. adunca* can be found in a paper by Moritz (1939).

REFERENCES:

BUMPUS, H. C., 1898. The breeding of animals at Woods Holl during the months of June, July and August. *Science,* **8**: 850-858.

COE, W. R., 1936. Sexual phases in Crepidula. *J. Exp. Zool.,* **72**: 455-477.

COE, W. R., 1938. Conditions influencing change of sex in mollusks of the genus Crepidula. *J. Exp. Zool.,* **77**: 401-424.

COE, W. R., 1948. Nutrition and sexuality in protandric gastropods of the genus Crepidula. *Biol. Bull.,* **94**: 158-160.

CONKLIN, E. G., 1897. The embryology of Crepidula, a contribution to the cell lineage and early development of some marine gasteropods. *J. Morph.,* **13**: 1-226.

CONKLIN, E. G., 1902. Karyokinesis and Cytokinesis in the maturation, fertilization and cleavage of Crepidula and other Gasteropoda. I. Karyokinesis. II. Cytokinesis. *J. Acad. Nat. Sci., Philadelphia, ser. 2,* **12**: 1–121.

CONKLIN, E. G., 1937. The genus Crepidula. *In:* Culture Methods for Invertebrate Animals, edit. by Galtsoff *et al.,* Comstock, Ithaca, pp. 531–532.

GOULD, H. N., 1950. Culturing *Crepidula plana* in running sea water. *Science,* **111**: 602–603.

MORITZ, C. E., 1938. The anatomy of the gasteropod *Crepidula adunca* Sowerby. *Univ. California Publ. Zool.,* **43**: 83–92.

MORITZ, C. E., 1939. Organogenesis in the gasteropod *Crepidula adunca* Sowerby. *Univ. California Publ. Zool.,* **43**: 217–248.

MOLLUSCA

(Gastropoda)

Haminea (formerly *Bulla*) *solitaria*

LIVING MATERIAL:

These small, hermaphroditic gastropods have a reduced shell and a relatively large foot. The adults burrow into the mud, about half an inch below the surface (although the egg-capsules are deposited at the surface), and can be collected from the mud flats of Hadley Harbor, close to the Middle Gutter, at Woods Hole, Mass. Although the adults are quite abundant during the breeding season, they seem to disappear during the rest of the year.

BREEDING SEASON:

June to September, with the peak between July 15 and August 15.

PROCURING AND HANDLING MATERIAL:

A. Care of Adults: If the adults are placed in large fingerbowls covered with cheesecloth, and supplied with a gentle stream of sea water, they will live and breed in the laboratory without any other special care.

B. Procuring Fertilized Ova: There is apparently no relation between capsule production and time of day. Animals have been known to produce, on the average, three to four capsules daily over a period of three weeks. During the last week, however, both eggs and capsules may be abnormal. The number of eggs in each capsule varies, but the average content is about two thousand (Smallwood, 1904b).

C. Preparation of Cultures: Eggs will develop normally in open fingerbowls of sea water if they are kept cool on a water table and have a daily change of sea water. This treatment allows normal development, even of eggs in ruptured capsules.

When the free-swimming larvae appear, they should be decanted daily to fingerbowls of fresh sea water. They will live for four to five days under these conditions. After this time, many die from starvation or because they become trapped and held in the surface film.

NORMAL DEVELOPMENT:

A. The Ovum: The fertilized, uncleaved egg is small, having a diameter of about 80 microns. It is enclosed in a thin, structureless membrane, and is very opaque. The ova are laid in spherical, soft gelatinous capsules with no apparent orientation. Capsules produced by laboratory animals average about half an inch in diameter, and, as noted above, contain about two thousand eggs, although this number varies considerably.

B. Cleavage: Shortly after fertilization two polar bodies are extruded. Cleavage is total and spiral, and often unequal. Smallwood (1904a) observed that in about 30 per cent of the eggs, one blastomere was markedly larger than the other.

141

The micromeres are strikingly large and clear. Gastrulation is apparently by epiboly.

C. Time Table of Development: The following schedule is given for temperatures of 24 to 26° C. Times are calculated from the appearance of the first polar body, which is reported by Smallwood (1904a) to appear about 15 minutes after the egg is deposited.

Stage	Time
First cleavage	85 minutes
Second cleavage	120 minutes
Third cleavage	200 minutes
Gastrulation	24 hours
Young veliger	48 hours
Well-formed, rotating veliger	72 hours
Hatching	96 hours

D. Later Stages of Development: A typical gastropod veliger is formed from the gastrula. In young forms, an opaque digestive tract can be seen, and beside it another dark mass which is probably unabsorbed yolk. A clear vesicle, which may represent a head kidney, is sometimes visible. In older veligers the alimentary tract becomes more complex; a triangular mouth, ciliated oesophagus, large ciliated stomach and a narrow intestine with one coil may be seen. A dark lobe, the liver, lies to the left of the stomach. An eyespot and a pair of statocysts develop. At hatching, the veliger is enclosed in a curved shell; the large, two-lobed velum, which protrudes from it, propels the free-swimming larva through the water.

REFERENCES:

BERRILL, N. J., 1931. The natural history of *Bulla hydatis* Linn. *J. Mar. Biol. Assoc.,* **17**: 567–571.

SMALLWOOD, M., 1901. The centrosome in the maturation and fertilization of *Bulla solitaria. Biol. Bull.,* **2**: 145–154.

SMALLWOOD, W. M., 1904a. Natural history of *Haminea solitaria* Say. *Amer. Nat.,* **38**: 207–225.

SMALLWOOD, W. M., 1904b. The maturation, fertilization, and early cleavage of *Haminea solitaria* (Say). *Bull. Mus. Comp. Zool., Harvard,* **45**: 259–318.

MOLLUSCA

(Gastropoda)

Ilyanassa obsoleta *

LIVING MATERIAL:

This snail is commonly found on mud flats in shallow water, and is abundant at Woods Hole, Mass. The species is dioecious.

BREEDING SEASON:

Egg-laying in the natural habitat at Woods Hole has been recorded from the last week in April (Mead, 1898) to mid-July. However, snails collected in June and kept in running sea water in the laboratory will continue to deposit egg-masses through August. Toward the end of the summer, unfertilized eggs are often deposited, and fertilized eggs may be fragile. Snails collected at Woods Hole from December 1 on through the spring months will, if kept in aquaria at room temperatures, lay abundantly. Difficulty has been encountered in obtaining eggs from snails collected between mid-summer and December (Clement, personal communication).

PROCURING AND HANDLING MATERIAL:

A. Care of Adults: These snails are very hardy and can be maintained in the laboratory in good breeding condition for a prolonged period. A new batch of adults usually takes several days to become acclimatized before they begin to spawn. As many as 250 animals can be kept in a large aquarium, provided there is a continuous flow of fresh sea water; however, 100 snails will provide an adequate supply of eggs for most purposes.

One or more minced clams should be provided for food every day.

A smaller number of adults (about 25 to 30) can be kept for at least a month in standing, aerated sea water, if they are removed to a separate container for feeding and then returned to the aquarium. This makes possible their use for certain types of embryological experiments at inland laboratories, where running sea water is not available. See "Special Comments" below.

If the wooden ends of the aquaria commonly used at Woods Hole are covered with removable glass plates, collection of egg capsules is greatly facilitated.

B. Procuring Fertilized Ova: Fertilization is internal, and 30 to 300 eggs are deposited in transparent capsules, which are produced singly or in groups. The snails usually climb up the sides of the aquarium to spawn, but congregate at the bottom of the tank to feed. If an irregular feeding schedule is followed, eggs will not be deposited on the day after the animals are fed.

Freshly-deposited capsules may be obtained if the snails are watched to determine the time of oviposition. The capsules are first visible at the pedal gland opening at the anterior, median part of the foot. After a capsule is fastened to

---

* We should like to express our appreciation to Dr. A. C. Clement for his helpful suggestions, and for much of the information on which this section is based.

the glass, the snail can be gently removed and the capsule transferred to a watch glass of pasteurized sea water (prepared by heating the water to 70 or 80° C. for 15 minutes, cooling it and shaking to aerate).

Clement (1952 and personal communication) describes the following methods for obtaining Ilyanassa eggs. A handy device for scraping the capsules from the aquarium walls is a razor blade mounted in a long wooden handle. The capsules are picked up and transferred with a long, wide-mouthed pipette. Excess jelly and the non-pasteurized sea water can be removed from the egg-capsule, before it is placed in the watch glass, by gently rolling it on a piece of paper towel or filter paper.

Using a binocular dissecting microscope, hold the capsule against the bottom of the watch glass, with a sharpened dissecting needle. With a pair of curved cuticle scissors, snip off the end of the capsule at a point where the eggs are not clustered. They are held in the capsule by a thick jelly which is soluble in water and which will ultimately dissolve. The eggs may be more rapidly freed, however, by exerting a very slow pressure on the capsule with a second needle.

C. Preparation of Cultures: Using a pipette, transfer the eggs to 35-mm. stender dishes (half-full of pasteurized sea water), placing about 10 to 20 eggs in a dish. Cover the dishes and place them in a large fingerbowl on a water table. Using this method, perfectly normal veliger larvae can be reared from decapsulated eggs (Clement, 1952).

D. Methods of Observation: Nuclear details of maturation, polar body formation and early cleavage stages are easily seen in fixed and stained, flattened, coverslip preparations. Accounts of two methods are given by Morgan (1933) and Tyler (1946).

The internal structure of the living veliger may be observed quite clearly in specimens mounted under a supported coverslip. The action of the velar cilia can be stopped by mounting the larvae in a 1% solution of urethane (Clement, 1952).

NORMAL DEVELOPMENT:

A. The Ovum: The fertilized, uncleaved egg is spherical, and measures about 166 microns in diameter (Clement, 1952). No membrane is visible. The ovum is very opaque, and contains a cap of granular cytoplasm around the animal pole, which is rich in mitochondria and lipid droplets (Clement and Lehmann, 1956). The remainder of the ovum is filled with coarse yolk spherules, which are largest in the vegetal hemisphere. In sea water, the egg tends to orient with the animal pole floating upward.

B. Fertilization and Cleavage: The history of the egg from deposition to first cleavage has been described by Morgan (1933). In the majority of inseminated, freshly-deposited ova, the first polar spindle is forming deep within the cytoplasmic cap; in others, some variation may be observed. After its formation, the spindle moves toward the polar surface and takes up a radial position. The first polar body is extruded shortly after this. As it is forming, the first polar (yolk or anti-polar) lobe appears. This lobe is inconspicuous; the only indication of its presence is a slight elongation along the polar axis, which gives the egg a top-like appearance. It is soon withdrawn and the egg remains spherical for about ten minutes or less. A second polar lobe develops and continues to enlarge for some time after the second polar body is fully formed. The second lobe is very broad and is more constricted from the rest of the cytoplasm than the first lobe. After about an hour the second lobe is resorbed, the egg rounds up, and the pronuclei come together and enlarge.

As the first cleavage spindle forms, the third polar lobe appears. In development and form, it is much like the second, although it ultimately becomes more constricted from the rest of the cell. After it has reached maximum size, the upper hemisphere of the egg broadens and flattens at the pole. A constriction appears in the region of the polar bodies, indicating the approach of the first cleavage. As the cleavage furrow cuts deeper between the blastomeres, the constriction delimiting the polar lobe also grows deeper, until a stage is reached where it is impossible to tell into which of the two blastomeres the lobe will flow. This is the trefoil stage. It lasts for several minutes; then a short, clear, yolk-free stalk can be seen connecting the polar lobe to one of the blastomeres. The stalk soon broadens as the contents of the lobe flow into the blastomere. The resulting blastomeres are unequal in size, for the larger CD cell contains the contents of the polar lobe. The fourth and final polar lobe appears during second cleavage in the vegetal region of the CD cell. The fourth lobe is of the same size as the third. After the cleavage is completed, there are three small cells: A, B and C, and a large cell, D, which contains the lobe substance. The first quartet of small, clear micromeres is cut off by a typical dexiotropic division; further divisions are very similar to those of Crepidula. The papers of Crampton (1896) and Clement (1952) may be consulted for further details.

C. Time Table of Development: Due to differences in maturity of the freshly-deposited ova, it is difficult to establish an exact chronology of development. After extrusion of the first polar lobe (between 15 and 50 minutes after egg deposition, according to Morgan, 1933), development is quite constant. The following table gives approximate rates of development at a room temperature of 23 to 24° C. The time is recorded from the initial appearance of the first anti-polar lobe.

Stage	Time
Egg spherical, first lobe withdrawn	11 minutes
Beginning of second polar lobe	21 minutes
Egg spherical, second lobe withdrawn	1 hour, 21 minutes
Appearance of third polar lobe	1 hour, 59 minutes
First cleavage	2 hours, 59 minutes
Second cleavage	4 hours, 9 minutes
Third cleavage	5 hours, 9 minutes
Ciliated, rotating embryo	2 days
Veliger	4–5 days

D. Later Stages of Development: The very young embryo is ciliated and rotates within the capsule; it contains a mass of opaque endoderm. There is no trochophore stage. The young veliger (five or six days) has a pigmented oesophagus, stomach and intestine. The velum bears large cilia and has a pigmented rim. Shell, operculum, foot, eyes, otocysts and heart are easily seen. At hatching (about seven to eight days), the larva swims actively by means of the velar cilia. The yolk is soon absorbed and details of the digestive tract may be seen (Clement, 1952).

SPECIAL COMMENTS:

This material can readily be used for class experiments in non-marine locations, since the animals breed readily after shipment in damp-pack. Slices of commercial frozen shrimp are a convenient and satisfactory food.

REFERENCES:

ANKEL, W. E., 1929. Über die Bildung der Eikapsel bei Nassa-Arten. *Verh. d. Deutsch. Zool. Ges.,* **33**: 219–230.

BUTROS, J. M., 1956. Simultaneous effects of metabolic inhibitors on the viscosity, surface rigidity and cleavage in Ilyanassa eggs. *J. Cell. Comp. Physiol.,* **47**: 341–356.

CLEMENT, A. C., 1935. The formation of giant polar bodies in centrifuged eggs of Ilyanassa. *Biol. Bull.,* **69**: 403–414.

CLEMENT, A. C., 1952. Experimental studies on germinal localization in Ilyanassa. I. The role of the polar lobe in determination of the cleavage pattern and its influence in later development. *J. Exp. Zool.,* **121**: 593–625.

CLEMENT, A. C., 1956. Experimental studies on germinal localization in Ilyanassa. II. The development of isolated blastomeres. *J. Exp. Zool.,* **132**: 427–446.

CLEMENT, A. C., AND F. E. LEHMANN, 1956. Über das Verteilungsmuster von Mitochondrien und Lipoidtropfen während der Furchung des Eies von *Ilyanassa obsoleta* (Mollusca, Prosobranchia). *Naturwiss.,* **43**: 478–479.

CRAMPTON, H. E., JR., 1896. Experimental studies on gasteropod development. *Arch. f. Entw.,* **3**: 1–19.

DAN, K., AND J. C. DAN, 1942. Behavior of the cell surface during cleavage. IV. Polar lobe formation and cleavage of the eggs of *Ilyanassa obsoleta* Say. *Cytologia,* **12**: 246–261.

MEAD, A. D., 1898. The breeding of animals at Woods Holl during the month of April, 1898. *Science,* **7**: 702–704.

MORGAN, T. H., 1933. The formation of the antipolar lobe in Ilyanassa. *J. Exp. Zool.,* **64**: 433–467.

MORGAN, T. H., 1935a. Centrifuging the eggs of Ilyanassa in reverse. *Biol. Bull.,* **68**: 268–279.

MORGAN, T. H., 1935b. The separation of the egg of Ilyanassa into two parts by centrifuging. *Biol. Bull.,* **68**: 280–295.

MORGAN, T. H., 1935c. The rhythmic changes in form of the isolated antipolar lobe of Ilyanassa. *Biol. Bull.,* **68**: 296–299.

MORGAN, T. H., 1936. Further experiments on the formation of the antipolar lobe of Ilyanassa. *J. Exp. Zool.,* **74**: 381–425.

MORGAN, T. H., 1937. The behavior of the maturation spindles in polar fragments of eggs of Ilyanassa obtained by centrifuging. *Biol. Bull.,* **72**: 88–98.

PELSENEER, P., 1911. Recherches sur l'embryologie des Gastropodes. *Mém. Acad. Roy., Belgique, ser. 2, Coll. IN-4°,* **3**: 1–167.

TYLER, A., 1946. Rapid slide-making method for preparation of eggs, protozoa, etc. *Coll. Net,* **19**: 50.

MOLLUSCA

(Gastropoda)

Lacuna vincta (Lacuna divaricata)

LIVING MATERIAL:

The adults are common on sea-weed at Nobska Beach.

BREEDING SEASON:

This has not been investigated in the Woods Hole, Mass., area. In European waters, the animals breed from January until June.

PROCURING AND HANDLING MATERIAL:

A. Care of Adults: Breeding adults can be maintained in laboratory aquaria. They should be supplied with Fucus or other sea-weed, for, as noted above, it is on these plants that the eggs are usually deposited.

B. Obtaining Gametes: The eggs are deposited in a clear, gelatinous capsule, which is covered by a thin, lens-shaped pellicle. The egg-mass is in the form of a ring which is often oval in outline. Although it measures only about 3 mm. across when freshly laid, it swells enormously during the course of development. Photographs of the egg-mass are available in the paper by Hertling and Ankel (1927).

NORMAL DEVELOPMENT:

A. Egg Characteristics: The eggs are golden, cream or greenish in color, and measurements of their diameter range from 103 to 180 microns (Lebour, 1937; Hertling and Ankel, 1927). Each egg is surrounded by an inner membrane and an outer capsule which swells as development proceeds. The number of eggs in each mass is large, varying between 1000 and 1200. They are sensitive to rising temperature, but apparently can withstand quite rigorous experimental treatment (Hertling, 1928).

B. Cleavage and Gastrulation: Cleavage is total, equal and of a typical spiral nature. Information concerning the nature of gastrulation is apparently not available.

C. Rate of Development: Development is slow, but fluctuates widely with the temperature. Hertling (1928) states that by the thirteenth day, the velum is visible. By the fifteenth day, the larvae are showing lively movements, and by the seventeenth day, the shell *anlage* appears. Hatching occurs on the twenty-sixth day. The exact temperature for the above developmental schedule is not given, but it is presumed to be slightly below 20° C.

D. Later Stages of Development: Lebour (1937) describes the newly-hatched veliger as having well-formed eyes, otocysts, foot, and operculum. The mouth is open. The shell consists of 1½ whorls, and is clear, colorless, and lacking in sculpturing. The velum has long cilia, and is marked by a brownish-red border. For diagrams of the larva, consult the papers of Lebour (1937) and Hertling (1928).

REFERENCES:

HERTLING, H., 1928. Beobachtungen und Versuche an den Eiern von Littorina und Lacuna. *Wiss. Meeres. Komm. Unt. Deutsch. Meere, N. F., Abt. Helgoland,* **17** (2) : 1-49.

HERTLING, H., AND W. E. ANKEL, 1927. Bemerkungen über Laich und Jugendformen von Littorina und Lacuna. *Wiss. Meeres. Komm. Unt. Deutsch. Meere, N. F., Abt. Helgoland,* **16** (7) : 1-13.

LEBOUR, M. V., 1937. The eggs and larvae of the British prosobranchs with special reference to those living in the plankton. *J. Mar. Biol. Assoc.,* **22** : 105-166.

MOLLUSCA

(Gastropoda)

Littorina obtusata (*L. littoralis*)

LIVING MATERIAL:

The adults are very abundant on fronds of Ascophyllum and Fucus in the Woods Hole, Mass., region. They can be shaken from the vegetation into a scrim dip-net. The animals are smaller than *L. littorea* and larger than *L. saxatilis*. The shell is almost without striations, and is compressed so that the spire seems to be lacking.

BREEDING SEASON:

This form has not been studied at Woods Hole. European workers (Pelseneer, 1911; Delsman, 1914) report that it breeds during the spring and summer months in European waters.

PROCURING AND HANDLING MATERIAL:

A. Care of Adults: The animals may be kept in aquaria supplied with running sea water; they should be furnished with a supply of sea-weed which must be renewed from time to time.

B. Obtaining Gametes: The egg-masses are deposited daily on the sea-weed (apparently never on the sides of the aquarium). If the masses are kept in running sea water, the eggs develop readily.

NORMAL DEVELOPMENT:

A. Egg Characteristics: The eggs are laid in oval or kidney-shaped gelatinous masses on sea-weed. The gelatinous material is transparent and faintly yellow in color. An egg-mass measures, on the average, 7 by 3 mm. (See the paper by Hertling and Ankel, 1927, for a diagram of the egg-mass.) The eggs are contained in a capsule and surrounded by an albuminous fluid; they are deposited in the germinal vesicle stage, but this lasts only a short time before the vesicle breaks down. Measurements of the egg diameter vary from 205 microns (Delsman, 1914) to 250 microns (Lebour, 1937). Fertilization apparently takes place before the eggs are laid.

B. Cleavage and Gastrulation: Cleavage is total, equal and spiral, with micromeres larger than those of *L. littorea* or *L. saxatilis*. Gastrulation is by epiboly and invagination.

C. Rate of Development: Development is said to be slow; at 13–14° C., the embryos hatch in three weeks, having passed the veliger stage within the capsule.

D. Later Stages of Development: Although the veliger stage is spent within the capsule, a well-formed velum is present. The veligers have a foot, operculum, single-whorled shell, kidney, ganglia, and a complex gut. At the time of emergence from the capsule, the larvae are fully-formed, crawling snails. See the papers by Delsman (1914) and Pelseneer (1911) for diagrams.

149

SPECIAL COMMENTS:

This species of Littorina is moderately common at Woods Hole, although *L. littorea* is found in greater abundance. The eggs of *L. littorea,* however, are laid in transparent capsules (with from one to nine eggs per capsule, according to Bequaert, 1943), and are planktonic, so that they are somewhat difficult to obtain and to study. The ova of *L. obtusata* are plentiful and relatively easy to study.

REFERENCES:

BEQUAERT, J. C., 1943. The genus Littorina in the western Atlantic. Johnsonia, no. 7, pp. 1–27.

DELSMAN, H. C., 1914. Entwicklungsgeschichte von *Littorina obtusata. Tijdschr. Nederl. Dierkundige Vereeniging, ser. 2,* **13**: 170–340.

HERTLING, H., AND W. E. ANKEL, 1927. Bemerkungen über Laich und Jugendformen von Littorina und Lacuna. *Wiss. Meeres. Komm. Unt. Deutsch. Meere, N. F., Abt. Helgoland,* **16** (7): 1–13.

LEBOUR, M. V., 1937. The eggs and larvae of the British prosobranchs with special reference to those living in the plankton. *J. Mar. Biol. Assoc.,* **22**: 105–166.

LINKE, O., 1935. Der Laiche von *Littorina (Melaraphe) neritoides* L. *Zool. Anz.,* **112**: 57–62.

PELSENEER, P., 1911. Recherches sur l'embryologie des Gastropodes. *Mém. Acad. Roy. Belgique, sér. 2,* **3**: 1–167.

MOLLUSCA

(Gastropoda)

Thais (formerly *Purpura* or *Nucella*) *lapillus*

LIVING MATERIAL:

Both adults and egg-capsules of this species are common on rocks in shallow water. They may be easily collected at low tide at Cuttyhunk or at Plymouth, Mass., where they are abundant. The sexes are separate.

BREEDING SEASON:

The limits of the breeding season have not been determined for the Woods Hole region, but there is evidence that the animals breed in early summer. At Plymouth, England, spawning occurs throughout the year, but the egg-capsules are most abundant in early summer.

PROCURING AND HANDLING MATERIAL:

A. Care of Adults: Only animals with a thick, toothed lip on the shell aperture should be selected for breeding purposes; individuals with a thin lip are immature (Moore, 1936). They can be kept in flowing sea water in an aquarium with a right-angled edge, or with a wire-screen top, to prevent their escape. Barnacles should be supplied regularly for food.

B. Procuring Fertilized Ova: Oviposition in the laboratory has been reported by Wilson (1900), but Portmann (1931) was unsuccessful in his attempts to obtain eggs in captivity. He recommends the use of capsules collected from their natural habitat.

C. Preparation of Cultures: Open the capsules by clipping off one end with a pair of fine scissors. If the capsules are now everted, the eggs will drop out of the cut end. Since the young embryos do not seem to develop normally unless they are associated with the yolk mass, it is doubtful whether they could be cultured outside the capsule. However, the veligers may be reared in fingerbowls of filtered sea water.

NORMAL DEVELOPMENT:

A. The Ovum: The mature ovum measures approximately 180 microns in diameter (Selenka, 1872), and is enclosed within a very delicate membrane. Individual egg-capsules are not formed, but 500 to 1000 ova are deposited with a clear gelatinous material in a long, slender vase-shaped capsule (8–9 mm. high, and 2 mm. across). The capsules are attached to the substrate by a short stalk with an expanded base.

B. Fertilization and Cleavage: Fertilization is internal and no membrane is elevated. Only a very few of the eggs (12 to 30, according to Carpenter, 1857) develop into normal embryos. The remainder never complete the maturation divisions, but instead, they fuse to form a column of yolk in the middle of the capsule, which is eventually consumed by the normal embryos. In normally

151

fertilized eggs, cleavage is total, unequal and spiral with prominent polar lobes formed. Gastrulation is by epiboly. Further details can be found in papers by Selenka (1872) and Pelseneer (1911).

C. Rate of Development: Development of this species is slow. The compact yolk mass is formed by the time gastrulation is completed, which is between four and eight days after fertilization. The embryos become attached to the developing yolk mass, which is usually absorbed by the tenth day. The young snails hatch from the capsules in about four months.

D. Later Stages of Development and Metamorphosis: The embryo, which attaches to the yolk mass, has a round, sparsely ciliated velum, a shell gland, a small foot, a pair of larval kidneys, and a large stomodeum and oesophagus. The intestine is short or lacking. Organogenesis ceases during the parasitic period, but after the yolk has been stored in the intestine, the embryo transforms into a typical veliger, with a well-formed velum, whorled shell, otocysts, eyespots, and a complex digestive tract. As metamorphosis approaches, the early larval heart and kidneys are replaced by adult organs. Tentacles appear and the velum slowly regresses. The metamorphosed larva, which emerges from the top of the capsule, is a miniature of the adult snail.

REFERENCES:

CARPENTER, W. B., 1855. On the development of the embryo of *Purpura lapillus*. *Trans. Micr. Soc., London,* **3**: 17–30.

CARPENTER, W. B., 1857. Remarks on MM. Koren and Danielssen's researches on the development of *Purpura lapillus*. *Ann. and Mag. Nat. Hist., ser. 2,* **20**: 16–21.

KOREN, J., AND D. C. DANIELSSEN, 1857a. Researches on the development of the Pectinibranchiata. *Ann. and Mag. Nat. Hist., ser. 2,* **19**: 353–366.

KOREN, J., AND D. C. DANIELSSEN, 1857b. Researches on the development of the Pectinibranchiata. *Ann. and Mag. Nat. Hist., ser. 2,* **19**: 433–442.

McMURRICH, J. P., 1886. A contribution to the embryology of the prosobranch gasteropods. *Stud. Biol. Lab., Johns Hopkins Univ.,* **3**: 403–450.

MOORE, H. B., 1936. The biology of *Purpura lapillus*. I. Shell variation in relation to environment. *J. Mar. Biol. Assoc.,* **21**: 61–89.

MOORE, H. B., 1938. The biology of *Purpura lapillus*. III. Life history and relation to environmental factors. *J. Mar. Biol. Assoc.,* **23**: 67–74.

PELSENEER, P., 1911. Recherches sur l'embryologie des Gasteropodes. *Mém. Acad. Roy., Belgique, ser. 2,* **3**: 1–167.

PORTMANN, A., 1925. Der Einfluss der Nähreier auf die Larvenentwicklung von Buccinum und Purpura. *Zeitschr. f. Morph. u. Okol. Tiere,* **3**: 526–541.

PORTMANN, A., 1931. Die Entstehung der Nähreier bei *Purpura lapillus* durch atypische Befruchtung. *Zeitschr. f. Zellforsch. u. mikr. Anat.,* **12**: 167–178.

SELENKA, E., 1872. Die Anlage der Keimblätter bei *Purpura lapillus*. *Niederländ. Arch. f. Zool.,* **1**: 211–218.

WILSON, H. V., 1900. Marine biology at Beaufort. *Amer. Nat.,* **34**: 339–360.

MOLLUSCA

(GASTROPODA)

Urosalpinx cinerea

LIVING MATERIAL:

The adults and vase-shaped egg-capsules of the oyster drill are found on rocks between tide levels. Near Woods Hole, Mass., they are abundant at Grassy Island (the Spindle) and at Sheep Pen Cove on Nonamessett Island. The sexes are separate. Males are easily recognized by the long, curved penis, which is located on the right side of the body behind the eye.

BREEDING SEASON:

Federighi (1931) and Nelson (1931) both observed that breeding begins when the water temperature has remained for at least a week above 20° C. At Woods Hole, the season begins late in May (Bumpus, 1898), and probably continues throughout the summer.

PROCURING AND HANDLING MATERIAL:

A. Care of Adults: The adults should be kept in aquaria provided with running sea water, and will remain in good condition if fed occasionally with barnacles, small mussels or clams. Food debris should be removed before putrefaction sets in. A ten-gallon tank has been found adequate for as many as 300 drills if it is kept free of debris (Federighi, 1937).

B. Procuring Fertilized Ova: Copulation probably occurs at night. The female creeps to the upper levels of the tank to spawn, and does so only once per season. On the average, oviposition lasts about a week; between 28 (Federighi, 1931) and 50 capsules (Nelson, 1931) are produced. In 24 hours a female deposits approximately four egg-capsules, containing a varying number of eggs. The capsules are 4–12 mm. high, with an operculum at the free end; the outer of the two capsule layers can be peeled off readily, permitting better observation of the embryos (Hancock, 1956). Embryos in different stages of development are contained within the capsules. At hatching, the young drill is able to feed on young oyster spat or thin-shelled Crepidula.

NORMAL DEVELOPMENT:

A. The Ovum: The fertilized, uncleaved egg is spherical, measuring approximately 240 microns in diameter (Lebour, 1937). It is white in color and opaque, and lacks a membrane. The eggs are deposited with an albuminous substance, which provides nourishment for the developing embryos, in a yellow, urn-shaped capsule. This has a short stem and an expanded base, and is laterally compressed. The latter feature distinguishes it from the somewhat similar capsule of Thais. (See the diagram by Federighi, 1937.)

B. Cleavage: Cleavage is unequal and spiral, with large polar lobes appearing during the first two divisions. Gastrulation is by epiboly. At about the time of

153

gastrulation, a hatching enzyme apparently is produced within the capsule; this dissolves the operculum (Hancock, 1956).

C. Rate of Development: There seems to be no detailed information pertaining to the developmental rate. The average time from fertilization to hatching at temperatures varying between 18 and 32° C. is 40 days (Federighi, 1931). Hancock (1956) reports that at temperatures of 14–21° C., the veliger stage is reached in about 24 days.

D. Later Stages of Development: Embryonic development is similar to that of most gastropods. The veliger is formed at an early stage. The foot appears precociously, before closure of the blastopore; both velum and shell are well developed. The intestine and anus are late in appearing. The velum is lost before hatching, and the young animal emerges as a well-formed snail. Details of development and figures of the larvae can be found in a paper by Brooks (1879). Hancock (1956) presents diagrams of the egg-capsules.

REFERENCES:

BROOKS, W. K., 1879. Preliminary observations upon the development of the marine prosobranchiate gasteropods. *Stud. Biol. Lab., Johns Hopkins Univ.,* **1**: no. 5, pp. 121–142.

BUMPUS, H. C., 1898. The breeding of animals at Woods Holl during the month of May, 1898. *Science,* **8**: 58–61.

CONKLIN, E. G., 1891. Preliminary note on the embryology of *Crepidula fornicata* and of *Urosalpinx cinerea. Johns Hopkins Univ. Circ.,* **10**: 89–90.

FEDERIGHI, H., 1931. Studies on the oyster drill (*Urosalpinx cinerea,* Say). *Bull. U. S. Bur. Fish.,* **47**: 85–115.

FEDERIGHI, H., 1937. Culture methods for *Urosalpinx cinerea. In:* Culture Methods for Invertebrate Animals, edit. by Galtsoff *et al.,* Comstock, Ithaca, pp. 532–536.

HANCOCK, D. A., 1956. The structure of the capsule and the hatching process in *Urosalpinx cinerea* (Say). *Proc. Zool. Soc., London,* **127**: 565–571.

LEBOUR, M. V., 1937. The eggs and larvae of the British prosobranchs with special reference to those living in the plankton. *J. Mar. Biol. Assoc.,* **22**: 105–166.

NELSON, J. R., 1931. Trapping the oyster drill. New Jersey Agric. Exp. Stat. Bull. no. 523.

MOLLUSCA

(CEPHALOPODA)

Loligo pealii

LIVING MATERIAL:

Mature animals are obtained from the fish traps at Barnstable and Buzzards Bay, and at Menemsha Bight, Martha's Vineyard, Mass. The sexes are separate. Among mature animals the males are usually longer and more slender, with the milk-white testis visible through the mantle near the posterior end; this region in the female is filled with a uniformly transparent mass of eggs. The accessory nidamental glands of the female are red during the breeding season and can usually be seen through the mantle.

Egg-strings can be collected at low tide along the sandy beaches of Nonamessett Island, where they are found floating free or attached to submerged objects in the shallow water.

BREEDING SEASON:

Females with mature eggs are available at Woods Hole, Mass., from May through July, although the majority of the animals are spent by mid-July.

PROCURING AND HANDLING MATERIAL:

A. Care of Adults: In order to keep adults even a day or two, they must be transported to the laboratory without undue disturbance in an adequate amount of sea water. Then they should be transferred to large aquaria with a constant supply of running sea water. On several occasions, the sexual activities of the adults and deposition of the egg-masses have been observed in the laboratory (Drew, 1911, 1919).

B. Procuring Gametes: Open both male and female by making a longitudinal section through the mantle from the siphon to the tip, cutting along the posterior (funnel) wall; remove the ink sac. In the female, tear the thin wall of the oviduct with forceps and shake the eggs into a large fingerbowl of sea water. If the eggs are fully mature, they separate readily from the ovary and appear as beautifully transparent as glass. Immature eggs are not transparent and will not develop. In the male, collect the bundles of spermatophores from the opening of the sperm duct, and transfer them to a watch glass of sea water. The spermatophores "explode" on contact with sea water, and a concentrated sperm suspension is thus obtained. If males are not available, sperm may be obtained from the sperm receptacle of the female, which is located in the collar between the head and the free edge of the mantle.

C. Preparation of Cultures: Add several drops of sperm suspension to the fingerbowl of eggs. After 20 to 30 minutes, transfer to a large dish filled with clean sea water. Keep the culture on a sea water table, and leave undisturbed for $2\frac{1}{2}$ to 3 hours; thereafter change the sea water at least twice a day.

Embryos of all stages are readily obtained from naturally-laid egg-strings, which can be kept in aquaria of running sea water. The egg-strings containing the older stages are usually darker and more weathered in appearance than those containing the young ones.   To release the embryos proceed as follows: Place an egg-string in a Syracuse dish.   Use two beading needles in the manner of knives cutting against one another, and cut the string in half.   Place the left needle so that the pressure forces several embryos clear of the jelly at the open end of one of the halves.   Keeping this needle in hand, puncture the chorion of one of the eggs with the tip of the right needle, and tear the chorion with a sharp jerk.   The pressure of the enclosed fluid will pop the embryo from the membrane.   When the exposed row of embryos has been removed, cut off the empty jelly and repeat the procedure.   If the eggs are not first forced clear of the jelly, the embryos are difficult to remove without injury; the older stages are procured more easily than the very young ones.

D. Methods of Observation:

To study intact spermatophores: Transfer intact spermatophores quickly into concentrated (40%) formaldehyde and fix for ten minutes.   (They will "explode" in a weaker solution.)   Rinse with distilled water for several minutes, transferring the spermatophores gradually from the formaldehyde.   Stain with Ehrlich's triacid for 5 to 10 minutes (6 drops of the stock solution to 8 cc. of distilled water; this amount will half-fill a Syracuse dish).   Rinse off the stain with distilled water and place the spermatophores on a slide under a coverslip.

To observe early development: For short periods, the developing eggs can be examined in depression slides.   To obtain a polar view of the cytoplasmic cap (which alone undergoes cleavage), it is necessary to mount the eggs in an upright position.   Place a small amount of vaseline (enough to cover the surface with a film) in a depression slide, fill the depression with sea water, add a few eggs and manipulate them with hair loops or fine needles so that they stand up.

Preparation of Slides: Because of the large amounts of yolk which they contain, squid embryos have a tendency to be friable and difficult to section, especially in the younger stages.   The amyl acetate technique may be used (see p. 225 of this manual) or the dioxan technique as outlined below:

1. Fix embryos in Bouin's solution, first anaesthetizing in sea water containing chloretone, if the embryos are highly motile.
2. Transfer the embryos from the fixative into pure dioxan.   Make two changes to fresh dioxan, at hourly intervals (total of three hours in dioxan).
3. Transfer to pure paraffin for one hour; change to a fresh paraffin bath for one hour, and then to a mixture of paraffin containing 8–10% bayberry wax for one hour.
4. Embed in paraffin-bayberry wax mixture.
5. Section at 5 or 6 microns and stain with Heidenhain's haematoxylin or with Prenant's triple stain.

NORMAL DEVELOPMENT:

A. The Unfertilized Ovum: The mature egg, from the oviduct of the female, is surrounded by a thick, closely applied, transparent chorion.   At the pointed end of the egg, there is a depression in the chorion and a minute canal, the micropyle, extending through it.   The opposite end of the egg is blunt, and the region between shows a bilaterality.   The more convex side is the future "anterior" or mouth side of the embryo. The egg is large and somewhat elongated in shape; it measures 1500 to 1600 microns in length and 1000 to 1200 microns in diameter (Williams, 1910). A thin cytoplasmic cap covers the yolk at the pointed pole; this cap will give rise to the embryonic structures.

The inseminated eggs are embedded in a gelatinous matrix, which is produced by glands of the oviduct, and covered by a jelly-membrane produced by the nidamental glands. The eggs in their jelly-coats are wound spirally around a central core.

B. The Spermatophore: This unique structure consists essentially of an outer envelope and a central core, with a fluid-filled space between. The envelope has a double wall, the outer and middle tunics, and at its small tip-end, an opening sealed by a cap bearing a long thin cap thread. The central core is attached at this "oral" end. It is made up of the elongated, opaque sperm mass and an ejaculatory apparatus, with flask-shaped cement body and spiral filament. The ejaculatory apparatus is enclosed within three membranes, the most conspicuous being the middle membrane. It is relatively thick and extends from the cement body to the cap end where it is permanently fused to the outer tunic. The outer membrane also begins at the cement body, but it is closely applied to the inner tunic, a structure which also encloses the sperm mass. The "oral" end of the inner tunic and outer membrane can be easily identified as a thickened ring around the middle membrane at a short distance from the cap.

When the spermatophore "explodes," the entire contents of the capsule evaginate at the "oral" end. The evaginated inner tunic and outer membrane form the sperm reservoir after the "explosion." During evagination the cement gland reaches the surface and bursts, releasing cement which forms a seal at one end of the reservoir. The middle membrane opens and is lost, along with the outer envelope of the spermatophore. The sperm, mixed with a gelatinous mass, ooze out slowly from the opposite, open end of the sperm reservoir; this process may extend over a period of hours or even days. Further details and illustrations of the spermatophore are to be found in papers by Drew (1911, 1919).

C. Fertilization and Cleavage: The entrance of the sperm through the micropyle of an inseminated egg is soon followed by a withdrawal of the cytoplasmic cap from the chorion, leaving a clear perivitelline space. Within an hour, two polar bodies are formed (Hoadley, 1930).

Cleavage is meroblastic, and, in contrast to other molluscan eggs, not spiral. The first cleavage plane coincides with the median plane of the future embryo (Watase, 1891). At the end of the first day, there is a gradual extension of the blastoderm about the yolk. The "blastocones," which are supposed to give rise to the yolk epithelium, are not very distinct in Loligo. The thickening of the margin of the blastoderm denotes the formation of the entomesoderm, and is thus the beginning of gastrulation.

D. Time Table of Development: There is considerable variation due to temperature differences. The following table gives only a rough approximation of the times after insemination at which given stages are reached.

Stage	Time
First polar body	20 minutes
Second polar body	1 hour

Stage	Time
First cleavage	3 hours
Blastoderm over top of egg	12 hours
"Gastrula:" thickened peripheral ring	24 hours
Blastoderm halfway over egg	2 days
Blastoderm nearly covers egg	3 days
Shell glands and eye-stalks appear	3½ days
Siphonal folds and arms appear, eyes project	5½ days
Siphonal folds fuse into a tube, eye-stalks prominent	6½ days
Hatching	11–12 days

E. Later Stages of Development: The blastoderm grows down to completely enclose the yolk at the ventral pole. Meanwhile at the opposite, or dorsal, pole the developing shell gland can be seen, with the mantle primordium underneath. The primitive mouth, seen as a slight ectodermal invagination, and a pair of large, rounded projections, the eye primordia, lie toward the anterior side. On the posterior side are the gill primordia, otocysts and the anterior and posterior siphonal folds, and near the equator the primitive arms can be seen. Rhythmical contractions of the yolk epithelium serve to circulate liquefied yolk material in the yolk sac vessels, which are continuous with the embryonic vessels (Portmann, 1926). As the embryo develops, the yolk sac gradually constricts. It continues into the embryo which is thus formed around a yolk core. The mantle and fins are easily recognized at this stage, but the shell gland has invaginated and is not visible. On the posterior side, the siphon is forming by concrescence of the anterior siphonal folds. The posterior siphonal folds, which will form the retractor muscles, continue as ridges to the anterior side. The anus is located between the gill primordia.

The pre-hatching embryo has very prominent eye-stalks, which contain primordia of the optic and cerebral ganglia, the so-called "white bodies," and a separate mass of yolk. The inner sector of the lens, which is formed by the outer part of the optic vesicle, is clearly visible as a club-shaped rod extending into the eye vesicle. The contractile mantle has overgrown the anus and gills, and later develops chromatophores which are equipped with muscles and innervated. The otocysts lie close together. Feather-like gills can be observed through the mantle. At their bases lie the branchial hearts and, between them, the systemic heart; all three pulsate.

When the yolk sac is nearly absorbed, the embryos adhere to the chorion by Hoyle's organ. This is a T-shaped structure, which is located on the posterior dorsal side of the mantle. The secretion from Hoyle's organ dissolves the chorion and the jelly, leaving a hole through which the embryo emerges, aided by pulsations of its mantle. Adherence to the chorion can be stimulated in late embryos by stroking the egg-string.

Illustrations of these stages may be found in a paper by Brooks (1880).

REFERENCES:

BROOKS, W. K., 1880. The development of the squid *Loligo pealii* (Lesueur). Anniv. Mem. Boston Soc. Nat. Hist., 1880, pp. 1–22.

DREW, G. A., 1911. Sexual activities of the squid, *Loligo pealii* (Les.). I. Copulation, egg-laying and fertilization. *J. Morph., 22* : 327–359.

DREW, G. A., 1919. Sexual activities of the squid *Loligo pealii* (Les.). II. The spermatophore; its structure, ejaculation and formation. *J. Morph., 32* : 379–435.

HOADLEY, L., 1930. Polocyte formation and the cleavage of the polar body in Loligo and Chaetopterus. *Biol. Bull., 58* : 256–264.

KORSCHELT, E., 1892. Beiträge zur Entwicklungsgeschichte der Cephalopoden. I. Die Entstehung des Darmkanals und Nervensystems in Beziehung zur Keimblatterfrage. Festschrift R. Leuckart, S. 347–373.

KORSCHELT, E., 1936. Cephalopoden. *In:* Vergleichende Entwicklungsgeschichte der Tiere, Gustav Fischer, Jena, Bd. 2, S. 968–1009.

MACBRIDE, E. W., 1914. Text-Book of Embryology. Vol. I. Invertebrata. Macmillan and Co., Ltd., London.

NAEF, A., 1928. Die Cephalopoden, Bd. 2, Embryologie. *Fauna und Flora des Golfes von Neapel, 35* : 1–347.

PORTMANN, A., 1926. Der embryonale Blutkreislauf und die Dotterresorption bei *Loligo vulgaris*. *Zeitschr. f. Morph. u. Okol. d. Tiere, 5* : 406–423.

PORTMANN, A., AND A. M. BIDDER, 1928. Yolk-absorption in Loligo and the function of the embryonic liver and pancreas. *Quart. J. Micr. Sci., 72* : 301–324.

RANZI, S., 1931a. Duplicitas cruciata in embrioni di Cefalopodi. *Pubbl. Staz. Zool., Napoli, 11* : 86–103.

RANZI, S., 1931b. Sviluppo di parti isolate di embrioni di Cefalopodi. (Analisi sperimentale dell'embriogenesi.) *Pubbl. Staz. Zool., Napoli, 11* : 104–146.

RANZI, S., 1937. Ricerche sulla fisiologia dell'embrione dei Cefalopodi. *Pont. Acad. Scient., Acta, 1* : 43–49.

SPEK, J., 1934. Die bipolare Differenzierung des Cephalopoden- und des Prosobranchiereies. *Arch. f. Entw., 131* : 362–372.

WATASE, S., 1891. Studies on Cephalopods. I. Cleavage of the ovum. *J. Morph., 4* : 247–302.

WILLIAMS, L. W., 1910. The anatomy of the common squid, *Loligo pealii*, Lesueur. E. J. Brill, Leiden, Holland, pp. 1–92.

ARTHROPODA

(CRUSTACEA)

Balanus eburneus *

LIVING MATERIAL:

This form is quite commonly found in the Woods Hole, Mass., region; the shell is low and broad in form, with a smooth, yellow-white exterior. It usually occurs at or below the low-water mark, on stones, shells, timbers, etc. Burbanck *et al.* (1956) collected *B. eburneus* in abundance at Rand's Harbor, in areas of fresh water inflow.

BREEDING SEASON:

Fish (1925) states that the breeding season of *B. eburneus* at Woods Hole extends from August to mid-November. At Beaufort, North Carolina, this barnacle apparently breeds from July to September (Costlow and Bookhout, personal communication).

PROCURING AND HANDLING MATERIAL:

A. Care of Adults: The animals should be kept in aquaria supplied with running sea water.

B. Procuring Embryos: Carefully chip away the calcareous portion of the basis. If the eggs are ripe and in the process of development, the egg lamellae are firm and, with care, may be removed intact. They should be placed in a finger-bowl of sea water; the eggs may be teased out with a needle.

C. Preparation of Cultures: The embryos and larvae are sensitive to temperature and oxygen changes. Therefore, the sea water in which they are kept should be changed frequently, and the cultures kept cool on a sea water table. Despite these precautions, the mortality rate is high. The addition of 200,000 to 400,000 units of penicillin per liter appears to reduce bacterial growth in the cultures (Costlow and Bookhout, 1957).

Aqueous extracts of mantle wall or body tissues, but not of egg-masses themselves, have been found to promote hatching and liberation of the nauplii (Crisp, 1956).

NORMAL DEVELOPMENT:

A. Fertilization and Cleavage: The available evidence indicates that barnacles normally are not self-fertile; however, Barnes and Crisp (1956) have collected some data which indicate that *B. perforatus* eggs occasionally develop either parthenogenetically or as a consequence of self-fertilization.

Fertilization in *B. eburneus* is internal; in the youngest stages of development, it is possible to observe the formation of the polar bodies, and the approach of the germ nuclei. This is best seen in preparations which have dried somewhat, so

---

* Dr. J. D. Costlow, Jr. and Dr. C. G. Bookhout supplied much of the information on which this section is based; we should like to express our appreciation to them.

that the eggs are slightly flattened.   Cleavage apparently is similar to that in the egg of Lepas, and gastrulation is by epiboly.

B. Time Table of Development: The over-all time for development of *B. eburneus* is quite short, as compared with that for many barnacles, and requires from 7 to 13 days (Costlow and Bookhout, 1957).   At 26° C., the following durations for the naupliar and cyprid stages were recorded by Costlow and Bookhout (1957) :

Stage	Duration
First naupliar	15 minutes to 4 hours
Second naupliar	1 to 2 days (average: 1 day)
Third naupliar	1 to 4 days (average: 1.5 days)
Fourth naupliar	1 to 4 days (average: 2 days)
Fifth naupliar	1 to 5 days (average: 2.6 days)
Sixth naupliar	2 to 4 days (average: 2.5 days)
Cyprid	1 to 14 days

C. Later Stages of Development: A three- and a five-segment stage are undergone by *B. eburneus* (Costlow and Bookhout, personal communication).   The organogeny of the developing embryo is complex; Groom (1894) gives diagrams of the early development and later phases of *B. perforatus.*

Free-swimming stages: Costlow and Bookhout (1957) describe the six naupliar and one cyprid stage of *B. eburneus,* giving setation formulae, specific morphological characteristics, frequency of molting, duration of intermolt periods, and time of complete development in the laboratory.   The use of a motile source of food, such as Arbacia plutei and Chlamydomonas, is necessary in order to maintain the animals throughout the larval period.

Setting and metamorphosis: Costlow and Bookhout (1953, 1956) describe methods for collecting the cyprid stage of *B. improvisus* and *B. amphitrite niveus.* They use six-inch plastic squares, which are suspended in water known to be inhabited by the adults.   Small squares of plastic, containing individual cyprids, may be cut from the larger collecting-square and observed, from either surface, under the microscope.   Metamorphosis of the cyprid into the "pin-head" stage is described for *B. amphitrite niveus* by Doochin (1951).   The subsequent development of the characteristic six mural plates of the adult barnacle is described for *B. improvisus* by Costlow (1956).

REFERENCES:

BARNES, H., AND D. J. CRISP, 1956.   Evidence of self-fertilization in certain species of barnacles. *J. Mar. Biol. Assoc.,* **35**: 631–639.

BURBANCK, W. D., M. E. PIERCE AND G. C. WHITELEY, JR., 1956.   A study of the bottom fauna of Rand's Harbor, Massachusetts: An application of the ecotone concept. *Ecol. Monog.,* **26**: 213–243.

COSTLOW, J. D., JR., 1956.   Shell development in *Balanus improvisus* Darwin. *J. Morph.,* **99**: 359–415.

COSTLOW, J. D., JR., AND C. G. BOOKHOUT, 1953.   Moulting and growth in *Balanus improvisus. Biol. Bull.,* **105**: 420–433.

COSTLOW, J. D., JR., AND C. G. BOOKHOUT, 1956.   Molting and shell growth in *Balanus amphitrite niveus. Biol. Bull.,* **110**: 107–116.

COSTLOW, J. D., JR., AND C. G. BOOKHOUT, 1957.   Larval development of *Balanus eburneus* in the laboratory. *Biol. Bull.,* **112**: 313–324.

CRISP, D. J., 1956. A substance promoting hatching and liberation of young in Cirripedes. *Nature,* **178**: 263.

DOOCHIN, H. D., 1951. The morphology of *Balanus improvisus* Darwin and *Balanus amphitrite niveus* Darwin during initial attachment and metamorphosis. *Bull. Mar. Sci. Gulf and Caribbean,* **1**: 15–39.

FISH, C. J., 1925. Seasonal distribution of the plankton of the Woods Hole region. Bur. Fish., Document no. 975.

GROOM, T. T., 1894. On the early development of Cirripedia. *Phil. Trans. Roy. Soc., London, ser. B,* **185**: 119–232.

ARTHROPODA

(Crustacea)

Emerita (formerly *Hippa*) *talpoida*

LIVING MATERIAL:

The sand crab, Emerita, is common on sandy beaches; the animals migrate, with the tide, up or down the beach. The females are about twice the size of the males; according to MacGinitie (1938), the males outnumber the females by a ratio of three to one during the early part of the breeding season.

BREEDING SEASON:

On the California coast, in May and June the season is at its height. However, females with eggs in young stages have been found as late as October. Females carry their eggs for a period of four to five months. It appears that in general, mating of the California forms takes place in the late spring or early summer, although females with eggs are found throughout the year.

The breeding season for this form in the Woods Hole, Mass., region has not been accurately determined, although females with eggs have been found in July and August (Bumpus, 1898).

PROCURING AND HANDLING MATERIAL:

A. Care of Adults: Animals may be kept in large fingerbowls which are three-fourths filled with sand. An abundant supply of running sea water, led in under the sand, should be provided. Molted exuviae occasionally appear on top of the sand layer; these should be removed promptly.

B. Procuring Gametes and Embryos: For details concerning the mating habits of Emerita, see the paper by MacGinitie (1938). The time of mating can be detected by observing the behavior of the animals; several males will gather around a female for as many as five days in advance of egg-laying. Sperm will be deposited in ribbons of mucus on the ventral side of the female; shortly afterward, the female begins the egg-laying process. Eggs are deposited under the telson, on the ventral surface of the abdomen; the process may occur over a period of three days. Diagrams of the male reproductive system of *Hippa pacifica* are presented by Matthews (1956).

C. Methods of Observation: Embryos may be removed from the egg-mass at any time, by holding the female gently, prying up the telson, and removing a few embryos with forceps.

Cleavage stages are more clearly observed if the embryos are first treated with 1% chromic acid, washed in water and mounted under mica coverslips. Older stages are more difficult to study satisfactorily; they should be killed, to whiten the embryonic area, using mercuric chloride. The embryonic regions begin to whiten in a few minutes; strong aceto-carmine (with a little sea water) should then be used. After a few minutes, put the eggs in 50% glycerine, which causes the stain to fade.

NORMAL DEVELOPMENT:

A. The Unfertilized Ovum: The eggs are orange to scarlet in color, and measure approximately 380 microns in diameter. They are attached to the egg-mass by thin stalks, and remain on the ventral surface of the female until the zoeae hatch; presumably, the eggs do not develop further if they are detached from the egg-mass.

B. Cleavage and Gastrulation: Divisions appear to be total, but there is some question as to whether the cleavage furrows actually penetrate the yolk mass. Cleavage stages are more frequently found in Emerita eggs than in Libinia eggs.

Gastrulation is similar to that in Libinia, and there is a corresponding development of the embryonic rudiments in the embryonic area. Fixation of the cells with mercuric chloride (as noted above) and study by reflected light will facilitate observations.

C. Later Stages of Development: The zoea larvae hatch from the egg membranes and may be kept in fingerbowls supplied with pieces of Ulva; the larvae should be fed diatoms.

REFERENCES:

BUMPUS, H. C., 1898. The breeding of animals at Woods Holl during the months of June, July and August. *Science, 8*: 850–858.

MACGINITIE, G. E., 1938. Movements and mating habits of the sand crab, *Emerita analoga. Amer. Midl. Nat., 19*: 471–481.

MATTHEWS, D. C., 1956. The origin of the spermatophoric mass of the sand crab, *Hippa pacifica. Quart. J. Micr. Sci., 97*: 257–268.

ARTHROPODA

(Crustacea)

Lepas anatifera

Living Material:

The goose barnacle is not indigenous to the Woods Hole, Mass., region; however, during the summer, timbers and wooden boxes with barnacles attached may sometimes drift into the harbor from the Gulf Stream.

Breeding Season:

The limits of the season are not known. Bigelow (1902) states that he found maturation stages early in June, whereas by July and August, young nauplii were prevalent.

Procuring and Handling Material:

A. Care of Adults: Sections of timbers with adherent barnacles may be placed in aquaria supplied with running sea water, in the laboratory, or larger timbers may be anchored in the Eel Pond. Detached animals will also live in an aquarium in the laboratory.

B. Procuring Gametes and Embryos: Lepas is hermaphroditic and can fertilize its own gametes; these embryos are then deposited in the mantle cavity in sheet-like ovigerous lamellae, where they continue to develop until they hatch as nauplii. If one wishes to examine the gametes, they can be procured by slitting a barnacle along the plate hinges and exposing the visceral mass. The testes lie at the stalk side of the body, and when the animal is in a breeding condition, they are white and swollen. The ovary is found by cutting the stalk lengthwise; young egg-masses are bright blue. In this condition, unfertilized eggs can be found; it has not been ascertained whether such eggs can be artificially inseminated. For cleavage stages, it is better to study the eggs which are obtained from the ovigerous lamellae.

If enough animals are available, a complete series, from egg to hatching larva, may be obtained at the same time. During development, there is a striking color change in the eggs of the lamellae: early cleavage stages are medium blue, later cleavage stages are light blue to blue-lavender. In pink-lavender lamellae, larvae can be seen inside the egg cases. Hatching stages are pink in color, while young to mature swimming nauplii accumulate in peach-colored masses. The chemistry of this color change has been studied by Ball (1944).

The lamellae lie as two sheets which are at first closely applied to the lower portion of the visceral mass and later are extended to cover the entire inside of the mantle cavity. When the lamellae are old enough to contain hatching stages, they are extruded from the body when the tentacles are molted. The bottom of the aquarium should therefore be inspected for these peach-colored sheets, which are about thumb-nail size.

The various stages may be isolated in separate fingerbowls. Bigelow (1902) states that the early embryos will not continue development outside the brood-chamber for a period of longer than five to ten hours. Late nauplii, however, will live for some time in fingerbowls of sea water.

C. Methods of Observation: To aid in the study of cleavage stages, it is helpful to stain with strong methyl green; the micromeres stain deeply, the macromeres, faintly. The stain, however, is transient.

NORMAL DEVELOPMENT:

A. The Unfertilized Ovum: The eggs are distorted while they are still in the ovary, but become spherical in shape after they are placed in sea water. According to Bigelow (1902) the first polar body is given off when the eggs leave the oviducts; whether or not fertilization occurs at this time, the vitelline membrane is elevated and lies, therefore, between the egg surface and the first polar body.

B. Fertilization and Cleavage: After fertilization, waves of slow contraction can be seen in the egg; Groom (1894) states that this process separates the proto-plasmic portions of the egg from the yolk. The egg has a rounded point at the vegetal pole and is blunt at the animal pole. Cleavage is total, unequal, and regular. For a complete account of cleavage and of the cell lineage of this form, see the paper by Bigelow (1902).

Costello (1948) has pointed out that the cleavage of Lepas can be homologized with that of spirally cleaving eggs by considering it to be cleavage by "monets" rather than by quartets.

C. Later Stages of Development and Metamorphosis: Groom (1894) gives an account of later development (as well as maturation and early cleavage stages). The papers of Bigelow (1902) and Groom (1894) contain illustrations of stages from the unfertilized ovum to the early unhatched larva. Groom continues the series to the mature nauplius larva.

REFERENCES:

BALL, E. G., 1944. A blue chromoprotein found in the eggs of the goose-barnacle. *J. Biol. Chem.,* 152: 627–634.

BIGELOW, M. A., 1902. The early development of Lepas. A study of cell-lineage and germ-layers. *Bull. Mus. Comp. Zool., Harvard,* 40: 61–144.

COSTELLO, D. P., 1948. Spiral cleavage. *Biol. Bull.,* 95: 265. (See, also, *Erratum, Biol. Bull.,* 95: 361.)

GROOM, T. T., 1894. On the early development of Cirripedia. *Phil. Trans. Roy. Soc., London, ser. B,* 185: 119–232.

ARTHROPODA

(CRUSTACEA)

Libinia emarginata and *L. dubia*

LIVING MATERIAL:

Libinia emarginata may be distinguished from the less commonly found *L. dubia* by the presence on its back of nine median spines, as contrasted with the six median spines characteristic of *L. dubia*. The animals occur on mud flats, and are abundant. The eggs are carried by the females on the legs; those egg-masses which are bright vermilion in color are best for study, since they contain the early stages. Later stages of development are chocolate-brown in color. Zoea and megalops larvae (of this and other crabs) are sometimes obtained by towing in the Hole at Woods Hole, Mass. Frequently, an electric light shining near the surface of the Eel Pond water (as, for example, the Nereis-collecting light commonly used) will attract vast numbers of larvae, which may then be dipped up.

BREEDING SEASON:

Bumpus (1898a) reported that females with eggs were collected at Woods Hole during the month of May and (1898b) that oviposition was observed as late as August 7. Thompson (1899) states that the larvae had disappeared from his collections by September 4.

PROCURING AND HANDLING MATERIAL:

A. Care of Adults: The animals should be kept in large aquaria supplied with running sea water.

B. Methods of Observation: Forceps may be used to pick the eggs and larvae from the legs of the female. Cleavage and subsequent stages of development can be studied in the living egg only with considerable difficulty, and it is therefore advisable to fix the embryos. The following methods are useful:

1. Place the eggs in strong aceto-carmine (in a very little sea water). After about ten minutes, transfer them to 50% glycerine, which causes the stain to fade.
2. Early embryos are readily studied after the addition of 1% chromic acid to a drop of sea water in which the embryos are contained. After about five minutes, wash the embryos in water and mount them on glass slides under mica coverslips.
3. Drop the older stages into *strong* mercuric chloride solution; the embryonic area will whiten in a few minutes.

Use *reflected* light and a low power of the microscope for observation of all stages which have been fixed.

Study of the zoea stage in the living condition requires that the larvae be anaesthetized (with magnesium sulfate or other agents). With the use of the higher powers of the microscope, such details as the muscles, compound eyes, contractile heart and intestine can be observed.

167

Normal Development:

A. Early Stages of Development: The early development of the centrolecithal egg of Libinia is essentially the same as that of the crayfish, Astacus. Since the paper by Reichenbach (1886) is in a journal which is not readily accessible, this account is based upon the summary given by MacBride (1914), and on the description by Brooks and Herrick (1892) of the cleavage of Alpheus and Stenopus.

The zygote nucleus occupies a central position in the fertilized egg and there divides. Protoplasmic division is said not to begin until after the fourth nuclear division, by which time the nuclei have migrated to the periphery. The daughter nuclei are at first internal but gradually migrate outward until they reach the surface. At this time the egg is imperfectly divided (by radiating planes of cytoplasm between masses of yolk granules) into a series of pillars, each of which contains one of the daughter nuclei. These are referred to as "columnar blastomeres." The yolk pyramids persist for only a short time; then the dividing planes disappear, and a flattened "skin" of cells remains, surrounding a large mass of yolk. This "skin" of cells is termed a "blastoderm." This stage corresponds to a blastula, the blastocoele being filled with an unsegmented mass of yolk.

Preceding the formation of the gastrula, there is an increase in the number of the blastoderm cells on one side of the egg; they are also thicker here and this becomes the ventral surface of the embryo. They press on one another laterally as they increase in number and become columnar in character, to form the ventral plate. This is on the future neural side of the embryo. Five circular areas develop in this ventral plate, in each of which the cells are arranged in concentric curves, and in lines radiating from a central point. These areas may be clearly distinguished in an embryo of this age after fixation with mercuric chloride, if it is examined by reflected light. The two anterior areas are the "cephalic lobes," or the rudiments of the paired eyes and cerebral ganglia. The thoracico-abdominal thickenings posterior to these constitute the next pair of rudiments. Just posterior to these, on the mid-line, is the central disc, or endodermic rudiment.

At the anterior margin of the endodermic rudiment, a groove develops. This is the beginning of the blastopore. The appearance of this groove (the endodermic groove) marks the beginning of the process of gastrulation. The endodermic groove later becomes a complete circle, as the periphery of the endodermal disc is invaginated, giving rise to the "endodermal button." As the button is carried in, a circular blastopore forms, later changing into an elliptical blastopore. The front border of the endodermic rudiment is the point of origin of the mesoderm. The endodermal tube becomes pinched off as a blind sac; much later, the proctodeum and stomodeum grow through to it. The proctodeum appears in between, and just posterior to the thoracico-abdominal rudiments, where the blastopore formerly was located. Other embryonic areas develop a short time after the first five. Three of these are the rudiments of the anterior paired appendages: first antenna (antennule), second antenna, and mandibles, and are characteristic of all crustacean larvae. When these rudiments appear, the stage is called a nauplius.

B. Rate of Development: About one month passes between spawning and the zoea stage.

C. Later Stages of Development: The nauplius stage has the first three pairs of appendages; later stages have five or more pairs of appendages, and the stomodeum, ventral fold, dorsal shield, telson and ganglia may be found. It is necessary to supply the older larvae with Ulva and diatoms.

REFERENCES:

BROOKS, W. K., AND F. H. HERRICK, 1892. The embryology and metamorphosis of the Macroura. *Mem. Nat. Acad. Sci.,* **5**: 325–574.

BUMPUS, H. C., 1898a. The breeding of animals at Woods Holl during the month of May, 1898. *Science,* **8**: 58–61.

BUMPUS, H. C., 1898b. The breeding of animals at Woods Holl during the months of June, July and August. *Science,* **8**: 850–858.

MACBRIDE, E. W., 1914. Text-book of Embryology. Vol. I. Invertebrata. Macmillan and Co., Ltd., London.

REICHENBACH, H., 1886. Studien zur Entwicklungsgeschichte des Flusskrebses. *Abh. Senckenberg. Naturforsch. Ges.,* **14**: 1–137.

THOMPSON, M. T., 1899. The breeding of animals at Woods Hole during the month of September, 1898. *Science,* **9**: 581–583.

ECHINODERMATA

(Asteroidea)

Asterias forbesi and *A. vulgaris*

LIVING MATERIAL:

Both species are moderately abundant, and are obtained by dredging off Vineyard Haven, near East Chop, Martha's Vineyard, Mass. The most reliable feature for distinguishing between them is the shape of the arms or rays; in *A. forbesi* the rays are stout and cylindrical and tend to be blunt at the tip, and in *A. vulgaris* they are flattened and taper to a point. The sexes are separate but cannot be distinguished on the basis of external characteristics.

BREEDING SEASON:

May, June and early July in the Woods Hole region. A few ripe females can be obtained in late July; however, it is not practicable to do experiments on a large scale after July 15. Formerly, starfish from the Hole produced viable gametes as late as the middle of August (R. S. Lillie, personal communication).

PROCURING AND HANDLING MATERIAL:

A. Care of Adults: Adults can be kept in good condition for a considerable period of time in aquaria supplied with running sea water, provided they are occasionally given mussels or small clams for food. If an animal sheds, it should be removed immediately from the aquarium, since it may induce shedding among the others. Dying or dead individuals should also be removed as promptly as possible.

B. Procuring Gametes: Shedding may sometimes be induced in mature animals by removing them from sea water and placing them on a board in the sun, or on the cement floor of the laboratory under the heat of a desk lamp. This method is reasonably effective in the case of the west coast starfish *Patiria miniata,* which normally sheds in the warm shallow water of tide pools at low tide. Usually, however, it is easier to obtain gametes as outlined below, than to depend on the occurrence of natural spawning.

Only animals with soft, bulging arms are fully ripe; it is a waste of time and material to open small, hard-skinned starfish in an attempt to obtain gametes. A small-bore pipette may be easily inserted into the arm of a ripe starfish, preferably near the central region, without causing injury; the few gametes thus obtained enable one to ascertain the sex of the animal rapidly.

After identifying a female, remove the punctured arm from the disc, and return the animal to an aquarium of running sea water to be used again. Injured animals will not, however, keep indefinitely; the gametes are rarely usable at the time the animal begins to undergo autotomy. Slit the detached arm along the mid-dorsal line to expose the bulging pair of ovaries, which are typically pale salmon in color. Then, with a pair of forceps, carefully detach each plume-like ovary by grasping it near its point of attachment at the proximal end, thus closing the gonoduct; rinse it in a large fingerbowl of filtered sea water. Transfer the ovary to a second bowl and allow the eggs to exude from the blunt end. *Do not cut up the ovary*. At the end of five minutes, remove the gonads to another container or discard them; the best eggs are those which exude first. Gently stir the contents of the fingerbowl and allow the eggs to settle. When they have done so, pour off the supernatant fluid and carefully replace it with an equal volume of filtered sea water. Leave the eggs undisturbed for 20 to 30 minutes; during this time small samples may be removed with a pipette for examination. Eggs carefully obtained from a ripe female, kept under proper conditions of coolness and with an adequate oxygen supply from the time of collection, should show 85 to 90 per cent germinal vesicle breakdown at approximately the same time.

From the detached arm of a male remove a single testis, white or ivory in color, and rinse it in clean sea water. A small piece of the blunt end should be cut off and placed in 200 cc. of filtered sea water.

C. Preparation of Cultures: The optimum period for fertilization is after the breakdown of the germinal vesicle and before the extrusion of the first polar body. Eggs with intact germinal vesicles are non-fertilizable; they may elevate a fertilization membrane but will not develop further. It is convenient, therefore, to inseminate when the distal end of the first maturation spindle begins to protrude above the previously smooth surface of the oöcyte in a moderate percentage of the eggs which have undergone germinal vesicle breakdown. To do so, add about five cc. of the sperm suspension, prepared as directed above, to a large fingerbowl of eggs. Immediately rotate the dish gently to ensure complete mixing. When the eggs have settled, the supernatant fluid should be decanted and an equal amount of sea water added. This procedure should be repeated at half-hour intervals, to eliminate the excess sperm which would otherwise foul the culture and prevent development of the late embryonic stages. There should be only one layer of well-spaced eggs on the bottom of a dish.

When the first swimming stages appear (after about 20 hours), pour off the upper half of the culture, containing the more normal swimming blastulae, into a series of tall battery jars. Add enough filtered sea water to fill the jars. Care must be taken to eliminate dead embryos or unfertilized eggs. In these tall jars evaporation is considerably reduced; however, the original level should be maintained by the addition of distilled water. It is essential that relatively few embryos be placed in a jar, if one wishes to raise older larvae. Aerate the cultures gently, using glass tubing rather than rubber hose for this purpose. Early bipinnaria may be obtained without special feeding, but diatoms must be added to the cultures in order to obtain brachiolaria or later stages. The culture jars should be kept at temperatures between 17 and 20° C., away from the direct sunlight (Larsen, 1937).

The egg of Asterias is very delicate as compared with most eggs used for routine laboratory work. Satisfactory results are not obtained unless adequate precautions are observed, including the following: (1) Avoid contamination of either type of gamete with perivisceral fluid; (2) avoid over-insemination; (3) avoid crowding of eggs; and (4) use only fresh, motile sperm.

D. Methods of Observation: The presence of a jelly-hull around these eggs may be demonstrated by using dim illumination, or by adding a trace of Janus green. Vital staining with neutral red is helpful in studying the larval stages.

An aqueous (sea water) extract from squid egg-string jelly has proved useful in the Embryology Course at Woods Hole, for slowing down or immobilizing the larval forms of certain echinoderms. (It is apparently not effective for Callocardia veliger larvae, however.) The extract is prepared as follows: Peel the outer covering from about four egg-strings, and cut up the strings in approximately 10 cc. of sea water. Allow the strings to remain in the sea water for one or two hours, then filter through a moderately coarse grade of filter paper. The extract will retain the ability to slow down or immobilize echinoderm larvae for at least two days, if it is kept under refrigeration. Two or three drops of the extract will quiet the larvae contained in one drop of sea water, in a depression slide. It is not necessary that the squid jelly used contain squid embryos; empty jelly-strings are equally effective for preparing extracts.

NORMAL DEVELOPMENT:

A. The Unfertilized Ovum: The egg of Asterias is very delicate and is surrounded by a jelly-hull. It is shed in the germinal vesicle stage, and on contact with sea water proceeds spontaneously to the first and second maturation divisions. The mature ovum contains a lightly pigmented yolk, pale yellow in color, through which (in later stages) the spindles of mitotic figures may sometimes be seen. The egg of *A. forbesi* measures about 110 microns in diameter (Fry, 1937).

B. Fertilization and Cleavage: Immediately after insemination, sperm may be seen on the jelly-surface of the eggs. Some will be attached by a tenuous filament to a fertilization cone which has arisen on the egg surface. The fertilization membrane elevates in a wave which begins at the cone and spreads rapidly around the egg. The sperm is drawn passively through the jelly to the cone, and after a pause the head piece is pulled through the membrane and enters the cone. Six minutes after insemination, the delicate sperm aster is formed and moves through the egg to fuse with the egg nucleus. It was in the egg of the starfish that Fol (1879) first observed the actual penetration of an egg by a spermatozoon. See the papers of Chambers (1930) and Colwin and Colwin (1956) for comments and additional observations.

The first two cleavages are meridional; they go through the animal and vegetal poles at right angles to each other. The third cleavage is horizontal; the eight cells of this stage are approximately equal in size. In the 16-cell stage, no definite arrangement of cells in rows occurs, and from this stage on, cleavage is irregular. Throughout the early cleavages the blastomeres exhibit a tendency to assume a spherical shape, resulting in a rather loose arrangement of cells. The perivitelline space is wider and the hyaline plasma membrane is thinner and weaker than in the Arbacia egg. These two conditions account, in part, for the loose connection between the blastomeres. Chambers has pointed out that in the absence of the fertilization membrane, the blastomeres tend to separate completely.

Eventually the cells become arranged in an epithelial wall enclosing the blastocoele. The surface cells acquire cilia and the blastula begins to rotate within the fertilization membrane. The two polar bodies are still visible, attached to the animal pole or lying loose within the perivitelline space. The embryo hatches in the late blastula stage.

C. Developmental Rate: No precise information is available. This is apparently due to the fact that few workers have obtained egg-batches showing uniform germinal vesicle breakdown.   According to Chambers and Chambers (1949), for example, the time of cleavage depends upon the exact time when the eggs are in- seminated during the maturation stages.   Their data indicate that if one waits until the egg is almost fully mature (*i.e.,* shortly before the second polar body is to be extruded) before inseminating, the eggs cleave about 103.5 minutes later, at 16° C.

Unfertilized Asterias eggs undergo maturation changes at 16–18° C., according to Chambers and Chambers (1949), as follows; the time is recorded from the moment of deposition of the eggs in sea water:

Stage	Time
Disappearance of nucleolus	8–9 minutes
Formation of first polar body	76–90 minutes
Formation of second polar body	105–119 minutes

D. Later Stages of Development and Metamorphosis:

Gastrulation: The vegetal pole area thickens and flattens, and invagination begins.   The blastopore is destined to become the anus.   The larva elongates along the animal-vegetal axis and gradually becomes pear-shaped.   The blind inner end of the archenteron becomes thin-walled and expands, and from it mesenchyme cells wander into the blastocoele.   In a slightly later gastrula, two out-pocketings of the distal end of the archenteron can be seen; they are the pri- mordia of the coelomic sacs.   While they are forming, the first sign of the change from radial to bilateral symmetry may be seen, namely, the bending of the ciliated archenteron toward the future ventral side of the embryo.

Dipleurula larva: By the time this larva is fully formed, the blind end of the archenteron has made contact with an ectodermal depression, the stomodeum, on the ventral body wall and has broken through to form the mouth.   Overhanging this is the oral lobe.   The ventral side of the dipleurula is convex in shape.   The entire surface is finely ciliated, and in addition there is a continuous ciliary band which is longitudinal with two cross-bars.   The longitudinal bands above the upper cross-bar loop toward the mid-line where they eventually meet.   Thus a frontal field, the pre-oral ciliary band, is separated on the upper ventral part of the larva, overhanging the oral field.   This separate frontal field is characteristic of asteroid larvae.   The alimentary tract consists of three parts, characteristic of echinoderm larvae: oesophagus (with a constriction near the entrance to the stomach), stomach, and intestine.   In lateral views, the bend of the intestine can be seen.   Ciliation occurs in the oral field and certain other parts of the tract.   The two coelomic vesicles are clearly visible at the lower end of the oesophagus, near its entrance into the stomach.   A subdivision of the vesicles is not yet clearly demarcated, but the narrow tube connecting the larger left coelomic vesicle with the dorsal body wall, the pore canal, and its opening, the madreporic pore, can be readily seen.   Loose mesenchyme cells are scattered in the body cavity, which is the persisting blastocoele.

The dipleurula (early bipinnaria) larva represents an early larval type common to Asteroidea, Echinoidea, Ophiuroidea, and Holothuroidea (see the book of Korschelt and Heider, 1936, vol. 1, p. 499).

Bipinnaria larva: This larva is characterized by a number of pairs of lobes or arms which grow out from the margin of the ectoderm and which carry along the ciliary band. They are not supported by a skeleton, and young stages may not have all the arms developed. Pairs of arms follow each other in quick succession; unpaired median dorsal, and paired antero-dorsal, postero-dorsal, postero-lateral, post-oral and pre-oral arms can be identified. The coelomic vesicles grow out into long tubes and fuse in the anterior part of the larva. No further subdivisions have yet occurred.

Brachiolaria larva: Unlike the bipinnaria arms, which are long hollow tubes, those of the brachiolaria, the brachia, are short, and contain diverticula of the coelom. They are not ciliated but bear small papillae, differentiated from their end discs; they can adhere to the substrate. A sucker, the gland cells of which secrete a sticky substance, is formed between the brachia. The developing disc, the future young starfish, can be seen.

Metamorphosis: In late stages of metamorphosis, the anterior part of the brachiolaria, in front of the disc, shrinks to form a stalk. This attaches firmly to the substrate by means of the sucker and brachia, and bears the Asterias *anlage* at its distal end. About one week is required for the young starfish to complete development, rupture the stalk, and crawl away.

For further details of these stages consult papers by Agassiz (1877), Gemmill (1914) and the text-book of MacBride (1914), all of which contain figures.

REFERENCES:

AGASSIZ, A., 1877. North American starfishes. I. Embryology of the starfish. *Mem. Mus. Comp. Zool., Harvard,* **5**: no. 1, pp. 1–83. First published in 1864.

CHADWICK, H. C., 1923. Asterias. Liverpool Mar. Biol. Comm. Mem., no. 25, pp. 1–63.

CHAMBERS, R., 1930. The manner of sperm entry in the starfish egg. *Biol. Bull.,* **58**: 344–369.

CHAMBERS, R., AND E. L. CHAMBERS, 1949. Nuclear and cytoplasmic interrelations in the fertilization of the Asterias egg. *Biol. Bull.,* **96**: 270–282.

COLWIN, L. H., AND A. L. COLWIN, 1955. Some factors related to sperm entry in two species of Asterias. *Biol. Bull.,* **109**: 357.

COLWIN, L. H., AND A. L. COLWIN, 1956. The acrosome filament and sperm entry in *Thyone briareus* (Holothuria) and Asterias. *Biol. Bull.,* **110**: 243–257.

COSTELLO, D. P., 1935. Fertilization membranes of centrifuged Asterias eggs. I. The effects of centrifuging before fertilization. *Physiol. Zool.,* **8**: 65–72.

DELAGE, Y., 1904. Élevage des larves parthénogénétiques d'*Asterias glacialis.* *Arch. de Zool. expér., 4e sér.,* **2**: 27–42.

FOL, H., 1879. Recherches sur la fécondation et le commencement de l'hénogénie chez divers animaux. *Mém. Soc. Phys. et Hist. Nat., Genève,* **26**: 12–397.

FRY, H. J., 1937. *Asterias forbesi. In:* Culture Methods for Invertebrate Animals, edit. by Galtsoff *et al.,* Comstock, Ithaca, pp. 547–550.

GEMMILL, J. F., 1914. VII. The development and certain points in the adult structure of the starfish *Asterias rubens,* L. *Phil. Trans. Roy. Soc., London, ser. B,* **205**: 213–294.

GOTO, S., 1898. The metamorphosis of *Asterias pallida,* with special reference to the fate of the body cavities. *J. Coll. Sci., Imp. Univ., Japan,* **10**: 239–278.

JUST, E. E., 1939. Basic Methods for Experiments on Eggs of Marine Animals. P. Blakiston's Son & Co., Inc., Philadelphia.

KORSCHELT, E., AND K. HEIDER, 1936. Vergleichende Entwicklungsgeschichte der Tiere. Vol. 1. G. Fischer, Jena.

LARSEN, E. J., 1937. The laboratory culture of the larvae of *Asterias forbesi. In:* Culture Methods for Invertebrate Animals, edit. by Galtsoff *et al.,* Comstock, Ithaca, pp. 550–553.

LILLIE, R. S., 1941. Further experiments on artifical parthenogenesis in starfish eggs, with a review. *Physiol. Zool.,* **14**: 239–267.

MACBRIDE, E. W., 1914. Text-Book of Embryology. Vol. I. Invertebrata. Macmillan and Co., Ltd., London.

NEWMAN, H. H., 1925. An experimental analysis of asymmetry in the starfish, *Patiria miniata. Biol. Bull.,* **49**: 111–138.

ECHINODERMATA

(ASTEROIDEA)

Henricia (formerly *Cribrella*) *sanguinolenta*

LIVING MATERIAL:

This small red starfish is not abundant at Woods Hole, Mass., although some can be obtained by dredging at Lackey's Bay. The sexes are separate and similar in appearance.

BREEDING SEASON:

The species is said to breed in the early spring (Clark, 1902). Mead (1898) noted that eggs were frequently laid in aquaria at Woods Hole during the third week in April. Larvae were obtained in tows during the month of May (Bumpus, 1898), and motile sperm are found as late as June.

At St. Andrews, Scotland, the breeding period extends from the beginning of February to the end of April (Masterman, 1902).

PROCURING AND HANDLING MATERIAL:

A. Care of Adults: Adults may be kept in aquaria or large fingerbowls, supplied with running sea water.

B. Procuring Gametes: It is not known whether artificial fertilization is successful in this species. Gametes can be obtained as follows: Cut off an arm along with a pie-shaped piece of the adjacent disc and, with forceps, remove the gonads (pale peach testis or orange-brown ovaries) from the base of the arm. Place them in a small dish of sea water, and allow the gametes to ooze out.

C. Preparation of Cultures: In normal development, the fertilized eggs are protected beneath the body of the female (Coe, 1912), where a brood-chamber is formed, roofed by the raised disc and enclosed by the bases of the arms. The embryos usually remain therein throughout their larval life, and during this period the female does not feed. However, if she is disturbed she will desert the brood permanently, and within a short time resume feeding. Meanwhile, the embryos develop quite normally.

Eggs and assorted larvae can be washed out of the brood-chamber with a pipette. They may be kept in fingerbowls, to which the more advanced larvae will attach. The sea water should be changed frequently, but no special feeding is necessary since there is an adequate supply of yolk.

NORMAL DEVELOPMENT:

A. The Unfertilized Ovum: The mature eggs are deep orange in color, and are opaque, due to the presence of a large amount of colored yolk. They are large and spherical in shape, and show some variation in size (800–1200 microns); the majority measure 1000 microns in diameter (Mead, 1898; Masterman, 1902).

B. Fertilization and Cleavage: Fertilization in this species has not been described. There is no definite pattern of segmentation, although the type most

175

frequently observed is holoblastic and unequal.   In all cases the egg is transformed gradually into a solid morula, and then, by outward migration of cells, into a blastula with a large blastocoele.   The forming blastula may be recognized by a number of transitory indented furrows which form on the surface.   Gastrulation is by invagination.   See the paper of Masterman (1902) for further details and illustrations.

C. *Rate of Development:* This is apparently rather slow.   The two-cell stage is reached in 6 hours (Mead, 1898) ; the larvae hatch in 8 to 10 days, and 6 to 10 days later begin their somewhat slow transformation into the adult form (Masterman, 1902).

D. *Later Stages of Development:* The hatching larvae are demersal, uniformly ciliated, and nearly spherical in shape.   They rapidly elongate to a somewhat barrel-shaped form, and develop a dorsal, tripod-like process.   The larval stages have neither arms nor mouth.   The orange-colored larvae swim about rather slowly for a few days, and then attach by means of the pre-oral process.   The larval body, with the exception of this process (which is reduced), is gradually molded into the pentagonal form of the adult.   Illustrations of the larval stages may be found in a paper by Masterman (1902).

REFERENCES:

Bumpus, H. C., 1898.   The breeding of animals at Woods Holl during the month of May, 1898.   *Science,* **8** : 58–61.

Clark, H. L., 1902.   The echinoderms of the Woods Hole region.   *Bull. U. S. Bur. Fish.,* **22** : 545–574.

Coe, W. R., 1912.   Echinoderms of Connecticut.   *Conn. State Geol. and Nat. Hist. Surv.,* **19** : 1–147.

Masterman, A. T., 1902.   The early development of *Cribrella oculata* (Forbes), with remarks on echinoderm development.   *Trans. Roy. Soc., Edinburgh,* **40** : 373–418.

Mead, A. D., 1898.   The breeding of animals at Woods Holl during the month of April, 1898.   *Science,* **7** : 702–704.

ECHINODERMATA

(Ophiuroidea)

Amphipholis (formerly *Amphiura*) *squamata*

LIVING MATERIAL:

This small brittle star is obtained by dredging at the head of Lagoon Pond, Martha's Vineyard, and at Provincetown, Mass., although it is not available in large numbers. It is found with *Ophioderma brevispina*. Amphipholis is hermaphroditic and viviparous, and is probably self-fertile (Fewkes, 1887).

BREEDING SEASON:

In New England, mature eggs and young in various stages of development have been obtained during the middle of the summer and on until the end of September (Fewkes, 1887; Coe, 1912). Animals obtained in the British Isles and New Zealand indicate that there may be a prolonged breeding period, which possibly extends throughout the year. At Plymouth, England, they are reported to breed from May to September (Garstang, 1931), but specimens collected in February, during an exceptionally cold winter, carried embryos of various stages (Fell, 1946).

PROCURING AND HANDLING MATERIAL:

A. Care of Adults: The animals may be kept in aquaria or petri dishes, supplied with fresh sea water which should be inoculated at intervals with diatoms, such as Skeletonema (Fell, 1946).

B. Procuring Gametes: The ova are produced singly, and are liberated directly into the bursae where they are fertilized. Attempts at artificial fertilization have been unsuccessful.

C. Preparation of Cultures: Embryos in various stages of development can be removed from the bursae or brood-pouches of a mature adult, using the method described by Fell (1946): The animal is anaesthetized using a $2\frac{1}{2}$–5% solution of menthol in sterile sea water. With fine tenotomy scalpel and forceps, the disc, with bursae attached, is separated from the arms and mouth skeleton and turned oral side upward. The free-swimming embryos are disentangled from the membranous walls by directing a stream of water from a hypodermic syringe into the bursae. The younger, attached embryos are excised with fine scissors.

The embryos should be pipetted through several washings of sterilized sea water, and then isolated in five-cm. watch glasses containing two to three ml. of "Erdschreiber" medium (Gross, 1937), which provides certain vital nutrient substances. The watch glass is set in a larger petri dish, together with a sterile swab of wet cotton wool. The whole set-up is placed on a water table in order to keep the temperature moderately constant. The medium should be renewed every fourth day. The embryos are very susceptible to bacterial toxins, but by using this method they may be kept for several weeks and will differentiate normally.

D. Methods of Observation: Polarized light is recommended for studying the developing skeleton in these rather opaque embryos.

NORMAL DEVELOPMENT:

A. The Unfertilized Ovum: The mature ovum is orange-red in color, and measures approximately 100 microns in diameter (Fell, 1946). It is enclosed within a thin membrane, which is closely associated with the underlying protoplasm. The egg is opaque, due to the presence of yolk, and is shed at the germinal vesicle stage.

B. Fertilization and Cleavage: Little is known about fertilization and cleavage in this species. Two polar bodies are extruded and are retained within the fertilization membrane. The early cleavages are presumably total and regular. A modified form of invagination produces a gastrula with a reduced blastopore and no true archenteron. The pigmentation becomes restricted to the cells giving rise to endoderm (Fell, 1946).

C. Developmental Rate: No details are available.

D. Later Stages of Development and Metamorphosis: The young embryo becomes attached soon after hatching to the wall of the bursa. It is a vestigial, bilaterally symmetrical and oval-shaped pluteus, which corresponds approximately to the central portion of a normal pelagic ophiopluteus. A reduced calcareous skeleton, oesophagus, stomach and intestine are present, but anus and mouth openings are lacking. The embryos are very opaque and contain a cluster of orange pigment near the "anal" pole. The primitive gut degenerates as the growing embryos are converted to a more transparent, pentagonal form. At this stage, the attachments atrophy, and the embryos break off and lie free in the cavities of the bursae. Here they complete their metamorphosis. The young animals crawl out of the bursae when they have attained the adult form. Figures of these stages are to be found in papers by Fewkes (1887), MacBride (1893), Metschnikoff (1869), and Fell (1946).

REFERENCES:

COE, W. R., 1912. Echinoderms of Connecticut. *Conn. State Geol. and Nat. Hist. Surv.,* **19**: 1–147.

FELL, H. BARRACLOUGH, 1946. The embryology of the viviparous ophiuroid *Amphipholis squamata* Delle Chiaje. *Trans. Proc. N. Z. Inst.,* **75**: 419–464.

FEWKES, J. W., 1887. On the development of the calcareous plates of Amphiura. *Bull. Mus. Comp. Zool., Harvard,* **13**: 107–150.

GARSTANG, W., 1931. *In:* Plymouth Marine Fauna. Second edition, Mar. Biol. Assoc., U. K., p. 295.

GROSS, F., 1937. Notes on the culture of some marine plankton organisms. *J. Mar. Biol. Assoc.,* **21**: 753–768.

LUDWIG, H., 1881. Zur Entwicklungsgeschichte der Ophiurenskelettes. *Zeitschr. f. wiss. Zool.,* **36**: 181–200.

MACBRIDE, E. W., 1893. The development of the genital organs, ovoid gland, axial and aboral sinuses in *Amphiura squamata;* together with some remarks on Ludwig's haemal system in this Ophiurid. *Quart. J. Micr. Sci.,* **34**: 129–153.

MACBRIDE, E. W., 1914. Text-Book of Embryology. Vol. I. Invertebrata. Macmillan and Co., Ltd., London, pp. 498–501.

METSCHNIKOFF, E., 1869. Studien über die Entwickelung der Echinodermen und Nemertinen. *Mém. d. l'Acad. Imp. des sci., St. Petersbourg,* 7è ser., **14**: 8, pp. 1–73.

ECHINODERMATA

(Ophiuroidea)

Ophioderma (formerly *Ophiura*) *brevispina*

LIVING MATERIAL:

These brittle stars are common in Lagoon Pond on Martha's Vineyard, Mass., where they are dredged from sandy bottoms among living and dead grasses and algae. The sexes are separate, and are similar in appearance.

BREEDING SEASON:

Grave (1916) states that the breeding season at Beaufort, N. C., is in June and July. At Woods Hole, Mass., observations indicate that spawning occurs during July and at least the first part of August.

PROCURING AND HANDLING MATERIAL:

A. Care of Adults: The animals should be kept in aquaria provided with a constant supply of sea water. They do not need to be fed, and will remain in good breeding condition for a considerable period of time. Fertile eggs, which developed normally through metamorphosis, have been obtained from Ophioderma after a month in a laboratory aquarium. During this period the same animals had previously produced several batches of eggs.

B. Procuring Gametes: Artificial insemination has not proved successful in this species, but naturally-shed eggs may be readily obtained during the evening, provided that the animals are in breeding condition. Grave (1916) states that the males begin to spawn about 8 P.M., and it has since been observed that this process of spawning may continue until midnight.

The animals should be removed at sunset from the aquarium to a fingerbowl containing sea water, placed near a window. The males will begin to shed sperm; the presence of sperm in the water seems to induce the females to release their eggs. When the sperm concentration is very dense, a great number of immature eggs are shed along with the mature ones (Grave, 1916).

C. Preparation of Cultures: It is important to transfer the eggs to fingerbowls of fresh sea water as soon as possible after shedding, as the dense sperm suspension tends to induce abnormal development. Since the eggs are relatively large, the transfer is easily accomplished with the aid of a pipette. Both eggs and young larvae should be removed to fresh sea water at least twice a day. The cultures should be covered and kept on a water table.

NORMAL DEVELOPMENT:

A. The Unfertilized Ovum: The egg is pelagic and floats to the surface as soon as it is released. It is very opaque, due to the presence of yolk. The color may vary from yellow to dark green, but within a single batch of eggs it is uniform. The average diameter of this egg is approximately 300 microns (Grave, 1916). The egg is probably shed after the formation of the polar bodies.

B. Fertilization and Cleavage: The eggs are fertilized as they are shed into the water. Cleavage is total and equal, closely resembling that of Asterias. A thick-walled hollow blastula is formed. Gastrulation is by invagination.

C. Rate of Development: At a laboratory temperature of 24° C., the early cleavages occur at half-hour intervals. A rotating blastula is formed in 10 to 12 hours, and a gastrula 18 to 20 hours after fertilization. At 48 hours, the rudiments of the arms are visible. At 96 hours, the first tube feet appear as small protuberances, and at 120 hours, some of the larvae are able to crawl along the bottom.

D. Later Stages of Development: The young, yolky, larvae are cone-shaped with a flattened blastoporic pole at the time of gastrulation. They are completely covered with cilia which enable them to move slowly through the water. As they gradually elongate, the blastopore is displaced ventrally and the stomodeal depression becomes visible. Two lateral thickenings next appear, just below the equator of the embryo. The blastopore now closes, and the cilia become concentrated in the form of four bands. Five groups of elevations soon appear about the stomodeum, on the ventral surface of the flattened oral disc. Each group consists of three elevations, the rudiments of the end tentacle and the first two tube feet of each arm. In the course of further development the arms elongate, additional tube feet are added, the ciliated bands are raised on ridges, and the old "anterior" pole of the larva degenerates. For diagrams of the larvae and for a description of the internal development, see the paper by Brooks and Grave (1899).

REFERENCES:

BROOKS, W. K., AND C. GRAVE, 1899. *Ophiura brevispina. Mem. Nat. Acad. Sci.,* **8**: 79–100. Also in *Mem. Biol. Lab., Johns Hopkins Univ.,* **4**: no. 5, pp. 79–100.

GRAVE, C., 1916. *Ophiura brevispina.* II. An embryological contribution and a study of the effect of yolk substance upon development and developmental processes. *J. Morph.,* **27**: 413–451.

ECHINODERMATA

(Ophiuroidea)

Ophiopholis aculeata

LIVING MATERIAL:

Ripe specimens of these brittle stars are usually not available at Woods Hole, Mass., but they may be dredged from the colder waters to the north. Bumpus (1898) received large numbers of them in good condition, shipped in artificially cooled containers from Nahant, Mass., to Woods Hole.

The sexes are separate. During the breeding season the gonads can be seen through the skin on the underside of the disc. The ovaries are yellowish-red and the testes white.

BREEDING SEASON:

Fewkes (1886) stated that animals at Eastport, Maine, breed in summer until mid-August. At Nahant, in 1898, ripe animals were obtained from mid-May to the end of June (Bumpus, 1898).

PROCURING AND HANDLING MATERIAL:

A. Care of Adults: The adults may be stored in aquaria in a cool place. It is advisable to obtain fresh material quite often.

B. Procuring Gametes: Ripe animals will usually spawn about 15 to 30 minutes after they are placed in sea water at room temperature. The males usually, but not always, spawn first. Eggs may be obtained by removing the ovaries, cutting them in two, and allowing the eggs to roll out. Eggs which tend to cling together instead of rolling out are immature and should be discarded. The best way to obtain ripe eggs is to isolate a shedding female in a small container, first rinsing the animal in tap water. The eggs are shed within a short time, and it is probable that all which are ripe are released (Olsen, 1942).

C. Preparation of Cultures: The eggs should be transferred to a fingerbowl of fresh sea water, where they may be inseminated by adding a small amount of sperm suspension. All the eggs are fertilized, and should receive a change of sea water after a short time. They need little care until after hatching. Olsen (1942) gives methods for feeding the larvae with cultured phytoplankton.

D. Methods of Observation: The study of the developing skeleton of these embryos is greatly facilitated by the use of polarized light.

E. Removal of Membranes: The fertilization membrane can be removed with the aid of a pipette. This is most easily accomplished immediately after its formation. Development of the denuded egg proceeds normally.

NORMAL DEVELOPMENT:

A. The Unfertilized Ovum: The mature egg is spherical in shape and measures approximately 105 microns in diameter (Olsen, 1942). It is surrounded by a gelatinous capsule, which disappears about 10 minutes after fertilization. Fewkes

(1886) described the egg as faintly green in color; the Norwegian variety is reportedly reddish-yellow or yellowish-brown (Olsen, 1942). The ovum is shed after the breakdown of the germinal vesicle.

   B. Fertilization and Cleavage: About one minute after fertilization, the fertilization membrane begins to elevate, leaving a small perivitelline space. The diameter across the fertilization membrane is approximately 130 microns. A transparent hyaline layer, consisting of two parts, can now be seen surrounding the yolky portion of the egg. The outer part, which is as clear as glass, remains on the egg surface throughout cleavage, while the inner, with dark radial stripes or shadows, sinks between the blastomeres during cleavage and surrounds them completely (Olsen, 1942). Soon after fertilization, the egg becomes irregular in shape, and remains thus until after the first cleavage. Meanwhile, two polar bodies are formed. They are retained for some time under the fertilization membrane, but not in any fixed position.

   The cleavage pattern is usually irregular (Olsen, 1942). An ovoid, ciliated blastula is formed. It hatches and rotates slowly to the surface. Gastrulation is by invagination. The two portions of the hyaline layer can be followed through to late larval stages. For figures of cleavage and gastrulation, consult the papers by Fewkes (1886) and Olsen (1942).

   C. Time Table of Development: Olsen (1942) reared the Norwegian form of this species in sea water at 8° C., and recorded the following times from fertilization for the early stages of development:

Stage	Time
First cleavage	3 hours
Second cleavage	5 hours
Third cleavage	5 hours, 45 minutes
Fourth cleavage	6 hours, 30 minutes
Fifth cleavage	7 hours, 30 minutes
Hatching (blastula)	24 hours
Gastrulation	27 to 48 hours
Young pluteus	3 to 4 days
Full-grown pluteus	about 30 days

These times agree with the few observations of the New England species recorded by Fewkes (1886); however, it is unlikely that his animals were reared at such a low temperature—none is indicated.

   D. Later Stages of Development and Metamorphosis: The larval gastrula transforms into a young pluteus, with a calcareous skeleton and rudimentary arms. By the fourth day the alimentary tract and primitive coelom are formed, and the arms have increased in size. Older larvae (about 17 days) are characterized by the development of a fourth pair of ciliated arms, and the exceptional length of the postero-lateral pair. The developing hydrocoele may be seen after 20 days, and by 30 days the pluteus is full grown. Metamorphosis begins with the formation of the adult skeleton, and has been described in detail by Olsen (1942). Figures of these stages may be found in papers by Fewkes (1886, 1887) and Olsen (1942).

BUMPUS, H. C., 1898. The breeding of animals at Woods Holl during the months of June, July and August. *Science,* **8**: 850–858.

FEWKES, J. W., 1886. Preliminary observations on the development of Ophiopholis and Echinarachnius. *Bull. Mus. Comp. Zool., Harvard,* **12**: 105–152.

FEWKES, J. W., 1887. On the development of the calcareous plates of Amphiura. *Bull. Mus. Comp. Zool., Harvard,* **13**: 107–150.

OLSEN, H., 1942. The development of the brittle-star *Ophiopholis aculeata* (O. Fr. Müller), with a short report on the outer hyaline layer. Bergens Mus. Årb., 1942, Naturv. Rekke, Nr. 6, S. 1–107.

ECHINODERMATA

(ECHINOIDEA)

Arbacia punctulata

LIVING MATERIAL:

Although it is possible in some species of echinoids to distinguish the sexes by external characteristics (see the papers by Marx, 1932, and Harvey, 1956b), no differentiating characteristics have, as yet, been described for the American sea urchin, *Arbacia punctulata*. The sexes are readily identified after the animals are opened, by the deep red or purple ovaries and the white testes, or, if unopened animals shed spontaneously, by the red eggs and the white sperm. Hermaphroditic animals are occasionally found (Boolootian and Moore, 1956).

At Woods Hole, Mass., the animals are obtained by dredging; they are, at the present time, rather scarce.

An exhaustive account of the life-history, embryology and metamorphosis of Arbacia is given by Harvey (1956a).

BREEDING SEASON:

From the middle of June until the middle of August (Harvey, 1956a), although the season may vary somewhat from year to year.

PROCURING AND HANDLING MATERIAL:

A. Care of Adults: In the laboratory, animals can be kept in aquaria provided with running sea water; they should not be crowded.

B. Procuring Gametes: The following methods may be used, (4) or (5) being preferable because of the present scarcity of Arbacia at Woods Hole:

(1) Cut around the peristome (on the oral surface) and remove the Aristotle's lantern, taking care not to injure the gonads. The perivisceral fluid should then be drained from the body and the animal, aboral surface down, placed to shed on a Syracuse watch glass which has been moistened with sea water. After each animal is opened, the hands of the investigator and all instruments used should be washed with running fresh water, to avoid contamination of the gametes of one sex with those of the other, or with body fluids. If the eggs are shed through the gonopores of the female into the Syracuse dish, they should be transferred within ten minutes to a fingerbowl containing 200 cc. of sea water. The sperm are best kept "dry," just as they exude from the testes.

(2) Cut around the test, about halfway between the mouth and the equator, and proceed as in (1) above. Shedding is more frequently obtained by this method, but there is also more likelihood of cutting the gonads, and of contamination with the perivisceral fluid.

(3) Cut as in (2) above, pour out the body fluid and remove the gonads (at the gonoduct end) with blunt forceps, spatula or spoon. The ovaries should be placed in 200 cc. of sea water in a fingerbowl, and allowed to shed. If undisturbed, the eggs are extruded in compact clumps or strings, without ovarian tissue,

and may be removed to a fresh dish by means of a wide-mouth pipette. If large quantities of eggs are desired, the ovaries should be allowed to shed for about 30 minutes, with occasional stirring; then pour them gently through cheesecloth (which has previously been washed in fresh water and soaked in filtered sea water) or bolting silk.

(4) Palmer (1937) induced spawning in Arbacia by injecting isotonic (0.53 M) KCl into the perivisceral cavity, and Tyler (1949) described a similar method, utilizing 0.5 cc. of 0.5 M KCl. Ripe animals begin to shed in a few minutes; the eggs can be collected by inverting the female in a dish of sea water, or by washing them gently from the surface of the test with a pipette. The sperm should be collected "dry." This method has the advantage that one is enabled to sex animals without sacrificing them, but there is some evidence (Harvey, 1956b) that eggs obtained in this manner do not develop normally. The animals may be returned to an aquarium, and will produce another batch of gametes in about three weeks, if fed periodically.

(5) Harvey (1953) has reported an electrical method (similar to a technique devised by Iwata, 1950, for Japanese sea urchins) for sexing Arbacia and inducing shedding. An alternating current of 10 volts (reduced by a transformer from ordinary 60-cycle, 110-volt current) is applied, using lead electrodes, to any two points on the test of the animal, which is placed, aboral side up, in a dish and covered with sea water. Almost immediately after the current is passed, the gametes will be extruded from each of the gonopores; when the current is stopped, the shedding ceases, to be resumed when the current is again applied. The gametes should be removed and used at once. Harvey points out that this method is of great value in laboratories where sea urchins have become scarce, since only the quantity of gametes desired is obtained and the animals need not be sacrificed.

C. Preparing Cultures: Two drops (0.2 cc.) of "dry" sperm may be diluted with 10 cc. of sea water (Just, 1939) in a watch glass, just before insemination; *do not use sperm which have been diluted more than 20 minutes,* and avoid a high sperm concentration, which leads to polyspermy and abnormal cleavage. Two drops of diluted sperm are sufficient for a fingerbowl of eggs. Stir the dish immediately.

NORMAL DEVELOPMENT:

A. The Sperm: After dilution with sea water, the sperm become intensely active, although they are immobile in concentrated suspension due, presumably, to the effects of high concentrations of carbon dioxide. Concomitantly, their ability to fertilize eggs is lost more rapidly in dilute than in concentrated suspensions. (See the papers by Lillie, 1915; Cohn, 1918; Hayashi, 1945.) "Dry" sperm kept in the cold (2° C.) may remain usable for several days; at room temperatures, dilute sperm suspensions often lose their fertilizing power in an hour or less.

The spermatozoon consists of three parts: head, middle piece and tail. These are 3.25 microns, 0.75 micron and 45 microns in length, respectively (Harvey and Anderson, 1943). The fibrillar axial filament of the tail protrudes a short distance beyond the end of the sheath.

B. The Unfertilized Ovum: A good batch of eggs from a ripe female should show uniformity of size, perfectly spherical form and complete absence of immature eggs (which are in the germinal vesicle stage). Both meiotic divisions are completed while the eggs are still in the ovary, and the polar bodies very seldom remain attached when the eggs are shed (Hoadley, 1934). Occasionally (especially from relatively unripe animals, or after maceration of the ovaries), eggs may be found that are in the germinal vesicle stage; this is recognizable in the living state by the large clear nucleus (as opposed to the small nucleus of the ripe egg) and nucleolus. Such eggs may exhibit some surface response to sperm (including the formation of "papillae"), but they do not develop after insemination. The ripe egg, 72 to 75 microns in diameter, has a small, clear nucleus; it contains uniformly-dispersed, pale yolk granules, and slightly larger red granules containing echino-chrome pigment, which is a substituted naphthoquinone related to the K vitamins (Ball, 1936; Hartmann *et al.*, 1939; Tyler, 1939). The nucleus is usually ex-centric in location. Since the polar bodies are not ordinarily present, the position of the nucleus with respect to the polar axis is not readily determined; occasionally, however, batches of eggs are obtained in which the polar bodies are still attached, and in these, observations by Hoadley (1934) have shown that the nucleus may lie in any part of the cytoplasm between the cortex and the center. In the trans-parent, gelatinous coat of the egg (about 30 microns wide), there is a funnel-shaped space which usually lies in the polar axis. The funnel is rendered visible by staining the jelly with Janus green, or by placing the eggs in a suspension of Chinese ink. For this purpose, the eggs should be taken immediately after shed-ding, because the "micropyle" (funnel) may disappear as the jelly swells after the eggs are shed into sea water. See the diagrams by Harvey and Dan (Harvey, 1956a, p. 84) of the membranes and layers of the fertilized, as compared with the unfertilized, egg.

C. Fertilization: Sperm penetration occurs very rapidly (apparently at any point on the egg), and it is usually difficult to study. Within a few seconds after insemination, the cortical responses of the egg begin; the vitelline membrane starts to elevate rapidly from the egg surface (in about five seconds), leaving a peri-vitelline space. This membrane hardens and thickens during the next five minutes, and, after alteration, is called the fertilization membrane. At the protoplasmic egg surface (which is at first slightly disrupted by the elevation of the vitelline mem-brane), a new, clear layer is formed about ten minutes after fertilization: the hyaline plasma membrane, which is apparently a calcium-proteinate, acting as a cement to hold the blastomeres together after cleavage. It disappears when the eggs are placed in calcium-free sea water. After insemination, the jelly-layer is often clearly delimited by the supernumerary sperm trapped near its surface. Moser (1939, 1940) has correlated the elevation of the vitelline membrane with the breakdown of certain cortical granules. These granules are embedded in the cortex, and are not easily displaced by centrifugation (as are the granules of the underlying fluid endoplasm). Runnström *et al.* (1944) state that the cortical granules contribute to the formation of the fertilization membrane.

D. Cleavage: About 15 minutes after insemination (at 20° C.) a sperm aster is visible as a spherical region containing clear rays which extend from a clear center; this configuration attains its maximum development 20 to 30 minutes after insemination. Then a clear streak appears in the egg, slightly above the equator, and 45 to 50 minutes after insemination, it is replaced by two clear areas, the asters of the first cleavage spindle. The first three cleavages divide the egg into eight blastomeres of equal size. The planes of the first two cleavages are meridional (in the polar axis), while that of the third is equatorial or horizontal (at right angles to the polar axis). The progress of the cleavage furrows in dividing eggs can be followed; the hyaline layer forms the surface of the furrow and later, when the cells flatten against one another, it forms the boundary between them. At the fourth cleavage, the four upper cells divide meridionally, forming eight equal mesomeres, while the lower four cells divide unequally and horizontally, to form four large macromeres; below them, at the vegetal pole, are four small, clear micromeres.

At the fifth division, the eight mesomeres divide equally and horizontally, forming two tiers of cells termed an_1 (at the animal pole) and an_2 (see the paper by Hörstadius, 1939), while the macromeres and micromeres divide meridionally. At the sixth cleavage, the an_1 and an_2 cells divide in a more or less radial direction, while the macromeres divide horizontally to form the veg_1 and veg_2 tiers of cells. Veg_2 cells are next to the micromeres, which have also divided at this time but which do not form distinct layers. Tiers of cells are not readily distinguished in later cleavage stages, and no special cell-layer designation is used after the 64-cell stage. It has been shown by Hörstadius (1939) that the an_1, an_2 and veg_1 cells form the ectoderm, the veg_2 cells form endoderm (gut) and part of the mesoderm (coelom), while the micromeres form the mesodermal skeleton components.

E. Time Table of Development: The following schedules of development have been observed at temperatures of 23° C. (data from Harvey, 1956a) and 20° C.; the time is recorded from insemination.

	Time at	
Stage	20° C.	23° C.
Formation of fertilization membrane	5 minutes	2 minutes
Formation of hyaline layer	10 minutes	2 minutes
Sperm aster appears	15 minutes	8 minutes
"Streak" stage	35 minutes	20–35 minutes
Cleavage asters	45–50 minutes	35 minutes
First cleavage	56–67 minutes	50 minutes
Second cleavage	107 minutes	78 minutes
Third cleavage	145 minutes	103 minutes
Blastula	6 hours	
Hatching of blastula	10 hours	7–8 hours
Gastrula	20 hours	12–15 hours
Pluteus	48 hours	24 hours
Metamorphosis	2 weeks	

Different batches of eggs vary slightly (1–2%) in average cleavage times; within a batch, most eggs will develop at the average rate, but some may vary by about 10%. Temperatures above 30–32° C. are lethal for Arbacia eggs.

F. Later Stages of Development: At the eight-cell stage, there is a very small central cavity which enlarges as cleavage continues, to form the blastocoele. About six hours after fertilization, a smooth-surfaced, spherical young blastula is formed, the wall of which is one cell in thickness. Cilia soon develop on the surface, and the blastula is rotated by their action within the fertilization membrane. The blastula hatches out of the fertilization membrane in about ten hours. It has been shown that the blastula releases a "hatching enzyme" at this time, which weakens and dissolves the membrane so that the blastula can break through. A tuft of long cilia develops at the animal pole of the blastula, which is the forward end when the embryo is swimming. At the base of this apical tuft the blastula wall is thickened, forming the apical plate. At the vegetal pole, the blastula wall becomes flattened, and the micromeres migrate into the blastocoele, forming the rudimentary mesenchyme which gives rise to the skeleton.

About 20 hours after fertilization, the cells at the vegetal pole invaginate to form a blind tube, the archenteron. This reaches the opposite end of the blastocoele in about five hours. The gastrula contains approximately one thousand cells, and its outer wall, as well as the wall of the archenteron, has a single layer of cells. The primary mesenchyme cells form a ring around the blastoporal end of the archenteron. Secondary mesenchyme and, later, the coelom are budded off from the tip of the archenteron.

At the completion of gastrulation, the tip of the archenteron turns to one side of the gastrula, which becomes flattened over an area extending from the animal pole nearly to the blastopore. This is the first sign of bilateral symmetry, the flattened area representing the ventral side of the embryo. The primary mesen-chyme cells aggregate in two groups, one on each postero-ventral side, and each group secretes a triradiate spicule, the beginning of the skeleton. Where the tip of the archenteron touches the ectoderm, there is formed a depression which later acquires an opening into the archenteron to become the stomodeum. The archen-teron becomes divided by two constrictions into oesophagus, stomach and intestine. The apical tuft disappears, a ciliated band surrounds the oral field, the embryo begins to elongate in the dorso-ventral axis, and the direction of swimming changes, so that the ventral side is forward.

After about 48 hours, the embryo enters the pluteus stage, which is fully de-veloped by the end of the third day. The original apical plate grows out in a ventral direction, to form the oral lobe which includes the stomodeum and the anterior part of the oesophagus. Two short outgrowths, the oral (antero-lateral) arms, are formed on the oral lobe, and, at the anal side, two longer anal (aboral or post-oral) arms grow out in the same general direction. The original triradiate spicules form skeletal rods which extend into the oral arms (oral rods), the anal arms (anal rods), dorsally through the body (body rods) and laterally (ventra! transverse rods). Each of the rods is made up of three or four parallel parts joined by cross-bars. Different species of sea urchins differ in this regard, so that the structure of the skeletal rods is a useful characteristic in hybridization studies.

The embryo continues to elongate in the dorso-ventral direction, and becomes pointed at the postero-dorsal end where the body rods meet. The axis running through oesophagus, stomach and intestine becomes J-shaped. The stomach ex-pands, to become a spherical structure which fills a large part of the body of the pluteus; sphincter muscles connect it with the oesophagus and intestine. The two coelomic sacs extend postero-laterally from the oesophagus; the one on the left side becomes larger and later acquires a dorsal opening called the pore canal. The right coelomic sac buds off cells to form the madreporic vesicle, but otherwise remains rudimentary. The left coelom undergoes extensive later development in the formation of structures of the adult sea urchin. These changes do not occur until the second week, when metamorphosis begins in properly fed larvae. The adult organs are built up in and around a structure called the "echinus rudiment," which is formed by the fusion of an invagination (the amniotic invagination) of the ectoderm on the left side with the mid-portion (hydrocoele) of the left coelom. The left side of the pluteus becomes, then, the future oral surface of the adult.

G. Special Methods of Observation: Dark-field illumination shows a bright, reddish "luminous" layer on the surface of the unfertilized egg. The luminosity diminishes and becomes paler after fertilization (Runnström, 1928; Ohman, 1945). The skeletal spicules and rods are best demonstrated by the use of a polarization microscope.

REFERENCES:

BALL, E. G., 1936. Echinochrome, its isolation and composition. *J. Biol. Chem.,* 114: vi.

BOOLOOTIAN, R. A., AND A. R. MOORE, 1956. Hermaphroditism in echinoids. *Biol. Bull.,* 111: 328–335.

COHN, E. J., 1918. Studies in the physiology of spermatozoa. *Biol. Bull.,* 34: 167–218.

DAN, K., 1954. The cortical movement in *Arbacia punctulata* eggs through cleavage cycles. *Embryologia,* 2: 115–122.

FRY, H. J., 1936. Studies of the mitotic figure. V. The time schedule of mitotic changes in developing Arbacia eggs. *Biol. Bull.,* 70: 89–99.

HARTMANN, M., O. SCHARTAU, R. KUHN AND K. WALLENFELS, 1939. Über die Sexualstoffe der Seeigel. *Naturwiss.,* 27: 433.

HARVEY, E. B., 1939. A method of determining the sex of Arbacia, and a new method of producing twins, triplets and quadruplets. *Coll. Net,* 14: 211.

HARVEY, E. B., 1940. A note on determining the sex of *Arbacia punctulata. Biol. Bull.,* 79: 363.

HARVEY, E. B., 1953. A simplified electrical method of determining the sex of sea urchins and other marine animals. *Biol. Bull.,* 105: 365.

HARVEY, E. B., 1956a. The American Arbacia and Other Sea Urchins. Princeton University Press, Princeton, N. J.

HARVEY, E. B., 1956b. Sex in sea urchins. *Pubbl. Staz. Zool., Napoli,* 28: 127–135.

HARVEY, E. B., AND T. F. ANDERSON, 1943. The spermatozoon and fertilization membrane of *Arbacia punctulata* as shown by the electron microscope. *Biol. Bull.,* 85: 151–156.

HAYASHI, T., 1945. Dilution medium and survival of the spermatozoa of *Arbacia punctulata.* I. Effect of the medium on fertilizing power. *Biol. Bull.,* 89: 162–179.

HOADLEY, L., 1934. The relation between the position of the female pronucleus and the polar bodies in the unfertilized egg of *Arbacia punctulata. Biol. Bull.,* 67: 220–222.

HÖRSTADIUS, S., 1939. The mechanics of sea urchin development, studied by operative methods. *Biol. Rev.,* 14: 132–179.

IWATA, K. S., 1950. A method of determining the sex of sea urchins and of obtaining eggs by electric stimulation. *Annot. Zool. Jap.,* 23: 39–42.

JUST, E. E., 1939. Basic Methods for Experiments on Eggs of Marine Animals. P. Blakiston's Son & Co., Inc., Philadelphia.

LILLIE, F. R., 1915. Studies of fertilization. VII. Analysis of variations in the fertilizing power of sperm suspensions of Arbacia. *Biol. Bull.,* 28: 229–251.

MARX, W., 1932. Zum Problem der Determination der Bilateralität im Seeigelkeim. (Nebst einem Beitrag zur Kenntnis des Geschlechtsdimorphismus einiger Seeigel.) *Arch. f. Entw.,* 125: 96–147.

MOSER, F., 1939. Studies on a cortical layer response to stimulating agents in the Arbacia egg. Parts I and II. *J. Exp. Zool.,* 80: 423–471.

MOSER, F., 1940. Studies on a cortical layer response to stimulating agents in the Arbacia egg. Parts III and IV. *Biol. Bull.,* 78: 68–91.

OHMAN, L. –O., 1945.   On the lipids of the sea-urchin egg.   *Arch. f. Zoologi,* **36A**: no. 7, 1–95.

PALMER, L., 1937.   The shedding reaction in *Arbacia punctulata. Physiol. Zool.,* **10**: 352–367.

RUNNSTRÖM, J., 1928.   Die Veranderung der Plasmakolloide bei der Entwicklungserregung des Seeigeleis.   *Protoplasma,* **4**: 388–514.

*RUNNSTRÖM, J., L. MONNÉ AND E. WICKLUND, 1944.   Mechanisms of formation of the fertilization membrane in the sea urchin egg.   *Nature,* **153**: 313–314.

TYLER, A., 1939.   Crystalline echinochrome and spinochrome: Their failure to stimulate the respiration of eggs and of sperm of Strongylocentrotus.   *Proc. Nat. Acad. Sci.,* **25**: 523–528.

TYLER, A., 1949.   A simple, non-injurious method for inducing repeated spawning of sea urchins and sand-dollars.   *Coll. Net,* **19**: 19–20.

ZEUTHEN, E., 1955.   Mitotic respiratory rhythms in single eggs of *Psammechinus miliaris* and of *Ciona intestinalis., Biol. Bull.,* **105**: 366–385.

ECHINODERMATA

(ECHINOIDEA)

Echinarachnius parma

LIVING MATERIAL:

The common sand dollar is found in isolated areas on sandy bottoms below low tide level, and is obtained in abundance by dredging at West Barnstable on Cape Cod Bay, Mass.

The sexes are separate, but it is impossible to distinguish the male from the female by superficial examination.

BREEDING SEASON:

The animals breed abundantly at Woods Hole, Mass., from at least the last week of March to the end of July; even in August, a limited amount of ripe gametes may be obtained (Bumpus, 1898a, 1898b; Mead, 1898).

PROCURING AND HANDLING MATERIAL:

A. Care of Adults: The adults may be kept indefinitely in an aquarium provided with a layer of clean sand and a continuous supply of fresh sea water. They can be fed on kelp, mussels, and other marine plants and animals.

B. Procuring Gametes: Tyler's method (1949) for procuring gametes is to inject isosmotic KCl ($0.5 M$) with a hypodermic syringe into the body cavity of the sand dollar, inserting the needle (25–27 gauge, ½- to ¾-inch) through the mouth in a direction as nearly parallel as possible to the oral surface. A single injection of 0.5 cc. of $0.5 M$ KCl into an animal about 30 cc. in volume will induce shedding of virtually all the ripe eggs or sperm. For smaller animals, the dose should be proportionately smaller (0.5–0.2 cc.). Shedding starts within a few seconds and is completed in 5 to 15 minutes. Unripe animals usually fail to respond. The eggs can be collected readily by immersing the animal in a large fingerbowl containing about 250 cc. of sea water. The sperm can be removed "dry" or in concentrated suspension.

This method does not injure the animals. More gametes are matured, provided the animals are well fed, and successive sheddings may be obtained at two-week intervals during the season. If only a small number of gametes is desired, a correspondingly small amount of KCl should be injected, and the animals may then be kept for further use.

The eggs of *Dendraster excentricus,* the common sand dollar of the Pacific Coast, may be obtained by this same method (Tyler, 1949). Their development is similar to that of *Echinarachnius parma.*

C. Preparation of Cultures: The eggs should be washed several times in sea water. To them add one drop of sperm suspension (one drop "dry" sperm in 10 cc. of sea water) and mix thoroughly. After about 10 minutes, when the eggs have settled, decant the sea water to remove the excess sperm, and add fresh sea water. Store the fingerbowls on the water table. The sea water should be changed once a day. Normal development will not take place at temperatures above 24° C.

The larvae can be reared to metamorphosis if they are transferred to large battery jars of sea water and provided with some surface sand from a stock aquarium containing a diatom culture. No further care is necessary. Details of the method for diatom culture may be found in a short paper by Grave (1902).

D. Removal of Membrane: The fertilization membrane may be easily removed by shaking the eggs in a test-tube, half-full of sea water, a few seconds after the membrane has elevated. Echinarachnius eggs are fragile and will not stand as much shaking as those of Arbacia.

NORMAL DEVELOPMENT:

A. The Unfertilized Ovum: The mature egg of this species measures approximately 135 microns in diameter, and is surrounded by a thick jelly-layer in which are suspended fine red pigment granules. The diameter across the jelly varies from 220 to 250 microns (Fewkes, 1886). The egg itself, free of the jelly, is yellow due to its yolk content.

B. Fertilization and Cleavage: In a matter of seconds (7–22) after sperm penetration, the vitelline membrane begins to elevate in a wave from the entrance point of the sperm around the egg cortex (Just, 1919a). The resulting perivitelline space is quite large. Cleavage is usually equal and regular until the 8-cell stage (Fewkes, 1886). There is a thinner hyaline plasma layer than in the Arbacia egg, and less regularity of cleavage. However, the cleavage pattern is not markedly different from that of Arbacia. A hollow, ciliated blastula, which rotates slowly within the fertilization membrane, is produced. Gastrulation is by invagination.

C. Time Table of Development: No temperature was recorded for the following schedule of development observed by Fewkes (1886). The times are calculated from fertilization.

Stage	Time
First cleavage	1½ hours
Second cleavage	2 hours
Third cleavage	3 hours
Blastula	10 hours

D. Later Stages of Development and Metamorphosis: The early larva is nearly spherical in shape and rests on a tripod formed by the two posterior arms and the single anterior lobe. Pigment can be seen at the anal pole. A rudimentary skeleton, primitive alimentary tract, and mouth and anal openings are present. As the larva matures, it becomes more and more helmet-shaped. At four days the oral, or anterior, arms begin to form, and by the end of a week the antero-lateral and antero-internal arms have been added.

The body of the older pluteus is elongated, and rounded at the anal region. The four pairs of ciliated arms are of equal length; all except the antero-internal pair contain clusters of dark red pigment granules at the distal ends of the calcareous supporting rods. The pigmentation extends along the arms and over the body wall. The pluteus is propelled freely, but not rapidly, through the water.

The young sand dollar, which is very different in shape from the adult, is formed about the left hydrocoele of the pluteus, which is gradually absorbed. It is almost completely opaque, due to the formation of pigment, spines, calcareous rods and plates. The body is rounded and plump, and the spines are proportionately large when compared with those of the adult. Further details and illustrations of the larval development can be found in a paper by Fewkes (1886).

REFERENCES:

BUMPUS, H. C., 1898a. The breeding of animals at Woods Holl during the month of May, 1898. *Science,* **8**: 58–61.

BUMPUS, H. C., 1898b. The breeding of animals at Woods Holl during the months of June, July and August. *Science,* **8**: 850–858.

CHILD, C. M., 1950. Differential modification of sand-dollar development in relation to temperature. *Physiol. Zool.,* **23**: 140–168.

FEWKES, J. W., 1886. Preliminary observations on the development of Ophiopholis and Echinarachnius. *Bull. Mus. Comp. Zool., Harvard,* **12**: 105–152.

GRAVE, C., 1902. A method of rearing marine larvae. *Science,* **15**: 579–580.

JUST, E. E., 1919a. The fertilization reaction in *Echinarachnius parma.* I. Cortical response of the egg to insemination. *Biol. Bull.,* **36**: 1–10.

JUST, E. E., 1919b. II. The role of fertilizin in straight and cross fertilization. *Biol. Bull.,* **36**: 11–38.

JUST, E. E., 1919c. III. The nature of the activation of the egg by butyric acid. *Biol. Bull.,* **36**: 39–53.

JUST, E. E., 1920. IV. A further analysis of the nature of butyric acid activation. *Biol. Bull.,* **39**: 280–305.

JUST, E. E., 1922. V. The existence in the inseminated egg of a period of special susceptibility to hypotonic sea-water. *Amer. J. Physiol.,* **61**: 516–527.

JUST, E. E., 1923a. VI. The necessity of the egg cortex for fertilization. *Biol. Bull.,* **44**: 1–9.

JUST, E. E., 1923b. VII. The inhibitory action of blood. *Biol. Bull.,* **44**: 10–16.

JUST, E. E., 1923c. VIII. Fertilization in dilute sea-water. *Biol. Bull.,* **44**: 17–21.

MEAD, A. D., 1898. The breeding of animals at Woods Holl during the month of April, 1898. *Science,* **7**: 702–704.

PEASE, D. C., 1941. Echinoderm bilateral determination in chemical concentration gradients. I. The effects of cyanide, ferricyanide, iodoacetate, picrate, dinitrophenol, urethane, iodine, malonate, etc. *J. Exp. Zool.,* **86**: 381–404.

PEASE, D. C., 1942a. Echinoderm bilateral determination in chemical concentration gradients. II. The effects of azide, pilocarpine, pyocyanine, diamine, cysteine, glutathione, and lithium. *J. Exp. Zool.,* **89**: 329–345.

PEASE, D. C., 1942b. Echinoderm bilateral determination in chemical concentration gradients. III. The effects of carbon monoxide and other gases. *J. Exp. Zool.,* **89**: 347–356.

TYLER, A., 1949. A simple, non-injurious method for inducing repeated spawning of sea urchins and sand-dollars. *Coll. Net,* **19**: 19–20.

ECHINODERMATA

(HOLOTHUROIDEA)

Leptosynapta inhaerens and *L. roseola*

LIVING MATERIAL:

Both these species may be obtained readily by digging near low water mark at the Northwest Gutter or Sheep Pen Cove, near Woods Hole, Mass., at Lagoon Pond, on Martha's Vineyard, or at Rand's Harbor. *L. roseola,* which is small and rose-colored, is usually found under stones, and *L. inhaerens,* which is 10 to 20 cm. in length and white in color, is found burrowing in sand and occasionally in black mud. Both species are hermaphroditic, but neither is self-fertile. The American form of *Leptosynapta inhaerens* has been considered by some workers to be distinct from the European form with this name, and perhaps should be called *L. tenuis* (Ayres). *Leptosynapta roseola* is sometimes referred to as *Leptosynapta (Epitomapta) roseola* (Verrill).

BREEDING SEASON:

The height of the breeding season in the Woods Hole region is at the end of June and early in July (Clark, 1899), but mature gametes are probably available throughout both months (Bumpus, 1898; Coe, 1912).

PROCURING AND HANDLING MATERIAL:

A. Care of Adults: The animals are very sensitive to environmental conditions and will fragment if they are not handled with extreme care. They can be kept in aquaria provided with running sea water and a deep layer of clean sand.

B. Procuring Gametes: The gonads, in the form of long, contractile white strands, are visible through the transparent body wall during the breeding season. If the body wall overlying them is punctured, the gonads will ooze out. Dissection of the strings with fine needles releases the gametes. In some animals, the gonad strings will contain mature sperm and immature ova; in others, they are full of eggs and the sperm-bearing parts are inconspicuous.

Free-swimming larvae have been raised from artificially-inseminated eggs of *L. roseola* (Coe, 1912), but for *L. inhaerens* it is necessary to obtain naturally-shed ova. Spawning in the latter species begins between 3 and 4 o'clock in the afternoon and continues until 5 or 6 P.M. In the laboratory, it is most frequently observed on the first two days following collection, although it does occur occasionally after that (Runnström, 1927). The males shed first and continue for a longer period than do the females. Details of the natural spawning of *L. roseola* have not been recorded.

C. Preparation of Cultures: Artificially-obtained eggs of *L. roseola* may be inseminated by adding a few drops of sperm suspension to a dish of eggs. Mix well, allow the eggs to settle, and then decant the supernatant fluid. Add filtered sea water. Naturally-inseminated eggs of either species can be collected with a pipette and transferred to a fingerbowl of filtered sea water. The cultures should be stored on a sea water table.

When free-swimming forms appear, pour the upper layers of the culture, containing them, into another dish. Fill the dish with fresh sea water. No feeding is necessary since the larvae develop through metamorphosis exclusively on their own yolk content.

NORMAL DEVELOPMENT:

A. The Unfertilized Ovum: The egg of *L. inhaerens* is very transparent and fragile. It is surrounded by a narrow coat of jelly. The ovum, on removal from the egg-string, is not quite spherical and measures between 190 and 209 microns in its longest diameter. The germinal vesicle is very large and contains a conspicuous nucleolus.

B. Cleavage: Segmentation is total and equal in both species. It is reported to be very regular in *L. inhaerens* (Coe, 1912); gastrulation is by invagination, and a free-swimming gastrula is produced (Runnström, 1927).

C. Rate of Development: Little has been recorded concerning the rate of development for these species. However, the free-swimming gastrula of *L. inhaerens* can be seen about 24 hours after fertilization.

D. Later Stages of Development and Metamorphosis: Both species produce free-swimming larvae. The three-day larva of *L. inhaerens* is barrel-shaped, with four distinct transverse bands of cilia. No auricularia larva is developed. The free-swimming life is short and the larva remains near the bottom. Illustrations of the larval development of *L. inhaerens* may be found in a paper by Runnström (1927).

E. Pre-Adults: Metamorphosed animals up to 5 cm. in length may be collected at night, swimming near the surface in Eel Pond (Costello, 1946).

REFERENCES:

BUMPUS, H. C., 1898. The breeding of animals at Woods Holl during the months of June, July and August. *Science,* **8:** 850–858.

CLARK, H. L., 1899. The Synaptas of the New England coast. *Bull. U. S. Bur. Fish.,* **19:** 21–31.

CLARK, H. L., 1907. The apodous holothurians. A monograph of the Synaptidae and the Molpadiidae. *Smithsonian Contr. to Knowledge,* **35:** no. 1723, pp. 1–231.

COE, W. R., 1912. Echinoderms of Connecticut. *Conn. State Geol. and Nat. Hist. Surv.,* **19:** 1–147.

COSTELLO, D. P., 1946. The swimming of Leptosynapta. *Biol. Bull.,* **90:** 93–96.

RUNNSTRÖM, S., 1927. Über die Entwicklung von *Leptosynapta inhaerens* (O. Fr. Müller). Bergens Mus. Årb., 1927, Naturv. rekke, Nr. 1, pp. 1–80.

ECHINODERMATA

(HOLOTHUROIDEA)

Thyone briareus

LIVING MATERIAL:

This sea cucumber is abundant at Woods Hole, Mass. It lies almost completely buried in mud or sand in shallow water, and may be collected from many of the inlets in the vicinity. One recommended location is Bowen's Pond, near Falmouth Heights; another is in the Gutters at Hadley Harbor.

The sexes are separate and similar in appearance. The genital papilla, found between the two dorsal tentacles, is reportedly larger in males, but this has proved too unreliable a characteristic for sex determination. The sex ratio is approximately five females to six males (Colwin, 1948).

BREEDING SEASON:

June and July, according to Bumpus (1898), but June and possibly earlier is suggested by Colwin (1948), who found that the capacity to spawn decreases markedly during the latter half of June. Mead (1898) observed that every female examined at the end of April was full of nearly ripe eggs, a fact which would certainly indicate a season beginning in May, but Just (1929) claimed that eggs obtained in April and May showed atypical responses to insemination. He believed they were unripe oöcytes, capable of responding to insemination but unable to develop. Until this has been further investigated, Colwin (1948) recommends the first half of June for embryological experiments with this material.

PROCURING AND HANDLING MATERIAL:

A. Care of Adults: Any medium- or large-sized animal should be a suitable source of gametes. It is advisable to store the animals overnight in containers supplied continuously with fresh sea water, at a temperature between 15° and 17° C.; the latter precaution discourages shedding, and the former ensures that much of the debris, which Thyone pumps through its gut, will be removed, thus facilitating the recovery of gametes. The animals should then be isolated in containers with enough sea water to permit them to expand fully— 6 × 7½-inch battery jars are excellent. The sea water should be changed once or twice a day (Colwin, 1948).

B. Procuring Gametes: Although active sperm and apparently mature eggs can be teased from the gonadal lobes, artificial insemination of such eggs has not proved successful (Ohshima, 1925a; Just, 1939). This failure is perhaps explained by the fact that ovarian eggs contain a large germinal vesicle, while those shed normally are in metaphase of the first maturation division.

Spawning is preceded by full expansion and the so-called "feeding movements" of the tentacles. Ohshima (1925a, 1925b) noted that although shedding normally occurs late in the afternoon of the day of collection, it could be induced at any time by placing the animals in a dim light; it did not occur in darkness. However,

196

Colwin (1948) observed some normal shedding throughout the day and even in total darkness, although evening seemed to be the optimum time to obtain gametes. She discounts light intensity as a factor primarily involved in the shedding reaction. Any stimulus strong enough to cause a contraction of the animal will interrupt the process.

Colwin's method (1948) for obtaining naturally-shed gametes is to isolate the animals in sea water warmed to room temperature (20–22° C.) for about five hours. Shedding may begin immediately or after an interval; it may not occur until after the sea water has been re-cooled (16–18° C.). A period of warming is, however, apparently necessary for the occurrence of shedding in the laboratory. Other unknown factors may increase the frequency, but injections of KCl have no such effect. A concentrated sperm suspension is obtained by placing a shedding male into a fingerbowl containing only a very small amount of sea water. The adults are removed from their respective containers as soon as shedding ceases.

Colwin and Colwin (1956) have recently described another method for obtaining Thyone gametes, involving electrical stimulation of the adults. However, they state (p. 252) that they have not observed cleavage in inseminated cultures prepared from such gametes.

C. Preparation of Cultures: A small amount of sperm suspension should be added to the dish of eggs. After a short interval, the sea water should be changed, and the dish covered and placed on a water table. The sea water must be changed several times a day.

The larvae emerge in about three days. They may be successfully reared if placed in large battery jars of sea water, provided with some surface sand from a stock aquarium containing a diatom culture; then they may be left without further care. Details of the method for diatom culture may be found in a short paper by Grave (1902).

NORMAL DEVELOPMENT:

A. The Unfertilized Ovum: The egg is hemispherical in shape, measuring 260 to 300 microns in the equatorial plane, and 200 to 300 along the egg axis, and is enclosed in a thick, striated, jelly hull, approximately 55 microns wide (Colwin and Colwin, 1956). It is opaque and yellow-brown in color. The ovum is shed at metaphase of the first maturation division, although Colwin and Colwin (1956) point out that in living eggs, the germinal vesicle often appears to be intact, perhaps due to persistence of its "residual substance."

B. Fertilization and Cleavage: The eggs are fertilized as soon as they are shed into the water, the sperm most frequently entering near the equator. The polar bodies are soon formed and extruded, the egg rounding up during their formation (Ohshima, 1925a). An equal and somewhat modified form of radial cleavage was briefly noted by Ohshima (1925a). Gastrulation is by invagination, and appears to be similar to that of Cucumaria (Ohshima, 1921). Illustrations of the fertilization cone and polar body formation may be found in papers by Ohshima (1925b), and by Colwin and Colwin (1956).

C. Time Table of Development: The following schedule is taken from the paper of Ohshima (1925a). The time is calculated from egg-laying, the temperature not being indicated.

Stage	Time
First polar body	20–30 minutes
Second polar body	50–60 minutes
First cleavage	120 minutes
Second cleavage	150 minutes
Third cleavage	180 minutes
Gastrula	18–20 hours
Emergence	3½ days

D. Later Stages of Development: The ciliated gastrula, with polar bodies still attached, enclosed, within its membrane, transforms into a dipleurula, and then, just before emergence, into a metadoliolaria larva. This type of development is similar to that of *Holothuria floridana,* described by Edwards (1909). The metadoliolaria has a large, overhanging pre-oral hood, five unbranched tentacles and a pair of ventral pedicels. This form creeps out of the egg membrane. During the course of later development, the pre-oral hood is resorbed (pentactula stage), the tentacles branch and increase in number to ten, the ventral pedicels increase in number, and calcareous plates appear in the skin. There is no free-swimming stage (Ohshima, 1925a).

REFERENCES:

BUMPUS, H. C., 1898. The breeding of animals at Woods Holl during the months of June, July and August. *Science,* 8: 850–858.

COLWIN, L. H., 1948. Note on the spawning of the holothurian, *Thyone briareus* (Lesueur). *Biol. Bull.,* 95: 296–306.

COLWIN, L. H., AND A. L. COLWIN, 1956. The acrosome filament and sperm entry in *Thyone briareus* (Holothuria) and Asterias. *Biol. Bull.,* 110: 243–257.

EDWARDS, C. L., 1909. The development of *Holothuria floridana* Pourtalés with especial reference to the ambulacral appendages. *J. Morph.,* 20: 211–230.

GRAVE, C., 1902. A method of rearing marine larvae. *Science,* 15: 579–580.

JUST, E. E., 1929. The production of filaments by echinoderm ova as a response to insemination, with special reference to the phenomenon as exhibited by ova of the genus *Asterias. Biol. Bull.,* 57: 311–325.

JUST, E. E., 1939. Basic Methods for Experiments on Eggs of Marine Animals. P. Blakiston's Son & Co., Inc., Philadelphia.

MEAD, A. D., 1898. The breeding of animals at Woods Holl during the month of April, 1898. *Science,* 7: 702–704.

OHSHIMA, H., 1921. On the development of *Cucumaria echinata* v. Marenzeller. *Quart. J. Micr. Sci.,* 65: 173–246.

OHSHIMA, H., 1925a. Notes on the development of the sea-cucumber, *Thyone briareus. Science,* 61: 420–422.

OHSHIMA, H., 1925b. Pri la maturigô kaj fekundigô ĉe la ovo de l'markukumoj. *Bulteno Scienca de la Facultato Terkultura; Kyuŝu Imp. Univ.,* 1: no. 2, pp. 100–106 (in Japanese and Esperanto).

PROTOCHORDATA

(ENTEROPNEUSTA)

Saccoglossus (Synonyms: *Balanoglossus=Dolichoglossus*) *kowalevskii*

LIVING MATERIAL:

These worm-like animals are 15 cm. or more in length; the proboscis is pinkish-yellow in color and the body orange-yellow. They are collected from sand flats in the Woods Hole, Mass., area. The sexes are separate.

BREEDING SEASON:

No specific information on this subject has been recorded, for animals in the Woods Hole region. Presumably they are ripe during the latter half of July, and in August.

PROCURING AND HANDLING MATERIAL:

A. Care of Adults: The animals may be kept in fingerbowls supplied with a layer of clean sand. A gentle stream of running sea water should be provided.

B. Procuring Gametes: Colwin and Colwin (1953) report that females will shed spontaneously in the laboratory, the number of eggs spawned ranging from a few dozen to more than a thousand; the usual number (depending somewhat on the size of the female) is 100–300. Sperm may be obtained by cutting into the testis of a ripe male and collecting the sperm, which ooze out, in a pipette.

C. Preparation of Cultures: Colwin and Colwin (1953) placed naturally-shed eggs in small glass dishes containing sand-filtered sea water; spermatozoa (obtained as described above) were added directly from the pipette in which they were collected (Colwin and Colwin, 1950). Several changes of fresh, sand-filtered sea water should be made following insemination, and at least two or three times daily thereafter. The egg of Saccoglossus is sensitive to a number of environmental factors, including temperature, and the Colwins routinely took precautions to assure that the temperature of the sea water did not rise above 25° C. The eggs should not be crowded. It is advisable to keep the culture dishes in moist-chambers which are surrounded by running sea water.

Pre-hatching larvae should be transferred to dishes containing small amounts of fine, clean sand. If this is not done, free-swimming larvae tend to become caught in the surface film of the water, and the older, crawling larvae may become trapped by the adhesion to glass surfaces of the mucus which they secrete. Feeding is apparently not necessary; Colwin and Colwin (1953) supplied older cultures with unfiltered sea water, which contains an adequate amount of food to supply the larvae for at least as long as 36 days.

Normal Development:

A. The Unfertilized Ovum: The eggs are opaque, and vary in color from whitish-grey to dark grey-blue (Colwin and Colwin, 1953); they are rather irregular in shape before fertilization, and measure, on the average, about 330 microns by 420 microns. The germinal vesicle usually breaks down before the eggs are shed, and is at the metaphase of the first maturation division when it passes from the body of the female. The egg may remain fertilizable for a considerable period of time after shedding.

B. Fertilization and Cleavage: Fertilization takes place at the metaphase of the first maturation division, the sperm apparently entering at any point on the egg surface (Colwin and Colwin, 1953). The first polar body is given off about ten minutes after insemination, and the second 30 to 40 minutes later. The position of the polar bodies bears no very constant relation to the exact position of the animal pole. The details of fertilization (including the formation of the fertilization cone and membrane elevation) are described by Colwin and Colwin (1954a, 1954b).

After fertilization, the eggs become spherical in shape and are about 350 microns in diameter; soon after the first polar body appears, a broad, shallow "girdle" constricts the equatorial zone, and 15–30 minutes after insemination, a pear-shaped stage is attained, the vegetal hemisphere constituting the large, blunt end and the animal hemisphere the narrower portion. Shortly before the second polar body appears, the egg again becomes spherical, and after the second polar body is given off, a "reversed pear-shape" is evident, in which the animal hemisphere is the large, blunt end and the vegetal hemisphere is the more pointed one. Once again, the egg rounds up, and shortly before the first cleavage, there is a shortening of the animal-vegetal axis.

The first cleavage is usually approximately equal, the furrow passing from the animal to the vegetal pole; the same holds true for the second division. The third cleavage is latitudinal, resulting in an animal and a vegetal tier of cells; the size ratio of the two tiers, with respect to one another, is variable. At the fourth cleavage, the animal tier of cells divides somewhat sooner than the vegetal tier, so that a transitory 12-cell stage is present, followed shortly by a 16-cell stage after the vegetal cells divide. The eight animal cells are divided into a single tier composed of two more or less parallel rows, each consisting of two large central cells with a smaller cell at each end. These two long rows of cells represent the dorsal and ventral sides, respectively, of the embryo, and their two ends are the future left and right sides of the embryo (Colwin and Colwin, 1953). The vegetal cells at the 16-cell stage are arranged in an upper tier of four large cells and a lower tier of four small cells.

The early blastula is somewhat flattened at the vegetal end, but later it becomes more nearly spherical. Gastrulation is by invagination, and the embryo rotates actively before closure of the blastopore begins; cilia are present (as a transverse ciliated band) in a ring around the blastopore.

C. Time Table of Development: The following schedule is based on data from the paper by Colwin and Colwin (1953); temperatures were from 20° to 25° C., and the times were recorded from insemination.

Stage	Time
First polar body	10 minutes
"Equatorial girdle"	12–17 minutes
Pear-shape	15–20 minutes
Second polar body	40–50 minutes
"Reversed pear-shape"	40–55 minutes
Sphere-shape	50–70 minutes
First cleavage	1¾ to 2½ hours
Second cleavage	2½ to 3¼ hours
Third cleavage	3½ to 3¾ hours
Fourth cleavage	3¾ to 4½ hours
Blastula	6–15 hours
Gastrula	13–24 hours
Elongation of gastrula	18 hours
Appearance of first pair of gill slits	3 days
Hatching	7 days

D. Later Stages of Development and Metamorphosis: About 18 hours after insemination, the late gastrula begins to elongate in an antero-posterior direction. The division of the body into proboscis, trunk and collar regions is next accomplished; this process usually is complete 48 hours after insemination. The larva acquires pigmentation except in the area of the posterior collar groove. The first pair of gill slits appears when the pharyngeal pouches become perforated at three to four days, and two or three additional pairs subsequently develop. Emergence of the larva from its membranes occurs by the seventh day, and an adhesive sucker is developed. Further details, and photographs of many stages in the development of this form, are to be found in the paper by Colwin and Colwin (1953).

REFERENCES:

Bateson, W., 1884. The early stages in the development of Balanoglossus (sp. incert.). *Quart. J. Micr. Sci.,* **24**: 208–236.

Bateson, W., 1885. The later stages in the development of *Balanoglossus kowalevskii,* with a suggestion as to the affinities of the Enteropneusta. *Quart. J. Micr. Sci.,* **25**: Suppl. 81–122.

Colwin, A. L., and L. H. Colwin, 1950. The developmental capacities of separated early blastomeres of an enteropneust, *Saccoglossus kowalevskii. J. Exp. Zool.,* **115**: 263–295.

Colwin, A. L., and L. H. Colwin, 1951. Relationships between the egg and larva of *Saccoglossus kowalevskii* (Enteropneusta): Axes and planes; general prospective significance of the early blastomeres. *J. Exp. Zool.,* **117**: 111–137.

Colwin, A. L., and L. H. Colwin, 1953. The normal embryology of *Saccoglossus kowalevskii* (Enteropneusta). *J. Morph.,* **92**: 401–453.

Colwin, L. H., and A. L. Colwin, 1954a. Fertilization changes in the membranes and cortical granular layer of the egg of *Saccoglossus kowalevskii* (Enteropneusta). *J. Morph.,* **95**: 1–45.

Colwin, L. H., and A. L. Colwin, 1954b. Sperm penetration and the fertilization cone in the egg of *Saccoglossus kowalevskii* (Enteropneusta). *J. Morph.,* **95**: 351–371.

PROTOCHORDATA

(Tunicata)*

Amaroucium constellatum

LIVING MATERIAL:

The adult colonies of this species form abundant dense clumps on rocks and piles, and may be collected from Lagoon Pond Bridge at Martha's Vineyard, Mass. They are conspicuous because of the orange color of the ascidiozooids, which shows through the tunics. The animals are hermaphroditic and viviparous.

BREEDING SEASON:

Late June to early September. Maximum reproduction has been observed during July and August (Scott, 1945).

PROCURING AND HANDLING MATERIAL:

A. Care of Adults: When material is brought to the laboratory, the healthy, uninjured colonies should be placed, uncrowded, in large glass dishes with running sea water. At convenient intervals, the colonies should be inspected; healthy ones can be identified by their expanded oral and atrial siphons, and all others should be discarded. Such cultures may be kept in running sea water for days and, by daily removal of dead members, these "seasoned" cultures will produce abundant tadpoles for at least two weeks.

B. Procuring Gametes: Fertilization of ovarian eggs has not been successful in this species.

C. Preparation of Cultures: The eggs are retained in brood-spaces along the length of the ascidiozooid. Segmenting eggs are found in the posterior and lower portions of the abdomen, and tadpoles are packed into the thoracic region. With the aid of a microscope it is possible to dissect out eggs and larvae, but they may be obtained with greater ease by squeezing a mass of freshly collected adults over a fingerbowl containing a small amount of sea water. Many highly colored fragments will be ejected along with the embryos. Fill the dish with water and decant the coarse particles which whirl to the top. Tadpoles and eggs of all stages of development will be found on the bottom of the dish (Grave, 1921). Pregastrula stages will not develop outside the brood-spaces, but later embryos can be cultured in fingerbowls, provided the sea water is changed several times daily.

The larvae are normally released at dawn. Freshly collected, adult colonies should be placed in flowing sea water overnight, and transferred at daybreak to a container near a window. Shedding can be postponed to a more suitable hour if ripe colonies are kept in shrouded containers or in a dark room. Within 15–30 minutes after the time when these colonies are brought into the light, swarms of active tadpoles usually appear. Following this procedure at 9 A.M. yields about one-third of the available tadpoles; if it is delayed until mid-afternoon, the yield

* We are grateful to Sister Florence Marie Scott, for a review of this and the subsequent sections on tunicate development, and for much helpful information.

is approximately doubled. The tadpoles gather at the top of the water, near the side of the container which is exposed to the light. They may be collected with a pipette and isolated in separate drops of sea water in Syracuse dishes. When they have attached firmly to the dishes, they can be stored in an inverted position in wooden racks, which are submerged in an aquarium supplied continuously with fresh sea water.

D. Methods of Observation: Since the inner follicle cells divide and become closely packed within the perivitelline space, they obscure most of the developmental processes following the first few cleavages. The early embryos, therefore, are best studied in the form of sectioned material. Temporary whole mounts may be made, however, and these are very useful. The material is fixed in Bouin's fluid and preserved and mounted in 70% alcohol in depression slides; coverslips should be sealed on with vaseline, to prevent evaporation. The eggs may be rotated, bringing all surfaces into view, by moving the coverslip. Since the yolk granules are now stained yellow, the relationship between the yolky cells and those containing only clear protoplasm is readily observed (Scott, 1945).

Metamorphosing and budding individuals may be examined in the watch glasses to which they are attached. Debris should be flushed out with care, and the specimens kept covered with sea water. They may be flattened, if necessary, by gently lowering a coverslip on them. Asexual reproduction begins in cultures about 17 days after the attachment of the tadpole.

Scott (1952) describes a method for making fixed and stained Feulgen preparations of metamorphosing individuals.

NORMAL DEVELOPMENT:

A. Egg Characteristics: The eggs, in metaphase of the first maturation division, are shed into brood-spaces. Because of the pressure there of surrounding eggs and larvae, they are often polyhedral in shape. When fixed, the egg measures 250 microns in diameter; it has a chorion, and an outer and inner layer of follicle cells. The outer follicle cells are tightly pressed against the chorion. The inner follicle cells multiply, as the egg cleaves, and completely fill the wide perivitelline space which formed after it was shed; the egg of Amaroucium contains more yolk than any of the ascidians whose embryology has been studied, and is therefore opaque (Scott, 1945).

B. Fertilization and Cleavage: The first polar body is extruded at fertilization. The basic pattern of mosaic development is essentially the same for all ascidians, but in Amaroucium, owing to the greater accumulation of yolk, the processes of cleavage and gastrulation are somewhat modified. The first cleavage is unequal. The four cells produced by the second cleavage are listed here in order of increasing size: right posterior, right anterior, left posterior, and left anterior. In the third cleavage, the dense yolky material becomes concentrated in the macromeres. Gastrulation occurs between the sixth and seventh cleavages. It is accomplished chiefly by epiboly, but this is accompanied by an involution of the mesoderm and a pseudo-invagination of the endoderm without the formation of an open archenteron. The closing blastopore is definitely skewed, due to a rapid growth of the right lip. (For further details, see the paper of Scott, 1945.)

C. Rate of Development: Development is relatively slow, because of the large, inert yolk mass. However, no specific data pertaining to the rate of development are available, since pre-gastrula stages will not develop when removed from the parent.

D. Later Stages of Development and Metamorphosis: A free-swimming urodele-like tadpole is formed, with a relatively large trunk, measuring 600 microns in length, and a tail which is approximately twice as long. The lateral tail fins are well formed. Three cup-shaped adhesive papillae are visible. The tunic is transparent and glassy; embedded within it are a few scattered test cells. The sensory vesicle is conspicuous and the sense organs within it are well developed. The "eye" is a complex structure, consisting of sensory and pigment cells and a series of three lenses. There is a hypophysis, with its associated ganglia, and a nerve cord which extends into the tail and lies to the left of the notochord. The atria are fused posteriorly, connecting at this point with the atrial siphon. Four horizontal rows of gill slits (7 to 9 to a row) pierce the large pharynx on either side, in the posterior region where it is in contact with the two atria. The pharynx bears a conspicuous endostyle along its antero-dorsal border, and contains a large, central yolk mass. The U-shaped digestive tract is well developed. In the body cavity, antero-ventral to the yolk mass, is a small pericardial sac containing the developing heart. Both these structures originate from the floor of the pharynx. Complete descriptions and diagrams of all larval stages can be found in papers by Scott (1934, 1946, 1952); descriptions of the free-swimming tadpole are available in papers by Grave (1920, 1921). Some of the factors affecting metamorphosis have been described by Lynch (1956).

The swimming tadpole moves in irregular spurts, rotating on the longitudinal axis in a manner similar to that of a paramecium (Grave, 1920). When first released, the tadpoles show an immediate positive phototropism which is then reversed, at times so rapidly that before they reach the lighted side of the container, they become negative to the light stimulus. They are negatively geotropic and are always found near the surface of the water until the time of metamorphosis; then this tropism also reverses and they seek the lower levels of the container.

The length of the free-swimming period varies from 10 minutes to as long as 100 minutes (Grave, 1920). In a large vessel, most of the larvae will attach on the side of the dish near the bottom, but in small dishes they often fail to make an attachment although they will continue to metamorphose normally. Temporary attachment is made by the suckers which come in contact with a solid object; final attachment is effected by the secretion of an adhesive substance by an adhesive organ. A secretion within the cup adheres to the surface and the larva can detach itself and attach in another place numerous times before metamorphosis commences. At the time of attachment, or even before this occurs, the tail tissue buckles and is drawn into the trunk region; more extensive test is formed, and metamorphosis has begun. At the end of two days, metamorphosis is completed; sensory pigment is scattered through the body or is being eliminated through the digestive tract (which has reached its adult status) and the animal is feeding. Within the first hour of metamorphosis the heart assumes its characteristic reversal of beat. By four or five days, the zooid is well formed. All regions of the body are in full evidence: the spacious thorax with oral and atrial siphons and expanded pharynx; abdomen with the digestive loop, conspicuous in the bright orange tint of the stomach; and the post-abdomen, marked by a thin-walled, light orange epicardial tube throughout its length and a large heart at its distal tip. The zooid continues to grow through a period of about three weeks before asexual reproduction is initiated. During this time the post-abdomen increases in size and becomes filled with "blood" cells. The epicardium is the agent af asexual reproduction and colony formation. The process of metamorphosis is described by Scott (1952).

E. *Asexual Reproduction:* Asexual reproduction is accomplished in this species by strobilization, *i.e.,* segmentation of the post-abdomen which contains the epicardial strand. It is known as "pharyngeal" or "epicardial" budding. At the time of constriction, the buds consist of an inner vesicle of epicardial origin and an outer covering of parental epidermis. The cavity between these layers is congested with body ("blood") cells of various kinds, predominant among which are the large nutritive cells. Present, also, in each segment is a portion of the tube of neural tissue which develops in the post-abdomen as an extension of the abdominal nerve and which increases in size with growth of the post-abdomen. All internal organs of the new individual form from epicardial tissue, a pharyngeal derivative, and are, therefore, endodermal in origin. All other organs originate from neural and epidermal tissues.

During strobilization of the post-abdomen of the parent, the heart is isolated in the terminal bud where it persists as the heart of that member; all other members regenerate a new heart.

The buds, while developing into new zooids, move up and take their place around the parent, thus either forming a new colony around a metamorphosed individual or increasing the area of an old one. Swarms of buds in all stages of growth and migration can usually be found at the bases of the tiniest finger-like projections of a large healthy colony. (Details of this process are described by Kowalevsky, 1874; Berrill, 1935; and Korschelt, 1936.)

REFERENCES:

BERRILL, N. J., 1935. Studies in tunicate development. IV. Asexual reproduction. *Phil. Trans. Roy. Soc., London, ser. B,* **225**: 327–379.

BRIEN, P., 1930. Contribution à l'étude de la régénération naturelle et expérimentale chez les Clavelinidae. *Ann. Soc. Roy. Zool. Belg.,* **61**: 19–112.

GRAVE, C., 1920. *Amaroucium pellucidum* (Leidy) form constellatum (Verrill). I. The activities and reactions of the tadpole larva. *J. Exp. Zool.,* **30**: 239–257.

GRAVE, C., 1921. *Amaroucium constellatum* (Verrill). II. The structure and organization of the tadpole larva. *J. Morph.,* **36**: 71–91.

GRAVE, C., 1935. Metamorphosis of ascidian larvae. *Pap. Tortugas Lab.,* **29**: 209–291. (Carnegie Inst., Wash., Publ. no. 452.)

KOWALEVSKY, A., 1874. Über die Knospung der Ascidien. *Arch. f. mikr. Anat.,* **10**: 441–470.

KORSCHELT, E., 1936. Vergleichende Entwicklungsgeschichte der Tiere, vol. 2. Jena.

LYNCH, W. F., 1956. Factors inhibiting metamorphosis in tadpoles of the tunicate *Amaroecium constellatum. Biol. Bull.,* **111**: 308.

MAST, S. O., 1921. Reactions to light in the larvae of the ascidians, *Amaroucium constellatum* and *Amaroucium pellucidum* with special reference to photic orientation. *J. Exp. Zool.,* **34**: 149–187.

SCOTT, SISTER FLORENCE MARIE, 1934. Studies on the later embryonic development of Tunicata: *Botryllus schlosseri* and *Amaroecium constellatum.* Ph.D. Dissertation, Columbia Univ., pp. 1–53.

206   AMAROUCIUM

Scott, Sister Florence Marie, 1945. The developmental history of *Amaroecium constellatum*. I. Early embryonic development. *Biol. Bull.,* **88**: 126–138.
Scott, Sister Florence Marie, 1946. The developmental history of *Amaroecium constellatum*. II. Organogenesis of the larval action system. *Biol. Bull.,* **91**: 66–80.
Scott, Sister Florence Marie, 1952. The developmental history of *Amaroecium constellatum*. III. Metamorphosis. *Biol. Bull.,* **103**: 226–241.

PROTOCHORDATA

(Tunicata)

Botryllus schlosseri

LIVING MATERIAL:

Botryllus is a small, compound ascidian which is abundant around Woods Hole, Mass. It is found encrusting rocks, wharves, floats, and even the related genus Molgula. The daisy-like pattern, formed by the iridescent pigment bands extending between the siphons of the colony members, makes it easily recognized. Botryllus is viviparous.

BREEDING SEASON:

June to September, although the reproductive period for any one colony seems to be relatively short (Grave and Woodbridge, 1924).

PROCURING AND HANDLING MATERIAL:

A. Care of Adults: These animals are easily maintained in large fingerbowls, supplied with a continuous gentle stream of sea water. Dead material should be removed, as it will rapidly foul the water.

B. Procuring Gametes: As is the case for other viviparous species of ascidians, artificial insemination in Botryllus has not proved successful.

C. Preparation of Cultures: Early developmental stages must be dissected from the atrial cavity. This is done by slitting open the zooids and stripping the embryos from the atrial walls. They can be collected with a pipette and transferred to fingerbowls of sea water, where they will continue their development (Scott, (1934). In any one colony, all the embryos are at the same stage of development.

To obtain free-swimming larvae, a considerable number of adult colonies should be collected during the morning and placed in large fingerbowls of fresh sea water, near a window but out of direct sunlight. Sexually mature colonies contain zooids which are relatively thick and which tend to mat together. If they are fully ripe, some colonies will begin to release larvae within a few minutes. According to Grave (1937), the number of larvae released reaches a maximum at noon, with only an occasional tadpole being set free in the early morning or late evening.

For the study of metamorphosis and budding, tadpoles should be isolated in separate drops of sea water in watch glasses. When the larvae are firmly affixed, the dishes can be stored in an inverted position in wooden racks. These are in turn submerged in an aquarium supplied with a constant flow of sea water.

An easy way to collect tadpoles for the study of metamorphosis and budding is to stand slides around the inner wall of a fingerbowl containing Botryllus colonies. The tadpoles will attach to the slides, which may then be replaced in running sea water, in open slide-boxes. The advantage of collecting in this fashion lies in the fact that such slides of Botryllus may be killed, fixed, stained and mounted for further study.

D. Methods of Observation: Metamorphosing and budding individuals can conveniently be studied in the watch glasses to which they are attached; debris should be flushed out gently. The specimens may be slightly flattened if a cover-slip is gently lowered to cover them.

NORMAL DEVELOPMENT:

A. Egg Characteristics: The living egg measures 420 microns in diameter, according to Berrill (1937); when fixed, it is 215 microns in diameter (Scott, 1934). The yolk is in the form of small, evenly distributed granules. The mature egg is shed into the atrial cavity, at metaphase of the first maturation division. It is surrounded by a chorion and an inner and outer layer of follicle cells. The inner follicle cells are sparsely scattered within the narrow perivitelline space; the outer follicle cells become fused with the outer wall of the peribranchial cavity, thus holding the developing egg in a fixed position. Two to six eggs are found in a single individual.

B. Fertilization and Cleavage: Fertilization probably occurs when the egg is shed into the atrial cavity, and cleavage is virtually the same as in other ascidians. Gastrulation occurs between the sixth and seventh cleavages, and is similar to that of Styela (Scott, 1934).

C. Rate of Development: Development in this form is relatively rapid; a free-swimming larva is produced in about 12 hours.

D. Later Stages of Development and Metamorphosis: The neural plate of the young embryo is wide in the future brain region and narrows posteriorly. The neural folds, which encircle it, are visible shortly before the round blastopore closes; as they fuse to form the neural tube, the tail becomes marked off from the trunk and turns sharply to the left. Into the tail bud grow the dorsal neural tube, lateral muscle bands, notochord, and a ventral strand of endoderm. As the tail develops, it encircles the body meridionally, and by the time it has grown halfway around the body, the neuropore (seen in the region of the brain vesicle in early stages) has closed. A clear region in the anterior, ventral portion of the trunk marks the position of the primitive enteric cavity.

Shortly after the closure of the neuropore, a rapid series of changes occurs in the brain vesicle, resulting in the formation of a sensory vesicle, with a single sense receptor, and an adjacent hypophysis and associated ganglia. A conspicuous dorsal groove is present in the epidermis. In later development this groove stretches between the siphons. The atrium is formed by a single dorsal invagination in the posterior region of the trunk. A row of vertical gill slits is formed on each side where the two lobes of this invagination come into contact with the posterior wall of the pharynx. The tunic, siphons, papillae, and ampullae develop relatively late in embryonic life. When fully formed, the larvae drop off into the atrium and are released through the atrial siphon. (See the paper by Scott, 1934, for further details.)

The free-swimming tadpole is smaller than that of Amaroucium, having a body length of only 320–400 microns. The translucent tunic contains scattered cells, and extends out over the tail in the form of vertical fins. At the anterior end of the trunk can be seen eight conspicuous, sac-like outgrowths of the mantle, which are destined to be parts of the still non-functional and incomplete circulatory system

(Grave and Woodbridge, 1924). Also extending from the anterior region of the mantle are three projections arranged in the form of a triangle. Each of these contains a basal ganglion connected to the central nervous system, and they are believed to be sensory (rather than adhesive) in function (Scott, 1934). The siphons are inconspicuous and non-functional during the free-swimming period. The deep dorsal groove is visible between the siphons. The sensory vesicle appears as a large, clear sac located just behind the ampullae; suspended within it by a slender stalk is the statolith, a dense black cup associated with light-sensitive elements (Grave and Riley, 1935). The pharynx is large and contains a prominent endostyle along its anterior border. It extends posteriorly around the sensory vesicle in the form of two lateral lobes, each of which is perforated by a vertical row of four to six gill slits. The mass of yolk, which is so conspicuous in the pharyngeal floor of the Amaroucium tadpole, is completely lacking in the tadpole of Botryllus. A small, undeveloped heart lies below the pharynx. The short oesophagus leads to a sac-like stomach which narrows to a small intestine, coursing upward to the atrium. In the tail, the central notochord, dorsal neural tube, lateral muscle bands, and ventral cord of endoderm are clearly visible.

When first released, the tadpoles are strongly attracted to light; this attraction lasts throughout the greater portion of the free-swimming life. There is a period of indifference to light stimulus before metamorphosis, and some indication of a negative phototropism immediately before fixation (Grave and Woodbridge, 1924). The initial response to gravity is negative, but this decreases as metamorphosis approaches.

The length of the free-swimming period varies from 13 minutes to 27 hours, although on the average metamorphosis occurs in about two hours. Grave (1935) and Grave and Nichol (1939) have done some interesting work in an attempt to analyze the conditions which influence the onset of fixation. The anterior end of the tadpole attaches and metamorphosis is extremely rapid. One of the most striking features of the process is the unfolding of the ampullae, which spread out around the base of the developing tunicate like the petals of a flower.

Tadpoles which have attached and have been growing for two days are usually oriented so that the oral and atrial siphons are directed away from the substrate. The large pharynx, shaped like a truncate cone, bears three rows of stigmata (visceral clefts) which allow water to pass out into the atrial cavity on either side. A rod-like endostyle lies on the underside of the pharynx. The stomach ordinarily appears as a yellow body under the atrial opening. The intestine, near its junction with the stomach, turns to one side and loops to empty near the atrium.

E. *Asexual Reproduction:* Colony formation in Botryllus is often accomplished by the so-called "atrial" type of budding. The first bud, or blastozooid, is formed by an invagination of one side of the atrium, and its subsequently differentiated parts are thus derived solely from ectoderm. It is furnished with a blood supply. This first blastozooid is single, but all the later buds are formed in symmetrical pairs. By one week after attachment, four rows of stigmata have developed in the pharynx of the oözooid, and probably three or four rows in the blastozooid. Buds of the second and third order may have formed. The same organ structures are visible in all these individuals, notwithstanding their diverse embryology, with the minor exception that the oözooid does not develop gonads. By re-orientation of the individuals, the completed colony develops a common atrial pit at its center, and separate pharyngeal openings at the periphery. (For further details consult the papers of Pizon, 1893; Berrill, 1941a, 1941b; Watterson, 1945.)

Recently, Oka and Watanabe (1957) have described a process of "vascular budding" in this form.

REFERENCES:

BERRILL, N. J., 1937. Culture methods for ascidians. *In:* Culture Methods for Invertebrate Animals, edit. by Galtsoff *et al.,* Comstock, Ithaca, pp. 564–571.

BERRILL, N. J., 1941a. The development of the bud in Botryllus. *Biol. Bull.,* **80**: 169–184.

BERRILL, N. J., 1941b. Size and morphogenesis in the bud of Botryllus. *Biol. Bull.,* **80**: 185–193.

GRAVE, C., 1935. Metamorphosis of ascidian larvae. *Pap. Tortugas Lab.,* **29**: 209–291. (Carnegie Inst., Wash., Publ. no. 452.)

GRAVE, C., 1937. Notes on the culture of eight species of ascidians. *In:* Culture Methods for Invertebrate Animals, edit. by Galtsoff *et al.,* Comstock, Ithaca, pp. 560–564.

GRAVE, C., AND P. A. NICHOL, 1939. Studies of larval life and metamorphosis in *Ascidia nigra* and species of Polyandrocarpa. *Pap. Tortugas Lab.,* **32**: 1–46. (Carnegie Inst., Wash., Publ. no. 517.)

GRAVE, C., AND G. RILEY, 1935. Development of the sense organs of the larva of *Botryllus schlosseri. J. Morph.,* **57**: 185–211.

GRAVE, C., AND H. WOODBRIDGE, 1924. *Botryllus schlosseri* (Pallas): The behavior and morphology of the free-swimming larva. *J. Morph.,* **39**: 207–247.

HERDMAN, E. C., 1924. Botryllus. *Mem. Liverpool Mar. Biol. Comm.,* **26**: 1–40.

OKA, H., AND H. WATANABE, 1957. Vascular budding, a new type of budding in Botryllus. *Biol. Bull.,* **112**: 225–240.

PIZON, A., 1893. Histoire de la blastogénèse chez les Botryllidés. *Ann. Sci. Nat., Zool., sér. 7,* **14**: 1–386.

SCOTT, SISTER FLORENCE MARIE, 1934. Studies on the later embryonic development of Tunicata: *Botryllus schlosseri* and *Amaroecium constellatum.* Ph.D. Dissertation, Columbia Univ., pp. 1–53.

WATTERSON, R. L., 1945. Asexual reproduction in the colonial tunicate, *Botryllus schlosseri* (Pallas) Savigny, with special reference to the developmental history of intersiphonal bands of pigment cells. *Biol. Bull.,* **88**: 71–103.

PROTOCHORDATA

(TUNICATA)

Ciona intestinalis

LIVING MATERIAL:

These large, solitary ascidians can sometimes be collected from the wharf piles at Oak Bluffs and Vineyard Haven, Mass., and from the salt water tanks on the roof of the Marine Biological Laboratory, at Woods Hole, when the tanks are emptied in September; they are not always obtainable. The animals are hermaphroditic and, under some conditions at least, self-fertile (Just, 1934a, 1934b). They are oviparous.

BREEDING SEASON:

Almost any time of the year, since Ciona is sexually mature above a certain size limit. Reproduction is seasonal only to the extent of the rhythm of the growth cycle (Berrill, 1937).

PROCURING AND HANDLING MATERIAL:

A. Care of Adults: Mature adults will continue to produce normal eggs for several days in the laboratory, provided they are not crowded. Place only a few together in a large fingerbowl and insure a constant supply of fresh sea water.

B. Procuring Gametes: The eggs are normally shed at daybreak, but Rose (1939), using Styela, has developed a method for postponing this until a more convenient time. The adults are stored in a dark place, such as a desk drawer, until eggs are needed; shedding occurs almost immediately upon return of the animals to light.

Artificial insemination in this species is highly successful, since the genital ducts contain only ripe gametes. These may be obtained by slitting open the test and pipetting the eggs and sperm from the oviduct and sperm duct, respectively. If necessary, fine scissors can be used to puncture the ducts. The eggs remain viable for 18 hours after removal. They should be passed through several changes of sea water before insemination, to free them of perivisceral fluid.

C. Preparation of Cultures: Naturally-spawned eggs should be collected with a small-mouthed pipette and placed in fingerbowls of fresh sea water. The artificially-obtained eggs should be inseminated with a sperm suspension sufficiently concentrated to impart a faint milkiness to the sea water in which the eggs are contained. Berrill (1937) routinely uses eggs and sperm from different individuals, which is a wise precaution even in this self-fertile species. After fertilization, the essential requirements for normal development are the complete removal of excess sperm and oviducal fluid, and, above all, the use of glassware chemically and organically clean, as Morgan (1945) has demonstrated.

The development of Ciona tends to become abnormal during the period of tail elongation; placing the cultures in a larger volume of water prevents this tendency

211

and makes it possible to rear individuals through metamorphosis to maturity. The sea water should be replaced three or four times during the course of development. Feeding must be initiated once the small ascidiozooid has attached. Ciona, according to Berrill (1947), grows readily in an inverted bell jar or in a battery jar, equipped with an aerator. The diatom Nitzschia is used as a basic food, and its culture, within the bell jar, is regulated by controlling the amount of light with a dark paper shield. Nutrient salts are added from time to time.

D. *Removal of the Chorion:* Berrill (1932, 1937) gives several methods for the removal of the chorion for experimental purposes; this technique involves the use of crab stomach juice or proteolytic enzymes. Berg (1956) digested the chorion off unfertilized eggs with a 3% solution of protease in sea water. For observation, the chorion may be removed by simply rolling the eggs under a coverslip (Conklin, 1905).

NORMAL DEVELOPMENT:

A. *The Unfertilized Ovum:* The diameter of this egg is between 150 and 170 microns, according to Conklin (1905) and Berrill (1935). The egg is surrounded by a chorion, and inner and outer layers of follicle cells, the latter being elongated and pyramidal in shape (Berrill, 1929). There is a perivitelline space (Conklin, 1905). The egg has a clear, transparent cortical layer, and either green or red pigment in the yolk granules; the former color indicates a physiologically young egg, the latter a physiologically old one (Berrill, 1929). The oöcyte proceeds to the metaphase of the first maturation division when it enters the oviduct, and is shed into the water at this stage.

B. *Fertilization and Cleavage:* Although possible, self-fertilization is not at all common in Ciona. Following insemination, two polar bodies are extruded. They are larger than the inner follicle cells and remain attached to, or embedded in, the egg, thus constituting an important landmark. The first two cleavages are equal and divide the egg into future right and left halves.

Berg (1956) isolated Ciona blastomeres at the four-cell stage, and by spectrophotometric methods demonstrated that the cytochrome oxidase activity of posterior blastomeres is about 2.7 times that of anterior blastomeres. He interprets his results to indicate a localization of mitochondria in the posterior blastomeres.

Gastrulation is by invagination and epiboly (Castle, 1896). (For further details of development, consult the papers by Conklin, 1905, and Duesberg, 1915.)

C. *Rate of Development:* Duesberg (1915) states that cleavage begins one hour after insemination, and that hatching occurs at 19 hours, whereas Conklin (1905) reported that the latter event took place 12 hours after insemination; the temperature was not recorded in these papers. At 16° C., hatching occurs at about 25 hours, according to Berrill (1935). He also noted gastrulation at 7 hours, closure of the blastopore at 11 hours, and the appearance of sensory pigment 19 hours after insemination at 16°C.

D. *Later Stages of Development and Metamorphosis:* The tadpole, which hatches by means of a proteolytic enzyme (Berrill, 1932), is urodele-like in appearance. It has vertical tail fins, three adhesive papillae for attachment, a sensory vesicle with both a statocyst and a light-sensitive organ, and a short intestine. The siphons are not prominent. The endostyle is easily seen. (See the diagrams by Willey, 1893; MacBride, 1914; Berrill, 1929.)

The free-swimming period may last from 6 to 36 hours, usually more than 12 hours (Berrill, 1935). At metamorphosis the tail is resorbed and the mouth and atrial siphons rotate to a dorsal position. A heart and two primary gill slits appear soon after attachment. The affixed anterior region of the tadpole grows out to form a stalk which lifts the trunk away from the substrate. Details and figures of metamorphosis are given by Willey (1893) and Berrill (1929).

REFERENCES:

BERG, W. E., 1956. Cytochrome oxidase in anterior and posterior blastomeres of *Ciona intestinalis*. *Biol. Bull.*, **110**: 1–7.

BERRILL, N. J., 1929. Studies in tunicate development. I. General physiology of development of simple ascidians. *Phil. Trans. Roy. Soc., London, ser. B*, **218**: 37–78.

BERRILL, N. J., 1932. The mosaic development of the ascidian egg. *Biol. Bull.*, **63**: 381–386.

BERRILL, N. J., 1935. Studies in tunicate development. III. Differential retardation and acceleration. *Phil. Trans. Roy. Soc.. London, ser. B*, **225**: 255–326.

BERRILL, N. J., 1937. Culture methods for ascidians. *In:* Culture Methods for Invertebrate Animals, edit. by Galtsoff *et al.*, Comstock, Ithaca, pp. 564–571.

BERRILL, N. J., 1947. The development and growth of Ciona. *J. Mar. Biol. Assoc.*, **26**: 616–625.

CARLISLE, D. B., 1951. On the hormonal and neural control of the release of gametes in ascidians. *J. Exp. Biol.*, **28**: 463–472.

CASTLE, W. E., 1896. The early development of *Ciona intestinalis*, Flemming (L.). *Bull. Mus. Comp. Zool., Harvard*, **27**: 201–280.

CONKLIN, E. G., 1905. The organization and cell-lineage of the ascidian egg. *J. Acad. Nat. Sci., Philadelphia, ser. 2*, **13**: 1–119.

DUESBERG, J., 1915. Recherches cytologiques sur la fécondation des Ascidiens et sur leur développement. *Contrib. to Embryol.*, **3**: 33–70. (Carnegie Inst., Wash., Publ. no. 223.)

HARVEY, L. A., 1927. The history of the cytoplasmic inclusions of the egg of *Ciona intestinalis* (L.) during oogenesis and fertilisation. *Proc. Roy. Soc., London, ser. B*, **101**: 136–162.

JUST, E. E., 1934a. On the rearing of *Ciona intestinalis* under laboratory conditions to sexual maturity. *Carnegie Inst., Wash., Year Book*, **33**: 270.

JUST, E. E., 1934b. Zoological researches. *Carnegie Inst., Wash., Year Book*, **34**: 280–284.

MACBRIDE, E. W., 1914. Text-Book of Embryology. Vol. I. Invertebrata. Macmillan and Co., Ltd., London.

MORGAN, T. H., 1945. The conditions that lead to normal or abnormal development of Ciona. *Biol. Bull.*, **88**: 50–62.

ROSE, S. M., 1939. Embryonic induction in the Ascidia. *Biol. Bull.*, **77**: 216–232.

WILLEY, A., 1893. Studies on the Protochordata. I. On the origin of the branchial stigmata, praeoral lobe, endostyle, atrial cavities etc., in *Ciona intestinalis*, Linn., with remarks on *Clavelina lepadiformis*. *Quart. J. Micr. Sci.*, **34**: 317–360.

ZEUTHEN, E., 1955. Mitotic respiratory rhythms in single eggs of *Psammechinus miliaris* and of *Ciona intestinalis*. *Biol. Bull.*, **108**: 366–385.

PROTOCHORDATA

(Tunicata)

Molgula citrina

LIVING MATERIAL:

Members of this species are sometimes gathered, together with individuals of *M. manhattensis*. from Eel Pond at Woods Hole, Mass. While their anatomy is almost identical, the two species are radically different in their mode of reproduction. *M. citrina* is viviparous, *M. manhattensis* oviparous.

BREEDING SEASON:

Mid-June to mid-September (Grave, 1926). The period of reproduction seems to depend on the size of the individual rather than on the time of year.

PROCURING AND HANDLING MATERIAL:

A. Care of Adults: Sexually mature individuals (those over five mm. in length) will continue to reproduce and release larvae when brought into the laboratory, if they are kept in vessels supplied with a gentle stream of sea water.

B. Procuring Gametes: It is apparently not possible to remove and then fertilize ovarian eggs of this species.

C. Preparation of Cultures: Rearing embryos outside the parent is difficult. Berrill (1935) suggests that they be raised in a thistle-tube, the large end of which is covered with bolting silk on which the eggs are placed, the other end being attached to a T-tube through which air is bubbled. The whole apparatus is submerged in sea water; further details can be found in the original article. Even with this set-up, the mortality rate is high, and it is better to take the stages desired for study directly from the atrial brood-chamber of the parent.

Larvae are released when the adults are exposed to light; no particular time of day seems to be optimal. Culture directions for the tadpole are similar to those given for *M. manhattensis* (see p. 216). This form is favorable for use in a study of metamorphosis.

NORMAL DEVELOPMENT:

A. The Unfertilized Ovum: The egg measures approximately 210 microns in diameter, and is very opaque due to the presence of a yellow-orange pigment in the densely packed yolk. The outer follicle cells form a markedly flattened layer over the surface of the chorion, while the inner follicle cells are closely packed into a narrow perivitelline space (see the paper by Berrill, 1931, Figure 2). The egg is shed from the oviduct at the metaphase of the first maturation division.

B. Fertilization and Cleavage: Fertilization and development take place within the atrial chamber of the parent. The first few cleavages are equal, dividing the egg into a right and a left half. Gastrulation is by invagination, between the sixth and seventh cleavages (Berrill, 1935).

214

C. Rate of Development: Details are not available, but development in this form is relatively slow. At 16° C., the tadpoles hatch by rupturing the chorion 150 hours after fertilization.

D. Later Stages of Development and Metamorphosis: The free-swimming larvae, although they bear the same superficial resemblance to urodele larvae as do those of Amaroucium or Botryllus, seem to be less highly specialized. They lack organs for attachment, and no gill slits are visible. The most conspicuous larval organ is a huge sensory vesicle containing a statolith; there is no "eye." The alimentary tract is very yolky and poorly differentiated. The atrium consists of two sacs joined dorsally and posteriorly; the siphons are inconspicuous. The tail-fins are vertical. A small bilobed pericardial sac lies anterior and ventral to the intestine. Eight thickenings in the mantle precede the formation of the ampullae (see the paper of Grave, 1926, for a diagram).

The free-swimming period is short, averaging less than three hours (Grave, 1926). Fixation can be accomplished at any region of the adhesive test, and is accompanied by tail shrinkage and the extension of 8 or 10 mantle projections, the ampullae. A very small percentage of larvae metamorphose within the egg membrane inside the atrial cavity. Details and diagrams of metamorphosis are available in papers by Grave (1926) and Berrill (1931).

REFERENCES:

BERRILL, N. J., 1931. Studies in tunicate development. II. Abbreviation of development in the Molgulidae. *Phil. Trans. Roy. Soc., London, ser. B,* **219**: 281–346.

BERRILL, N. J., 1935. Studies in tunicate development. III. Differential retardation and acceleration. *Phil. Trans. Roy. Soc., London, ser. B,* **225**: 255–326.

GRAVE, C., 1926. *Molgula citrina* (Alder and Hancock). Activities and structure of the free-swimming larva. *J. Morph.,* **42**: 453–471.

PROTOCHORDATA

(Tunicata)

Molgula manhattensis

LIVING MATERIAL:

Adults are abundant on the floats and wharf piles around Woods Hole, Mass. They are far more common than *M. citrina*, but in the past workers have often confused the two species. Since *M. citrina* is viviparous and releases larvae instead of eggs, there is little reason for this mistake in identification. The animals are hermaphroditic.

BREEDING SEASON:

Probably there is no fixed season. Individuals over 12 mm. in length seem to breed continuously (Berrill, 1931).

PROCURING AND HANDLING MATERIAL:

A. Care of Adults: These animals keep very well when placed in large finger-bowls on the water table. A continuous gentle stream of sea water should be supplied and dead material removed promptly, since the water will foul very rapidly.

B. Procuring Gametes: For experimental work it is usually advisable to obtain naturally-shed eggs. Molgula sheds soon after dawn; however, this process may be delayed by placing several animals in large fingerbowls, and keeping them in the dark until they are needed. They will usually shed about 15 minutes after they are brought into the light.

Eggs and sperm may also be obtained by cutting open the tests of individuals over 12 mm. in length, and pipetting gametes from the genital ducts. This procedure may yield immature as well as mature eggs, since the oviducts in Molgula are short. The eggs should be passed through several changes of sea water, to free them of perivisceral fluid.

C. Preparation of Cultures: Naturally-shed eggs should be pipetted to finger-bowls of fresh sea water. To artificially-obtained eggs, enough sperm should be added to cause a faint milkiness in the water. The water should be replaced after one or two hours. It is probably advisable to use gametes from different individuals.

The bowls of fertilized eggs should be kept on a water table, and the water changed three or four times during subsequent development. As soon as the larvae begin to swim, they should be decanted or pipetted to fingerbowls of fresh sea water or, if a study of metamorphosis is desired, isolated in separate drops of sea water in Syracuse dishes. When they have firmly attached to these dishes, sea water should be added. The dishes with attached larvae can be stored in an inverted position in wooden racks which are submerged in aquaria of running sea water.

D. Removal of the Chorion: The chorion can be digested off with the stomach juice of crabs or with proteolytic enzymes, before or after fertilization (Berrill, 1932, 1937). This technique is useful for experimental purposes.

NORMAL DEVELOPMENT:

A. The Unfertilized Egg: The egg is opaque, with colored yolk; measurements of its diameter vary from 100 microns (Conklin, 1905) to 115 microns (Grave, 1926). Outer follicle cells, which are rounded, form a compact layer around the chorion, and a few inner follicle cells are present. A perivitelline space is visible. In the oviduct the germinal vesicle breaks down, and the egg proceeds to the metaphase of the first maturation division. Eggs are shed at this stage and remain in it until fertilization or death. (See the paper by Berrill, 1931, for further details.)

B. Fertilization and Cleavage: The eggs are fertilized as they are shed into the water. Cleavage is equal up to the fourth division, and separates the egg into future right and left halves, as in Styela. Gastrulation occurs between the sixth and seventh cleavages, and is a rather specialized form of true invaginative gastrulation.

C. Rate of Development: Berrill (1931) states that at 19° C. the blastopore is closed and the tail bud visible in four hours; hatching occurs in 8 to 11 hours. Secretion of the test, caudal degeneration, and outgrowth of the ampullae (*i.e.,* metamorphosis) occur 18 to 24 hours after insemination.

D. Later Stages of Development and Metamorphosis: The larvae normally hatch by means of enzymatic digestion of the chorion. The free-swimming urodele-like tadpoles have vertical tail-fins and a large sensory vesicle containing an otolith which is not destroyed during metamorphosis. There are no gill slits or adhesive papillae visible, and the siphons are undeveloped. The alimentary tract is poorly developed and very yolky. For diagrams of larvae, see the papers by Berrill (1931) and Grave (1926).

A few of the early stages of metamorphosis are figured by Berrill and by Grave. As has already been indicated, fixation is followed by tail degeneration and the outgrowth of a long, primary ectodermal ampulla. When this is fully formed, additional ampullae appear, and in the final state there are two present on one side of the body and three on the other. Pulsations appear early in the primary ampulla, which probably has a respiratory function.

REFERENCES:

BERRILL, N. J., 1931. Studies in tunicate development. II. Abbreviation of development in the Molgulidae. *Phil. Trans. Roy. Soc., London, ser. B,* **219**: 281–346.
BERRILL, N. J., 1932. The mosaic development of the ascidian egg. *Biol. Bull.,* **63**: 381–386.
BERRILL, N. J., 1937. Culture methods for ascidians. *In:* Culture Methods for Invertebrate Animals, edit. by Galtsoff *et al.*, Comstock, Ithaca, pp. 564–571.
CONKLIN, E. G., 1905. The organization and cell-lineage of the ascidian egg. *J. Acad. Nat. Sci., Philadelphia, ser. 2,* **13**: 1–119.
GRAVE, C., 1926. *Molgula citrina* (Alder and Hancock). Activities and structure of the free-swimming larva. *J. Morph.,* **42**: 453–471.

PROTOCHORDATA

(Tunicata)

Perophora viridis

LIVING MATERIAL:

These small green ascidians are found in abundance on sea-weed, wharf piles, etc., and may be collected from Lagoon Pond bridge at Martha's Vineyard, Mass. They are hermaphroditic and viviparous.

BREEDING SEASON:

August and September, according to Berrill (1937). However, Grave and McCosh (1923) indicate a shorter breeding period for Woods Hole, namely, the first half of August. Bumpus (1898) reports that ripe specimens of this species were taken throughout July.

PROCURING AND HANDLING MATERIAL:

A. Care of Adults: The animals are relatively hardy and will continue to breed and produce larvae in the laboratory, provided they are kept in large dishes with a constant supply of fresh sea water.

B. Procuring Gametes: Artificial insemination, using gametes pipetted from the genital ducts, has not been successful for this species.

C. Preparation of Cultures: Fertilized eggs, in various stages of development, can be obtained from the atrial brood-chamber by slitting open the test of an adult. They are difficult to rear outside the parent, although some success has been attained using the thistle-tube apparatus described by Berrill (1935a). The mortality rate decreases with advanced stages.

Older larvae can be obtained by placing dishes of adults before a window. The number of larvae released starts to increase at 8 A.M., reaches a maximum about 10 A.M., and declines by 11 A.M.; only a few are released throughout the rest of the day. This is a form well suited to the study of metamorphosis in ascidians; for such a study, the tadpoles should be isolated in separate drops of sea water in watch glasses. When the larvae have attached, the dishes may be stored in an inverted position in wooden racks which are submerged in aquaria constantly supplied with running sea water.

Bud formation is perhaps best observed in young cultures. If a small piece of the colony is affixed with vaseline to a watch glass which is stored in running sea water, stolons will be extended over the surface of the glass and new blastozooids formed at intervals along them. Within two weeks, a series of well-formed buds will be present.

D. Methods of Observation: To examine metamorphosing or budding individuals, remove a watch glass from the rack and gently flush out any debris; avoid

218

exposing the surfaces of the animals to air during the examination. If specimens are growing upright, they may be flattened by gently lowering a coverslip on them.

Normal Development:

A. The Unfertilized Ovum: This egg measures 240 microns in diameter. It has a very thin membrane and practically no perivitelline space. The ovum is yellowish in color. The germinal vesicle ruptures and the first maturation spindle is formed when the egg enters the oviduct.

B. Fertilization and Cleavage: Perophora eggs leave the oviduct one at a time, already fertilized, and pass into the atrial brood-chamber, where they are retained throughout development. Cleavage and gastrulation are similar to those of Styela (see p. 222). Gastrulation is by a rather specialized form of invagination, and occurs between the sixth and seventh cleavages (Berrill, 1935a).

C. Rate of Development: Development is relatively slow, and at 16° C. the interval between successive cleavages is approximately four hours. Gastrulation begins about 45 hours after insemination, the blastopore closes after 60 hours, sensory pigment appears after 120 hours, and the rupture of the chorion occurs about 185 hours after insemination (Berrill, 1935a). Grave and McCosh (1923) reported that the average free-swimming period lasts five hours.

D. Later Stages of Development and Metamorphosis: The translucent green larvae are rather similar to those of Amaroucium, having three cup-like adhesive papillae and horizontal tail-fins. The attachment papillae have cones of secretion projecting from the center of the cups. The sensory vesicle is enormous and contains an eye with lens, as well as a statocyst. Hypophysis, definitive ganglion, and sub-neural gland are present. There are four rows of horizontal gill slits on the right side and six on the left. Both the siphons and endostyle are well formed. The heart is functional and shows a characteristic reversal of beat. Further details and diagrams are available in the paper by Grave and McCosh (1923); Berrill (1935a) gives some details of metamorphosis.

E. Asexual Reproduction: Perophora exhibits the type of budding designated as "septal." The stolons, which branch irregularly over the substrate, have central mesenchymal septa separating the outgoing and ingoing blood streams. In bud formation, there first appears a hypertrophy of the epidermis between the tip of the stolon and the last formed zooid. Beneath this evagination, the cells of the vascular septum proliferate and grow out to form a hollow vesicle within the epidermal bulge. The epidermal covering of the bud forms the epidermis of the new zooid, and the indifferent mesenchyme of the inner sac forms all the remainder of the blastozooid. In Perophora, the bud never loses its connection with the stolon and is, therefore, vascularized by the common blood stream of the colony. For further details see the papers by Huxley (1921) and Berrill (1935b).

REFERENCES:

Berrill, N. J., 1935a. Studies in tunicate development. III. Differential retardation and acceleration. *Phil. Trans. Roy. Soc., London, ser. B,* **225**: 255–326.

Berrill, N. J., 1935b. Studies in tunicate development. IV. Asexual reproduction. *Phil. Trans. Roy. Soc., London, ser. B,* **225**: 327–379.

Berrill, N. J., 1937. Culture methods for ascidians. *In:* Culture Methods for Invertebrate Animals, edit. by Galtsoff *et al.,* Comstock, Ithaca, pp. 564–571.

BUMPUS, H. C., 1898. The breeding of animals at Woods Holl during the months of June, July and August. *Science,* **8**: 850–858.

GRAVE, C., AND G. K. McCOSH, 1923. *Perophora viridis* (Verrill). The activities and structure of the free-swimming larva. *Washington Univ. Stud., Sci. ser.,* **11**: 89–116.

HUXLEY, J. S., 1921. Studies in dedifferentiation. II. Dedifferentiation and resorption in Perophora. *Quart. J. Micr. Sci.,* **65**: 643–697.

RITTER, W. E., 1897. Budding in compound ascidians, based on studies on Goodsiria and Perophora. *J. Morph.,* **12**: 149–238.

PROTOCHORDATA

(Tunicata)

Styela (formerly *Cynthia*) *partita*

LIVING MATERIAL:

Styela is a simple ascidian with a hard tunic and small granular tubercles on and about the papillae bearing the apertures. It is brownish or yellow in color, and up to 25 mm. in length. Occasionally, the animals are found in groups although, as noted above, the form is not a colonial one. They are quite common around Woods Hole, Mass.

BREEDING SEASON:

June to September, according to Berrill (1937).

PROCURING AND HANDLING MATERIAL:

A. Care of Adults: The animals live well in the laboratory, if they are adequately supplied with sea water. High temperatures should be avoided.

B. Procuring Gametes: Although it is hermaphroditic, Styela is ordinarily self-sterile. Eggs and sperm are shed between 4 and 7 P.M., and fertilization takes place when the ripe gametes from two different individuals are mixed. The usual method of obtaining Styela eggs and embryos has been to mince the gonads from a large number of individuals, in a dish of sea water. This liberates all stages in the maturation of eggs and sperm, and usually at least a few eggs will be fertilized (whatever the time of day or night) and will begin normal development.

Rose (1939) has described a method of controlling natural spawning in the laboratory; it works well except for a few weeks in mid-summer, when the animals are spent. The adults are kept in the dark until eleven or twelve hours before fertilization is desired; then an artificial day is started, by turning on a 40-watt electric light, placed about 18 inches from the animals. Eggs and sperm are discharged in clouds at the desired time. The same batch of animals can be induced to shed a number of times on successive days.

NORMAL DEVELOPMENT:

A. The Unfertilized Ovum: The mature unfertilized egg is approximately 150 microns in diameter, and has a tough membrane, the chorion, to which a few follicle cells adhere at the outer surface. Between the chorion and the egg surface, there are small, spherical inner follicle cells ("nurse cells"), which contain yellow granules. The peripheral layer of the egg is clear and contains minute yellow granules, and the central part of the egg consists of grey yolk platelets. The germinal vesicle is large and clear, and is excentrically placed, near the animal pole; it ruptures and maturation begins at about the time when the eggs are discharged. The maturation spindle remains at the metaphase of the first division until the sperm enters.

B. Post-Fertilization Changes: The sperm enters at or near the vegetal pole (Conklin, 1905a) ; maturation continues, and two polar bodies are given off. An extensive re-arrangement of the cytoplasm now occurs : within two to eight minutes after fertilization, the clear, yellowish peripheral material streams to the lower pole, over the yolk, followed by the clear protoplasm from the animal pole. This process is best studied using daylight for illumination ; the microscope diaphragm should be open as far as possible.

The grey yolk rises to occupy the upper pole, except for the space which surrounds the maturation spindle. Soon the yellow substance accumulates on one part of the lower hemisphere, where it assumes a crescentic form. Immediately above the broad part of the yellow crescent, there is a layer formed by the clear cytoplasm.

The different pigmented regions of the egg correspond closely to the various embryonic areas with specific presumptive developmental fates. The yellow pigment area, at the posterior vegetal region, forms the "yellow crescent," which is presumptive mesoderm. The ventral and anterior portion of the vegetal hemisphere, which has the slate grey color of the yolk, forms endoderm and small amounts of mesoderm ; it also contributes to a portion of the neural plate. The animal hemisphere material, which is light grey in color because of the presence of clear protoplasm beneath the peripheral yolk, forms the body epidermis and a portion of the neural plate. The animal pole becomes the ventral-anterior side of the larva, while the vegetal pole is the future dorsal side.

C. Cleavage and Gastrulation: The first cleavage is equal, separating the two "horns" of the yellow crescent from one another and bisecting the clear protoplasm anterior to the yellow region. The second cleavage is nearly equal, vertical, and at right angles to the first. The two posterior cells contain only a small amount of yolk and practically all the yellow crescent substance. The two anterior cells, on the other hand, contain much yolk and almost no yellow crescent material. There is an equal division of the clear protoplasm to the four cells. At the third cleavage, which is horizontal, the yellow crescent substance is almost entirely confined to the two posterior dorsal cells. The planes of cleavage at the fourth division vary in different quadrants, but the cells do not overlap the sagittal plane of the embryo. Two of the antero-dorsal cells and two of the postero-ventral cells of the 16-cell embryo are crowded away from this sagittal plane, but all the other cells touch it. The dorsal and ventral hemispheres at this stage are mirror images of one another. The yellow pigment lies in four posterior cells. Division in the dorsal (vegetal) hemisphere precedes that in the ventral (animal) hemisphere at the fifth cleavage, and cleavage in the anterior part of each hemisphere precedes that in the posterior part. When the 32-cell stage is reached, the yellow substance is almost entirely confined to six dorso-posterior cells, three on each side of the midline. They give rise to mesoderm and mesenchyme. Six yolk-filled cells at the vegetal pole, anterior to the yellow mesoderm cells, give rise to endoderm. Four cells at the anterior border of the embryo (just below the equator) and two just above the equator produce the notochord and neural plate. All the other cells are ectodermal.

Gastrulation is by epiboly. The gastrula passes through disc-shaped, saucer-shaped and cup-shaped stages, starting at the seventh cleavage. As it finally becomes egg-shaped, the blastopore assumes the form of a "T," the stem of the "T" being bordered by the yellow mesoderm-mesenchyme cells. The cells overhanging the cross-bar of the T-shaped blastopore constitute its dorsal lip. They overgrow it, finally engulfing the yellow cells which are then seen only dimly through the translucent ectoderm.

D. Time Table of Development: The following approximate schedule for the development of normally-shed Styela eggs is from the classic monograph of Conklin (1905a). If eggs are obtained from "minced" cultures, cleavage is delayed, the eggs apparently maturing at variable intervals after coming into sea water. Time is recorded from insemination; the temperature is not specified, although Conklin states that these observations were made during the evening hours.

Stage	Time
First cleavage	40 minutes
Second cleavage	70 minutes
Third cleavage	100 minutes
Fourth cleavage	120 minutes
Fifth cleavage	140 minutes
Sixth cleavage	160 minutes
Seventh cleavage (beginning of gastrulation)	180 minutes
Eighth cleavage	200 minutes
Neural plate	5 hours
Fully-formed tadpole	12 hours

REFERENCES:

VAN BENEDEN, É., AND CH. JULIN, 1884. La segmentation chez les Ascidiens et ses rapports avec l'organization de la larve. *Arch. de Biol.,* **5**: 111–126.

BERRILL, N. J., 1929. Studies in tunicate development. I. General physiology of development of simple ascidians. *Phil. Trans. Roy. Soc., London, ser. B,* **218**: 37–78.

BERRILL, N. J., 1937. Culture methods for ascidians. *In:* Culture Methods for Invertebrate Animals, edit. by Galtsoff *et al.,* Comstock, Ithaca, pp. 564–571.

CASTLE, W. E., 1896. The early embryology of *Ciona intestinalis,* Flemming (L.). *Bull. Mus. Comp. Zool., Harvard,* **27**: no. 7, pp. 203–280.

COHEN, A., AND N. J. BERRILL, 1936. The early development of ascidian eggs. *Biol. Bull.,* **70**: 78–88.

CONKLIN, E. G., 1905a. The organization and cell-lineage of the ascidian egg. *J. Acad. Nat. Sci., Philadelphia, ser. 2, part 1,* **13**: 1–119.

CONKLIN, E. G., 1905b. Mosaic development in ascidian eggs. *J. Exp. Zool.,* **2**: 145–223.

CONKLIN, E. G., 1905c. Organ-forming substances in the eggs of ascidians. *Biol. Bull.,* **8**: 205–230.

CONKLIN, E. G., 1931. The development of centrifuged eggs of ascidians. *J. Exp. Zool.,* **60**: 1–120.

ROSE, S. M., 1939. Embryonic induction in the Ascidia. *Biol. Bull.,* **77**: 216–232.

CHORDATA (Vertebrata)

(Teleostei)

Fundulus heteroclitus and F. majalis

LIVING MATERIAL:

The sexes of both species of Fundulus are quite easily identified and obtained. The mature *F. heteroclitus* female is pale olive in color and usually has no definite bars or spots, although young females may have indistinct, dark, transverse bars on the sides; the dorsal fin is non-pigmented. The adult male of this species is a dull, dark green color, with narrow, ill-defined transverse bars composed of silvery spots; the dorsal fin is black-pigmented, in a mottled pattern.

The pale olive *F. majalis* female has a pattern of heavy, black longitudinal stripes on the sides, and a non-pigmented dorsal fin. The sides of the somewhat darker male bear approximately 12 broad, dark transverse bars, and there is a striking black patch on the dorsal fin.

BREEDING SEASON:

Material is best and most abundant, as a rule, during the first three weeks of June, but small numbers of fertilizable eggs have been procured through July 15 at Woods Hole, Mass.

PROCURING AND HANDLING MATERIAL:

A. Care of Adults: Fish are usually delivered by the M. B. L. Supply Department in mixed lots, but it is advisable to segregate the sexes, to prevent spawning. Males and females should be placed in separate aquaria until needed, and after they have been stripped, they should be removed to a discard tank. An adequate supply of running sea water is, of course, essential.

B. Procuring Gametes: Both eggs and sperm are obtained by "stripping": the fish is held firmly in one hand while gentle pressure is applied to its abdomen with the thumb and forefinger of the other hand. As these fingers are drawn towards the anus of the fish, the pressure forces out the gametes. If the fish is held in front of a strong light source during the stripping process, the eggs may be seen passing through the oviduct which runs along the anal fin.

C. Preparation of Cultures: Strip the eggs into a clean four-inch fingerbowl which has been moistened with filtered sea water. Strip the milt into a small amount of sea water, and mix the suspension with the eggs in ¼ inch of sea water. The eggs should be inseminated as soon as possible after they are obtained from the body of the female. After 30–45 minutes, change the sea water and leave the eggs in about a ¼- to ½-inch depth of sea water. Keep the fingerbowl covered with a glass plate to prevent evaporation; do not allow the eggs to clump or accumulate in one spot. The water should be changed at least twice daily.

D. Methods of Observation: To remove the sticky outer jelly layer, roll the eggs on a piece of filter paper or paper towel until the surface of the outer membrane is left smooth and clean. This same procedure should be followed daily for stock cultures, in order to prevent clumping of the eggs.

For experimental work, where it is essential to obtain development as nearly normal as possible, the eggs are usually examined uncovered in shallow depression slides; they may be manipulated with hair loops. For classroom study, when the eggs are to be observed over long periods of time and a specific orientation is desired, either of the following methods is suggested: (1) Place the eggs in sea water in special culture slides having a depression of 1.7 to 1.8 mm. (slightly less than the diameter of the eggs); it is then possible to roll the eggs to the desired position by moving the coverslip. (2) If these special slides are not available, the eggs may be placed in a drop of sea water on an ordinary glass slide and covered with a very thin, flexible sheet of mica; water is then withdrawn (using lens or filter paper) until capillary attraction causes a pressure on the egg, so that it can be rotated as in the previous method.

Recently, Trinkaus and Drake (1956) have described a method for the *in vitro* culture of Fundulus blastoderms isolated from the subjacent periblast and yolk mass.

E. Permanent Total Preparations: Fix the eggs in Stockard's solution (formalin, 5 parts; glacial acetic acid, 4 parts; glycerine, 6 parts; distilled water, 85 parts). This turns the protoplasm white but leaves the yolk transparent. The fixative may be used as a preservative, or the material can be transferred to 10% formalin after two days.

F. Preparation of Eggs for Sectioning: Eggs to be sectioned must be dechorionated before fixation, so that fluids can penetrate to the interior. (For details of this process, see the paper by Nicholas, 1927.) The following schedule for dehydration and embedding is useful.

1. Fix in Bouin's or Zenker's solution, 12–24 hours.
2. Dehydrate as usual through the alcohol series (up to and including 95% alcohol), leaving the eggs in each for one hour.
3. Absolute alcohol, two hours—use several changes.
4. Equal parts absolute alcohol and amyl acetate, two hours.
5. Amyl acetate, 24–48 hours.
6. Equal parts amyl acetate and paraffin, 12 hours (incubate at 30°).
7. Three changes of infiltrating paraffin (15 minutes in each); embed in 56–58° paraffin.

NORMAL DEVELOPMENT:

A. The Unfertilized Ovum: Eggs stripped from a female fish into diluted sea water (70% fresh water, 30% sea water) retain the morphological characteristics of freshly-extruded eggs, including the yolk platelets, oil drops, membranes, etc. A micropyle is present, but it must be observed before removal of the chorionic jelly.

B. Fertilization and Cleavage: In order to follow all the pre-cleavage changes, it is important to (1) record the exact time of insemination, and (2) transfer the eggs *immediately* to a slide (see above) for observation. Polar bodies have not been described for Fundulus eggs, and it is not certain what stage the egg nucleus is in at the time of fertilization. No fertilization membrane is given off.

There is a gradual accumulation of the egg protoplasm at one pole of the egg, 25–35 minutes after fertilization, to form the blastodisc or germ-disc. A groove on the surface of this blastodisc is the first indication of cleavage; it usually occurs two to three hours after fertilization. The cleavages continue for a considerable period without much change in the over-all form from that of the original blastodisc; this is called the period of the high blastula. Details of the process of cleavage are given by Oppenheimer (1937).

C. Time Table of Development: The following schedule is based on observations made at room temperatures which approximated 22–25° C. Times are recorded from insemination.

Stage	Time
Blastodisc formation	25–35 minutes
First cleavage	2–3 hours
Four-cell stage	2½–3½ hours
Eight-cell stage	4–5 hours
Sixteen-cell stage	4½–5½ hours
Early high blastula (Oppenheimer Stage 8)	10 hours
Late blastula (Oppenheimer Stage 9)	12 hours
Expanding blastula (Oppenheimer Stage 11)	17 hours
Early gastrula; embryonic shield (Oppenheimer Stage 12)	1 day
Middle gastrula; keel (Oppenheimer Stage 13)	2 days
Late gastrula; closure of blastopore (Oppenheimer Stages 14–15)	2½–3 days
Formation of brain and auditory capsules; 4–14 somites (Oppenheimer Stage 18)	3½ days
Heart-beat, embryonic circulation (Oppenheimer Stage 20)	4 days

D. Later Stages of Development: The periblast appears 16–24 hours after fertilization. The uncleaved protoplasm around the margin of the group of blastomeres is called the marginal periblast, while that beneath the blastodisc (visible only in sections) is the central periblast. At about this same time, the large, pinkish periblast nuclei may be visible. The nuclei of the marginal row of cells gradually become free of cell outlines, continue their divisions and migrate into the marginal periblast, converting it into a nucleated but non-cellular structure. Subsequent to the nucleation of the periblast, the blastoderm changes in form and size, and the embryo is now referred to as a blastula. Soon the margin of the blastodisc thickens (due both to a peripheral increase in cells and to a thinning of the central part of the disc), to form the germ-ring; this structure is best observed in eggs of *F. majalis.*

During the next few hours, the germ-ring grows completely over the surface of the yolk mass, so that the uncovered portion of the egg (the blastopore) is finally covered. This process of blastopore closure occurs after the first stages of formation of the embryonic axis. Under favorable conditions, it is sometimes possible to observe the beginning of gastrulation; a slight indentation appears at the edge of the germ-ring, usually when the yolk is about one-fourth covered. Staining with neutral red (one or two drops of a 0.5% solution in a Syracuse dish of sea water) may make easier the identification of the germ-ring and periblast.

While the germ-ring is extending around the yolk, the embryonic axis is being established. The first indication of this process is a cellular thickening, the embryonic shield, resulting from a more active movement of cells in one region of the germ-ring. It is usually initiated when the blastoderm has covered from one-quarter to one-third the surface of the yolk. When the blastoderm has spread to cover approximately one-half the yolk, the embryonic shield has become a bluntly triangular area, extending from the margin of one portion of the germ-ring almost to the center of the blastoderm. The shield can best be identified in profile view. As the blastoderm spreads over the surface of the yolk, the embryo grows rapidly in length, and becomes segmented; this segmentation is confined to the mesoderm.

It is suggested that embryos be removed from the chorion for observation of the later developmental stages. Although this de-chorionation is rather difficult at early stages, it can readily be accomplished later, with the use of sharpened forceps or beading needles. Injury to the yolk sac should be avoided.

After hatching, the young fish may be studied in detail if they are anaesthetized with chloretone. The paper by Oppenheimer (1937) contains further details of developmental stages.

REFERENCES:

AGASSIZ, A., AND C. O. WHITMAN, 1885. The development of osseous fishes. I. The pelagic stages of young fishes. *Mem. Mus. Comp. Zool., Harvard,* **14**: no. 1, part 1, pp. 1–56.

AGASSIZ, A., AND C. O. WHITMAN, 1889. The development of osseous fishes. II. The pre-embryonic stages of development. Part First. The history of the egg from fertilization to cleavage. *Mem. Mus. Comp. Zool., Harvard,* **14**: no. 2, part 2, pp. 1–40.

BREDER, C. M., JR., 1948. Field Book of Marine Fishes of the Atlantic Coast from Labrador to Texas. G. P. Putnam's Sons, New York. (Rev. ed.)

CLAPP, C. M., 1891. Some points in the development of the toad-fish (*Batrachus tau*). *J. Morph.,* **5**: 494–501.

CLAPP, C. M., 1898. Relation of the axis of the embryo to the first cleavage plane. Biol. Lectures M. B. L., Wood's Holl, Mass., pp. 139–151.

NEWMAN, H. H., 1907. Spawning behavior and sexual dimorphism in *Fundulus heteroclitus* and allied fish. *Biol. Bull.,* **12**: 314–348.

NEWMAN, H. H., 1915. Development and heredity in heterogenic teleost hybrids. *J. Exp. Zool.,* **18**: 511–576.

NEWMAN, H. H., 1918. Hybrids between Fundulus and mackerel. A study of paternal heredity in heterogenic hybrids. *J. Exp. Zool.,* **26**: 391–421.

NICHOLAS, J. S., 1927. The application of experimental methods to the study of developing Fundulus embryos. *Proc. Nat. Acad. Sci.,* **13**: 695–698.

NICHOLAS, J. S., AND J. M. OPPENHEIMER, 1942. Regulation and reconstitution in Fundulus. *J. Exp. Zool.,* **90**: 127–157.

OPPENHEIMER, J. M., 1937. The normal stages of *Fundulus heteroclitus*. *Anat. Rec.,* **68**: 1–15.

RUSSELL, A., 1939. Pigment inheritance in the Fundulus-Scomber hybrid. *Biol. Bull.,* **77**: 423–431.

SOLBERG, A. N., 1938. The development of a bony fish. Prog. Fish. Cult., no. 40, pp. 1–19.

SUMNER, F. B., 1903. A study of early fish development. Experimental and morphological. *Arch. f. Entw.,* **17**: 92–149.

TRINKAUS, J. P., AND J. W. DRAKE, 1956. Exogenous control of morphogenesis in isolated Fundulus blastoderms by nutrient chemical factors. *J. Exp. Zool.,* **132**: 311–347.

WILSON, H. V., 1889. The embryology of the sea bass (*Serranus atrarius*). *Bull. U. S. Fish Comm.,* **9**: 209–278.

CHORDATA (Vertebrata)

(Teleostei)

Menidia sp.*

Living Material:

Two species (and probably several sub-species) of the common silversides are available in the Woods Hole, Mass., area. Menidia is characterized by the presence of a longitudinal silvery stripe, which runs along the flanks of the adult.

It is difficult to distinguish between *Menidia menidia* and *M. beryllina* solely on the basis of external morphology of the adults, although *M. beryllina* is somewhat smaller than *M. menidia* and has a colorless peritoneum, as opposed to the black peritoneum of *M. menidia*. The eggs of *M. beryllina* are somewhat smaller than those of *M. menidia,* and each has 8 to 14 attaching threads per egg, in contrast to the larger number (about 40) characteristic of the egg of *M. menidia*. All the attaching threads of the *M. menidia* egg are of approximately equal size, but Moulton (personal communication) reports that one thread of the egg of *M. beryllina* is notably larger (by a factor of two or three) than the remaining ones. Further details may be found in the book by Breder (1948).

During the breeding season, the females of both species are considerably plumper than the males, but other criteria for distinguishing between the sexes are somewhat unsatisfactory. Often, the females in a school of Menidia out-number the males (Kendall, 1901).

The adults were formerly very abundant in the Eel Pond, and some are still available there, as well as at other collecting sites (frequently in the same locales as Fundulus). Kendall (1901) reported that Menidia was common at that time about the wharves in Great Harbor, at Woods Hole.

Breeding Season:

From mid-June to mid-July; the last two weeks in June are probably most favorable (Moulton, personal communication). Bumpus (1898) reported that eggs are also obtainable early in June.

Procuring and Handling Material:

A. Care of Adults: The fish live well in aquaria supplied with running sea water, but it is important that they be transferred to such aquaria as soon as possible after collection.

B. Procuring Gametes: Eggs and sperm are obtained by stripping the fish (see the section on Fundulus, p. 224 of this manual). Some immature eggs (which lack the characteristic attachment threads) are usually obtained from the females; such eggs are pale in color and smaller than ripe eggs, and do not tend to cling together as do mature eggs.

* Much of the material on which this section is based was obtained from Dr. James M. Moulton, to whom we are most grateful.

C. Preparation of Cultures: Eggs may be inseminated by the same general methods described for Fundulus. The cultures are best kept on the sea water table; a temperature of 18 to 19° C. is apparently most favorable (Moulton, personal communication).

D. Methods of Observation: The attachment threads may be cut off close to the egg surface, using a sharp scalpel or razor blade. (See, also, the methods used for observation of Fundulus eggs.)

NORMAL DEVELOPMENT:

A. The Unfertilized Ovum: The egg of *M. beryllina* is approximately 0.75 mm. in diameter (Breder, 1948), while that of *M. menidia* is somewhat larger and measures about 1.2 mm. in diameter (Nichols and Breder, 1927). The eggs of both species are clear and somewhat yellowish in color, and two to three oil droplets (which later coalesce into one) are present. The attachment threads arise from a very circumscribed area of the chorion, 180 degrees from the future site of origin of the blastodisc (Moulton, personal communication).

B. Fertilization and Cleavage: The sperm enters the egg through a micropyle. Polar bodies have not been observed in developing Menidia eggs (Moulton, personal communication), and the stage of the egg nucleus at the time of fertilization is not known. Formation of the germinal disc and cleavage are, in general, similar to the same processes in the Fundulus egg. During the course of development, the egg of Menidia becomes free within the chorion, so that the position of the attachment threads is no longer a criterion of the polar axis.

C. Time Table of Development: The development of Menidia eggs is slow; Moulton (personal communication) observed the following schedule, at a temperature of 18–19° C. The times are recorded from insemination.

Stage	Time
Germinal disc	By 40 minutes
First cleavage	60 minutes **
Eight to 32 cells	3 hours, 50 minutes
Beginning of expanding blastula	16 hours, 20 minutes
Early embryonic shield; germ-ring halfway around yolk	27 hours, 35 minutes
Beginning of gastrulation	36 hours
Yolk plug; optic vesicles to closed blastopore	39 hours, 35 minutes
Eyes formed; heart beating	6 days
Hatching	15 days

D. Later Stages of Development: The later development is like that of Fundulus, except that by four days, the eggs are clear and transparent, so that observation of the embryo is easier. The large oil droplets coalesce approximately 16 hours after insemination, to form a single drop. At six days, the eyes are well formed, the heart is beating and Kupffer's vesicle is clearly visible. The circulatory system in a 48-hour embryo is diagrammed by Clark and Moulton (1949). Shortly before hatching, the chorion becomes very soft and flabby.

** From the paper by Bumpus (1898); the temperature is not specified.

Figures of many stages in the development of *M. menidia* are available in the paper by Kuntz and Radcliffe (1917).

SPECIAL COMMENTS:

The localization of the egg attachment threads to a circumscribed area, together with the small number of oil droplets, facilitate study of this form, especially in early stages (Clark and Moulton, 1949). Thus, the eggs of Menidia have some advantages over those of Fundulus, for both study and experimentation.

In addition, the spawning season of Menidia is usually somewhat more prolonged than that of Fundulus.

REFERENCES:

BREDER, C. M., JR., 1948. Field Book of Marine Fishes of the Atlantic Coast from Labrador to Texas. G. P. Putnam's Sons, New York. (Rev. ed.)

BUMPUS, H. C., 1898. The breeding of animals at Woods Holl during the months of June, July and August. *Science,* **8**: 850–858.

CLARK, E., AND J. M. MOULTON, 1949. Embryological notes on Menidia. *Copeia,* 1949, no. 2, pp. 152–154.

KENDALL, W. C., 1901. Notes on the silversides of the genus Menidia of the east coast of the United States, with descriptions of two new subspecies. *Rep. of the Commissioner, U. S. Comm. of Fish & Fisheries,* **27**: 241–267.

KUNTZ, A., AND L. RADCLIFFE, 1917. Notes on the embryology and larval development of twelve teleostean fishes. *Bull. U. S. Bur. Fish.,* **35**: 87–134.

NICHOLS, J. T., AND C. M. BREDER, JR., 1927. The marine fishes of New York and southern New England. *Zoologica,* **9**: 1–192.

CHORDATA (Vertebrata)

(TELEOSTEI)

Tautogolabrus [*=Ctenolabrus*] *adspersus*

LIVING MATERIAL:

Pelagic eggs may be obtained from the scup (*Stenotomus chrysops*) and the mackerel (*Scomber scombrus*), but must be stripped and fertilized immediately, as the fish are taken from the traps. The cunner, Tautogolabrus, is more useful for the study of pelagic egg development, for it may be brought to the laboratory and stripped as needed. Fish of this genus are quite common.

Cunners should be caught on the same day they are to be used; females are ordinarily obtained only after 12 noon. The male has a somewhat brighter green color than the female, and can also be distinguished by its bright red cloacal lining.

BREEDING SEASON:

This is usually concurrent at Woods Hole, Mass., with the breeding season for Fundulus (June and, occasionally, part of July).

PROCURING AND HANDLING MATERIAL:

A. Care of Adults: The sexes should be segregated and the animals maintained in large aquaria with adequate supplies of running sea water.

B. Procuring Gametes: Eggs are stripped into a four-inch fingerbowl containing a small amount of filtered sea water; milt is stripped into a large fingerbowl containing sufficient sea water to cover the bottom. It is almost essential to use several layers of cloth for holding the fish while they are being stripped, because they are extremely active and slimy, and have very sharp spines in the dorsal fin.

C. Preparation of Cultures: As soon as possible after stripping, the sperm suspension should be poured into the dish containing the eggs, and the time recorded. Let the mixture stand undisturbed for one-half minute, then add fresh sea water and decant into a graduate cylinder or an Erlenmeyer flask, adding sufficient sea water to bring the meniscus to near the top of the cylinder, or to the neck of the flask. Viable eggs will float to the top and collect at the edge of the meniscus. They should then be pipetted off and placed in covered four-inch fingerbowls containing ¼ inch filtered sea water. Store the dishes on the sea water table where they will keep cool; pelagic eggs of this type are very sensitive to such environmental factors as temperature and oxygen supply.

Only glass-clear eggs are suitable for study; if ova show the slightest opacity, they are either immature or dead. Similarly, the presence of bits of tissue adhering to eggs indicates that they are immature and should be discarded. To obtain later stages of development, not more than three to six embryos should be placed per four-inch fingerbowl; the sea water should be changed twice daily and dead (opaque) embryos removed immediately.

D. Methods of Observation: For observing the formation of polar bodies, the blastodisc and early cleavage, it is advantageous to place the microscope in a horizontal position, so that the blastodisc may be studied in a profile view; it is difficult to observe the polar bodies by any other method.

NORMAL DEVELOPMENT:

A. The Unfertilized Ovum: The egg is approximately 0.8 to 1.0 mm. in diameter; it is, as noted above, transparent and contains no oil droplets.

B. Fertilization and Cleavage: The polar bodies, which appear as small, clear beads on the surface of the blastodisc, are given off 5 to 10 minutes after insemination. Cleavage is rapid, occurring about once every 20 minutes at temperatures of 16 to 18° C.; the nuclei are sometimes visible between divisions, as pinkish bodies.

C. Later Stages of Development: Because of the beautiful clarity of the egg, this form is very favorable for the study of later stages of teleost development, including the formation of the germ-ring, embryonic shield and Kupffer's vesicle. Development is rapid and hatching occurs in about four days. The details of embryogenesis are described by Newman (1915), Kuntz and Radcliffe (1917) and Breder (1948). Diagrams are available in the paper by Kuntz and Radcliffe (1917).

REFERENCES:

BREDER, C. M., JR., 1948. Field Book of Marine Fishes of the Atlantic Coast from Labrador to Texas. G. P. Putnam's Sons, New York. (Rev. ed.)

KUNTZ, A., AND L. RADCLIFFE, 1917. Notes on the embryology and larval development of twelve teleostean fishes. *Bull. U. S. Bur. Fish.,* **35**: 89–134.

NEWMAN, H. H., 1915. Development and heredity in heterogenic teleost hybrids. *J. Exp. Zool.,* **18**: 511–576.

NICHOLS, J. T., AND C. M. BREDER, JR., 1927. The marine fishes of New York and southern New England. *Zoologica,* **9**: 1–192.

CHORDATA (Vertebrata)

(TELEOSTEI)

Other Teleost Eggs of the Woods Hole, Mass., Region, Suitable for Experimental Use

I. *Cyprinodon variegatus* (broad killifish)

A. Breeding season: June through mid-July.

B. Developmental rate: Moderately rapid; hatches in 5–8 days.

C. Egg characteristics: Demersal; 1.3–1.5 mm. in diameter; spherical, slightly yellow; yolk almost transparent and colorless; fibrous, sticky coat; small oil droplets present; micropyle visible.

D. Special comments: Females with ripe eggs are rather difficult to obtain. The larvae live well in fingerbowls of sea water.

E. Pertinent references: Breder (1948); Newman (1907, 1915).

II. *Opsanus tau* (toadfish)

A. Breeding season: June and July.

B. Developmental rate: Very slow; hatches in 10–26 days.

C. Egg characteristics: Demersal; 5 mm. in diameter; large adhesive disc at center of vegetal pole, opposite micropyle; deep amber in color.

D. Special comments: Fairly readily obtained; the eggs are found attached inside submerged objects (tin cans, old boots, etc.), or they can be inseminated artificially (by allowing the eggs to flow from the opened ovary into a dish containing just enough water to cover them; fertilize after the eggs have attached to the dish).

E. Pertinent references: Clapp (1891, 1898, 1899); Sumner (1903); Wallace (1899).

III. *Scomber scombrus* (mackerel)

A. Breeding season: Mid-May to June and very early July.

B. Developmental rate: Rapid; usually hatches in 60 to 72 hours.

C. Egg characteristics: Pelagic; 1.2 mm. in diameter; faintly pink in color, transparent; one large oil globule; very sensitive to changes in temperature, 16° C. being optimum.

D. Special comments: The eggs are fairly readily obtained; females contain enormous numbers of eggs, but they must be stripped at the fish traps. Even at optimum temperatures, the mortality rate is high.

E. Pertinent references: Newman (1915, 1918); Russell (1939); Worley (1933).

IV. *Stenotomus chrysops* (scup)

A. Breeding season: Early June.

B. Developmental rate: Very rapid; hatches in 48 hours.

C. Egg characteristics: Pelagic; 0.8 mm. in diameter; colorless and very transparent; one large oil droplet.

D. Special comments: *Mature* females are rather difficult to obtain, but large numbers of eggs may be obtained from a single female. The fish must be stripped as soon as the eggs are ripe. Hatched embryos will live for a few days in fingerbowls of sea water.

E. Pertinent references: Breder (1948); Newman (1915).

V. *Strongylura marinus* (billfish)

A. Breeding season: June.

B. Developmental rate: Slow; the time of hatching has apparently not been recorded.

C. Egg characteristics: Demersal; 3 mm. in diameter; very clear and transparent; long tufts of adhesive threads.

D. Special comments: Not very common; probably it is best to strip and inseminate the eggs at the fish traps, although this can be done later, at the laboratory. The percentage of fertilized eggs is not very high, but the enormous numbers of eggs obtained from one female often assure a good supply of eggs. Embryos can be raised to the hatching stage.

E. Pertinent references: Breder (1948).

VI. *Syngnathus fuscus* (pipefish)

A. Breeding season: Mid-May through June or possibly early July. Males with young in their brood-pouches have been found in July and early August.

B. Developmental rate: Not known.

C. Egg characteristics: Pelagic; carried by male in a ventral brood-pouch; 0.75–0.85 mm. in diameter; nearly opaque; contains numerous orange oil droplets.

D. Special comments: Large numbers of eggs and larvae are found in the brood-pouches of the males—as many as 200. Eggs apparently cannot successfully be removed from the brood-pouch until the yolk sac is completed, but after that time, they will develop in fingerbowls of sea water.

E. Pertinent references: Agassiz and Whitman (1885); Cohn (1904); Huot (1902); Cunningham (1895).

REFERENCES:

AGASSIZ, A., AND C. O. WHITMAN, 1885. The development of osseous fishes. I. The pelagic stages of young fishes. *Mem. Mus. Comp. Zool., Harvard*, 14: no. 1, part 1, pp. 1–56.

BREDER, C. M., JR., 1948. Field Book of Marine Fishes of the Atlantic Coast from Labrador to Texas. G. P. Putnam's Sons, New York. (Rev. ed.)

CLAPP, C. M., 1891. Some points in the development of the toad-fish (*Batrachus tau*). *J. Morph.*, 5: 494–501.

CLAPP, C. M., 1898. Relation of the axis of the embryo to the first cleavage plane. Biol. Lectures M. B. L., Wood's Holl, Mass., pp. 139–151.

CLAPP, C. M., 1899. The lateral line system of *Batrachus tau*. *J. Morph.*, 15: 223–264.

COHN, L., 1904. Ueber die Bruttasche von *Syngnathus typhle*. *Anat. Anz.*, 24: 192–199.

CUNNINGHAM, J. T., 1895. Experiments and observations made at the Plymouth Laboratory. II. The development of the egg in flat fishes and pipe-fishes. *J. Mar. Biol. Assoc.*, 3: 258–270.

Huot, A., 1902. Recherches sur les poissons lophobranches. *Ann. des Sci. Nat., Zool., sér. 8,* **14**: 197–288.

Newman, H. H., 1907. Spawning behavior and sexual dimorphism in *Fundulus heteroclitus* and allied fish. *Biol. Bull.,* **12**: 314–348.

Newman, H. H., 1915. Development and heredity in heterogenic teleost hybrids. *J. Exp. Zool.,* **18**: 511–576.

Newman, H. H., 1918. Hybrids between Fundulus and mackerel. A study of paternal heredity in heterogenic hybrids. *J. Exp. Zool.,* **26**: 391–421.

Russell, A., 1939. Pigment inheritance in the Fundulus-Scomber hybrid. *Biol. Bull.,* **77**: 423–431.

Sumner, F. B., 1903. A study of early fish development. Experimental and morphological. *Arch. f. Entw.,* **17**: 92–149.

Wallace, L. B., 1899. The germ-ring in the egg of the toad-fish (*Batrachus tau*). *J. Morph.,* **15**: 9–16.

Worley, L. G., 1933. Development of the egg of the mackerel at different constant temperatures. *J. Gen. Physiol.,* **16**: 841–857.

SUMMARY OF EGG CHARACTERISTICS

Genus	Page	Approx. size of egg	Stage of nucleus at time of fertilization	Rate of devel.	Jelly or second. membrane	Abundance at Woods Hole	Breeding season at Woods Hole
Amaroucium	202	250 μ	Meta I	Slow	Chorion	Common	June–Sept.
Amphipholis	177	100 μ	Ger. vesicle	?	None	Not common	July–Sept.
Amphitrite	59	100 μ	Meta I	Rapid	None	Moderate	June–Aug.
Arbacia	184	73 μ	Both pol. bods.	Mod.	Jelly	Not common	June–Aug.
Arenicola	61	120 μ	Meta I	Slow	Jelly	Moderate	June, July
Asterias	170	110 μ	GV breakdown	Mod.	Jelly	Moderate	May–July
Aurelia	32	120 μ	?	Slow	None	Variable	July–Sept.
Balanus	160	?	First pol. bod.	Rapid	?	Common	Aug.–Nov. 15
Barentsia	48	?	?	?	None	Common	July–Sept.?
Botryllus	207	200–400 μ	Meta I	Rapid	Chorion	Common	June–Sept.
Bougainvillia	4	?	?	Slow	None	Moderate	June–Aug.
Bugula	51	?	?	Mod.	None	Common	June–Nov.
Busycon	135	1000 μ	?	Slow	Capsule	Not common	Aug., Sept.
Callocardia	103	49–60 μ	GV breakdown	Slow?	Jelly	Moderate	July?
Campanularia	6	160 μ	?	?	None	Common	June, July
Cerebratulus	44	120 μ	GV breakdown	Slow	Chorion	Not common	July
Chaetopleura	100	180 μ	Meta I	Mod.	Chorion	Common	June–Sept.
Chaetopterus	63	100 μ	Meta I	Rapid	None	Moderate	June, July
Ciona	211	160 μ	Meta I	Mod.	Chorion	Variable	Jan.–Dec.
Cirratulis	67	104 μ	Meta I	Rapid	None	Common	July, Aug.?
Cistenides	69	55 μ	GV breakdown	Mod.	None	Common	?
Clava	8	131 μ	?	Mod.	None	Moderate	June, July
Clymenella	71	150 μ	Meta I	?	None	Variable	May
Crassostrea	105	45–54 μ	Ger. vesicle	Mod.	None	Moderate	June 15–Aug. 15
Crepidula	137	136–182 μ	Meta I	Slow	Capsule	Common	June 15–Aug. 15
Crisia	53	18 μ	?	?	None	Common	?
Cumingia	108	62 μ	Meta I	Rapid	Jelly	Not available	June 15–Sept. 15
Cyanea	34	?	Both pol. bods.?	?	None	Variable	March–May
Cyprinodon	233	1.4 mm.	?	Mod.	Chorion	Not common	June–July 15
Diopatra	73	235 μ	GV breakdown	Rapid	Jelly	Common	?
Echinarachnius	191	135 μ	Both pol. bods.	Mod.	Jelly	Common	Apr. 1–July 31
Electra	55	79 μ	?	Mod.	None	Common	?
Emerita	163	380 μ	?	?	?	Common	July, Aug.?
Ensis	111	65 μ	Ger. vesicle	Rapid	None	Common	July?
Eudendrium	10	230 μ	?	Mod.	None	Common	July, Aug.
Eutima	12	?	?	Rapid	None	Not common	?
Fundulus	224	1.8 mm.	?	Rapid	Chorion	Common	June
Gonionemus	14	70 μ	Both pol. bods.	Mod.	Jelly	Not common	July 1–Sept. 30
Gonothyrea	16	102 μ	GV breakdown?	Mod.	None	Not common	July, Aug.
Haminea	141	80 μ	Meta I	Rapid	Capsule	Variable	June–Sept.
Harmothoë	76	50–78 μ	?	Rapid	None?	Moderate	Apr. 15–May 31
Henricia	175	1000 μ	?	Slow	?	Not common	April?
Hoploplana	40	100 μ	Ger. vesicle	Slow	Capsule	Moderate	June–Sept.
Hydractinia	18	160–170 μ	Sec. pol. bod.	Mod.	Jelly	Moderate	June–Aug.
Hydroides	77	67–72 μ	Ger. vesicle	Mod.	None	Common	June–Nov.
Ilyanassa	143	166 μ	GV breakdown?	Mod.	Capsule	Common	Apr. 24–July 15
Lacuna	147	103–180 μ	?	Slow	Capsule	Common	?
Lepas	165	185 μ	First pol. bod.	Rapid	None	Variable	?
Lepidonotus	81	65 μ	?	Slow	None	Common	May
Leptosynapta	194	190–209 μ	?	Mod.?	Jelly	Common	June, July
Libinia	167	1 mm.	?	Slow	None	Common	May–July?
Littorina	149	205–250 μ	GV breakdown?	Slow	Jelly	Common	?
Loligo	155	1500 μ	GV breakdown?	Slow	Jelly	Common	May–July 15
Mactra	113	53–56 μ	Ger. vesicle	Rapid	None	Moderate	June–Aug.
Menidia	228	1 mm.	Both pol. bods.?	Slow	Chorion	Moderate	June 15–July 15
Metridium	36	100–160 μ	Both pol. bods.	Mod.?	None	Common	June, July
Mnemiopsis	38	?	?	Rapid	None	Variable	May–July
M. citrina	214	210 μ	Meta I	Slow	Chorion	?	June 15–Sept. 15
M. manhatten.	216	100–115 μ	Meta I	Rapid	Chorion	Common	Jan.–Dec.
Mya	117	58–80 μ	GV breakdown?	Mod.	Jelly	Not common	June–Aug.?
Mycale	1	Small	?	?	None	?	Sept., Oct.?
Mytilus	119	70 μ	Meta I	Mod.	None	Common	June–Sept. 15
Nereis	83	140 μ	Ger. vesicle	Mod.	Jelly	Moderate	June–Sept.
Nucula	122	90 μ	Both pol. bods.?	Rapid	None	Not common	?
Obelia	21	130 μ	GV breakdown?	Mod.	None	Common	June–Aug.
Ophioderma	179	300 μ	Both pol. bods.?	Rapid	None	Common	July–Aug. 15
Ophiopholis	181	105 μ	GV breakdown	Slow	None	Not available	?
Opsanus	233	5 mm.	?	Slow	Adh. disc	Moderate	June, July
Pecten	124	63 μ	GV breakdown?	Mod.	Jelly	Common	June 15–Aug. 15
Pedicellina	49	60 μ	First pol. bod.?	?	Shell	Moderate	?
Pennaria	23	237–500 μ	Both pol. bods.	Rapid	None	Common	July 15–Sept.

Abbreviations used:

Meta I: Metaphase of the first maturation division.
Ger. vesicle: Germinal vesicle.
Both pol. bods.: Both polar bodies have been extruded.
GV breakdown: Germinal vesicle breakdown.
Adh. disc: Adhesive disc present on surface of chorion.
?: Reliable information is apparently not available.

SUMMARY OF EGG CHARACTERISTICS—*Continued*

Genus	Page	Approx. size of egg	Stage of nucleus at time of fertilization	Rate of devel.	Jelly or second. membrane	Abundance at Woods Hole	Breeding season at Woods Hole
Perophora	218	240 μ	Meta I	Slow	Chorion	Common	Aug. 1–15?
Phascolosoma	57	150–180 μ	Meta I	Rapid	None	Common	June 15–Sept.
Platynereis	89	180–200 μ	Ger. vesicle	Rapid	Jelly	Not common	July–Aug. 21
Podarke	91	63 μ	Meta I	Rapid	None	Common	July, Aug.
Podocoryne	26	?	Before GV brkdwn.	?	None	Not common	June, July
Polychoerus	42	220 μ?	Ger. vesicle	Slow	Capsule	Not common	June–Aug.
Sabellaria	93	60 μ	GV breakdown	Mod.	Jelly	Common	June–Aug.
Saccoglossus	199	420 μ	Meta I	Mod.	None	Common	?
Scomber	233	1.2 mm.	?	Rapid	Chorion?	Moderate	May 15–July 1
Spisula	113	53–56 μ	GV breakdown	Rapid	None	Moderate	June–Aug.
Stenotomus	233	0.8 mm.	?	Rapid	Chorion?	Not common	Early June
Sthenelais	98	110 μ	GV breakdown?	Mod.	None	Not common	?
Strongylura	234	3 mm.	?	Slow	Chorion?	Not common	June
Styela	221	150 μ	Meta I	Rapid	Chorion?	Common	June–Sept.
Syngnathus	234	0.8 mm.	?	?	Chorion?	Moderate	May 15–June 30
Tautogolabrus	231	0.9 mm.	GV breakdown?	Rapid	Chorion	Common	June
Teredo	127	55–60 μ	?	Slow	None	Common	May–Oct. 15
Thais	151	180 μ	?	Slow	Capsule	Common	?
Thyone	196	200–300 μ	Meta I	Mod.	Jelly	Common	June
Tubularia	28	400 μ	GV breakdown?	Mod.?	None	Common	June, July
Turritopsis	30	116 μ	Both pol. bods.	Rapid	None	Not common	?
Urosalpinx	153	240 μ	?	Slow?	Capsule	Common	Late May–Aug.
Venus	130	70–73 μ	Meta I	Mod.	None	Common	June 15–Aug. 15
Yoldia	133	150 μ	Both pol. bods.	Rapid	None	Common	?

INDEX

Acoelous turbellarian, 42.
Actinulae of Tubularia, 29.
Agar-bottomed operating dishes, xv.
AGASSIZ A., 39, 174, 227, 234.
AGASSIZ, L., 35.
Alkaline NaCl, use of in denuding
  Nereis eggs, 84.
  Sabellaria eggs, 94.
ALLEN, C. M., 29.
ALLEN, M. J., 75.
ALLEN, R. D., 115.
ALLMAN, J. G., 11.
Alternation of generation in hydroids, 3 ff.
Amaroucium constellatum, 202.
AMEMIYA, I., 107.
AMIRTHALINGHAM, C., 126.
Amphineura, 100.
Amphipolis squamata, 177.
Amphitrite ornata, 59.
Anaesthetization of larvae
  of Amphipholis, 177.
  of Cerebratulus, 45.
  of Crepidula, 138.
  of Fundulus, 277.
  of Ilyanassa, 144.
  of Libinia, 167.
  of Cumingia, 109.
ANDERSON, T. F., 189.
ANDREWS, E. A., 75.
Anemone (Metridium), 36.
ANKEL, W. E., 146, 148, 150.
Annelida, 59 ff.
Anthozoa, 36 ff.
Antibiotic, use of in culture medium for Balanus, 160.
Arbacia, disappearance of, at Woods Hole, ix.
Arbacia plutei as food for Balanus larvae, 161.
Arbacia punctulata, 184.
Arenicola cristata, 61.
Arthropoda, 160 ff.
Asterias, 170.
Asteroidea, 170 ff.
Atrial budding in Botryllus, 209.
Attachment threads of Menidia egg, 228.
Aurelia aurita, 32.
Autotomy in Asterias, 170.
Axiation
  of Fundulus embryo, 227.
  of Pedicellina embryo, 49.
  of Saccoglossus embryo, 201.
AYERS, J. C., 118.

BAKER, E. G., 24.
Balanoglossus, 199.

Balanus eburneus, 160.
BALL, E. G., 166, 189.
BALLARD, W. W., 19, 24.
Barentsia laxa, 48.
Barnacle, 160.
Barnacles as food for Thais adults, 151.
BARNES, E. W., 118.
BARNES, H., 161.
BARROIS, J., 54.
BATESON, W., 201.
BATTLE, H. I., 118, 121.
BECKWITH, C. J., 19.
BELDING, D. L., 115, 118, 126, 132.
VAN BENEDEN, É., 223.
BENOIT, P., 29.
BEQUAERT, J. C., 150.
BERG, W. E., 121, 213.
BERRILL, N. J., 5, 17, 19, 24, 27, 29, 142, 205, 210, 213, 215, 217, 219, 223.
BIDDER, A. M., 159.
BIGELOW, M. A., 166.
Billfish, 234.
Bipinnaria larvae of Asterias, 173.
Blastocones of squid embryo, 157.
Blastodisc of Fundulus egg, 225
  of Tautogolabrus egg, 232.
Blastopore, fate of in Hydroides embryo, 79.
BONNEVIE, K., 56.
BOOLOOTIAN, R. A., 189.
Borers (Teredo), 127.
BORG, F., 54.
Botryllus schlosseri, 207.
Bougainvillia superciliaris, 4.
Brachiolaria larvae of Asterias, 174.
BREDER, C. M., JR., 227, 230, 232, 234.
Breeding season extension
  for oyster, 106.
  for clam (Venus), 131.
BRESSLAU, E., 43.
BRIEN, P., 205.
Brittle star, 177 ff.
Broad killifish, 233.
BROOKS, W. K., 13, 31, 107, 154, 159, 169, 180.
Bryozoa, 48 ff.
Budding in Botryllus, 209.
Bugula, 51.
Bulla, 141.
BUMPUS, H. C., 62, 68, 75, 76, 82, 99, 118, 121, 139, 154, 164, 169, 176, 183, 193, 195, 198, 219, 230.
BUNTING, M., 19, 27.
BURBANCK, W. D., 72, 161.
Bursa of Amphipholis, 177.
Busycon, 136.

239